Anno 1729

Richd Hartshorn · Jno Smitheman · Wm Hayward · J^n^o Purcell

Lightmor · Sand holes · Cole mere · Coa...

Big St · Lump Do · Big St · Big St · Big St · Coaks · Big St

Old-blast-Furn^s Dr to Sund^y acco^ts carry^g coals from Apr^l 27 to May 25

To Roger Cock Carry^g — 2 8 · 0 4
To Francis Parton D^o — 0 6 · 2 – · 12 –
To Wm Bazlewood D^o — 0 4 · 2 4
To Geo Ashwood D^o — 0 6 · 6 3
To Jno Brook D^o — 1 6
To Richd Hazlewood D^o — 1 5
To Richd Williams D^o — 1 3 · 0 1 · 0 2 – 3/4 · 263
To Geo Burras D^o — 0 4 · 0 2 2 1/2 · 255
To Wm Griffiths D^o — 0 4 · 1 4 · 0 4 7 · 270
To Jno Crippen D^o — 1 4 · 0 3 4 · 171
0 4 · 0 1 0 · 102 — 4 – 11 1/2

New Blast Furn^s Dr to Sund^y acco^ts for D^o in D^o time

To Roger Cock Carry^g — 28 5 · 0 5 · 1 9 · 30 2 · 11 – · 259
To Jno Brook D^o — 3 1 · 0 4 · 4 16 9 · 283
To Richd Bazlewood D^o — 8 2 · 0 8 · 16 6 · 2 7 · 1 8 5 3/4 · 248
To Richd Williams D^o — 4 4 · 0 2 · 10 1 · 9 8 · 2 3 · 1 6 11 1/2 · 263
To Geo Burras D^o — 5 – · 2 11 · 1 7 · 1 11 0 · 255
To Wm Griffiths D^o — 0 3 · 0 6 · 4 2 · 1 2 6 3/4 · 270
To Jno Wooley D^o — 1 7 · 0 1 11 · 171
To Jno Crippen D^o — 1 3 · 0 4 · 0 4 0 · 161
To Francis Parton D^o — 1 2 · 2 6 · 0 2 8 · 102
To Wm Bazlewood D^o — 1 – · 2 – · 1 5 · 4 1 · 0 14 1 1/2 · 266
To Geo Ashwood D^o — 0 2 · 2 1 · 4 4 · 8 – · 0 10 8 · 219
1 11 6 1/4 · 136 — 13 10 7 3/4

Upper Air Furn^s Dr to Sund^y acco^ts for D^o in D^o time

To Geo Burras Carry^g — 5 6 · 5 5 · 0 1 · 1 3 · 271
To Roger Cock D^o — 1 3 · 0 1 · 1 1 7 · 270
0 1 10 3/4 · 283 — 1 3 5 3/4

New Air Furn^s Dr to Sund^y acco^ts for D^o in D^o time

To Geo Burras carry^g — 2 – · 0 5 · 206
To Roger Cock D^o — 0 9 · 0 3 7 3/4 · 270
0 2 – 3/4 · 283 — 5 8 1/2

Generall Charges Dr to Sund^y acco^ts for D^o in D^o time

To George Burras Carry^g — 1 – · 3 1 · 3 5 · 246
To Roger Cock D^o — 0 5 · 0 12 9 1/2 · 270
0 9 8 1/4 · 283 — 13 5 3/4

Totals: 69 7 · 2 11 · 5 9 · 25 5 · 32 4 · 12 8 · 5 7 · 38 4 · 49 4 · 5 1 — 19 14 3 1/4

Sund^y acco^ts are Drs to Richd Hartshorn for coals from his pits ye M^o — 268

Old Blast Furn^s for — 8 5 · 0 6 · 2 9 6 1/2 · 258
New Blast Furn^s For — 51 2 · 2 11 · 5 3 · 15 12 6 1/4 · 259
Upper Air Furn^s For — 7 0 · 1 18 6 · 271
New Air Furn^s For — 2 – · 0 11 – · 206
Generall Charges For — 1 – · 0 5 6 · 246 — 20 17 1 1/4

Sund^y acco^ts are Dr to Jno Smitheman for Coals from his pits ye m^o — 261

Old Blast Furn^s for — 2 4 · 0 9 9 1/4 · 238
New Blast Furn^s For — 23 1 · 4 12 5 1/4 · 259 — 5 2 2 1/2

Sund^y acco^ts are Dr to Willm Hayward for coals from his pits ye M^o — 247

Old Blast Furn^s For — 22 5 · 0 8 · 1 4 · 8 2 · 1 16 8 3/4 · 258
New Blast Furn^s For — 9 5 · 1 9 · 4 2 · 30 2 · 2 18 10 1/4 · 259
Upper Air Furn^s For — 5 6 · 0 1 · 0 8 4 3/4 · 271
New Air Furn^s For — 1 4 · 0 2 1 · 206
General Charges For — 3 1 · 0 4 7 3/4 · 246 — 5 10 8 1/2

Sund^y acco^ts are Dr to John Purcell for coals from his Pits this month — 276

Old Blast Furn^s For — 0 5 · 0 3 – 1/2 · 258
New Blast Furn^s For — 43 4 · 5 1 · 13 7 – 1/2 · 259
Upper Air Furn^s For — 1 3 · 0 7 4 · 271
Generall Charges For — 4 1 · 1 2 7 1/4 · 246 — 15 – – 1/4

Sund^y acco^ts are Dr to Richard Johnson getting Coals this month — 256

Old Blast Furn^s for — 22 5 · 3 16 1 1/4 · 258
New Blast Furn^s For — 9 5 · 1 12 9 · 259 — 5 8 10 1/4
Vide a Contract ... [illegible]

PUBLISHERS' NOTE

This 1989 edition is substantially a fascimile reproduction of the original edition of 1953, with the additions and amendments noted below. It was revised by Dr. Arthur Raistrick and was produced for the Ironbridge Gorge Museum Trust in conjunction with the Sessions Book Trust. Additional material has been provided by Stuart B. Smith, Director of the Ironbridge Gorge Museum, and picture research has been carried out by Michael A. Vanns, Assistant Curator. The Publishers are grateful for a grant towards publication from Christopher Cadbury.

(a) Illustrations: completely revised. Details on pp. xiv–xvi.

(b) Chapter 15: new (1989) text by Arthur Raistrick, replacing the original (1953) text.

(c) Chapter 16: new (1989) text by Stuart Smith.

(d) Postscript: new (1989) text by Arthur Raistrick, replacing the original (1953) text.

(e) Index: revised to incorporate the new materials.

(f) Corrigenda: the author wishes the reader to note the following changes to his original (1953) text:–

p. ix, line 4: for '14' read '13'.

p. 3: this family tree has been revised and updated in the light of new information.

p. 15, line 36: for 'about 1930' read 'in 1929'.

p. 40, line 10: for '1711' read '1709'.

p. 47, note 2: to delete 'the house which was later called Sunniside, and which keeps that name to the present.'

p. 71, line 19: for 'house of the later Darbys, White House, or Sunniside', read 'house of Abiah and Abraham II, Sunniside'.

p. 102, line 1: for '1658' read '1638'.

p. 103, line 34: for 'may have been a rebuilding or enlargement' read 'was a rebuilding'.

p. 144, line 18: for 'Dinnington' read 'Donnington'.

p. 149, line 20: for 'Kinneil House, Stirlingshire' read 'Kinniel House, Linlithgowshire'.

The front cover illustration is from *The Upper Works at Coalbrookdale*, a hand-coloured engraving of 1758 by Francois Vivares (1709–80) after Thomas Smith (d. 1767) and George Perry (1719–71), and shows a Newcomen engine cylinder being drawn by a team of horses in front of the Works.

The back cover illustration shows Coalbrookdale, an original watercolour of 1951 by John Piper RA (b. 1903).

DYNASTY OF IRON FOUNDERS

Arthur Raistrick was born in Yorkshire in 1896 and educated at Bradford Grammar School and Leeds University, where he gained an MSc degree in Civil Engineering and MSc and PhD degrees in Geology. From 1945 to 1970 he was Extramural Tutor at the Universities of Leeds, Durham and Newcastle, and a lecturer for the Workers' Educational Association from 1922. He was actively involved in industrial archaeology for more than 40 years and was President of the Industrial Archaeology Unit of Bradford University as well as being an Honorary Curator of Coalbrookdale Museum, Vice-President of the Ironbridge Gorge Museum Trust and an Honorary Life Member of the Newcomen Society.

He has the Honorary degree of DLit from Leeds and Bradford Universities.

In 1988 he was awarded the Silver Medal of the Yorkshire Archaeological Society.

He is married and has one adopted daughter.

A prolific writer throughout his life, three of his other books are:

The London (Quaker) Lead Company: 1692-1905: Two Centuries of Industrial Welfare **1938** The Friends' Historical Society, London.

Quakers in Science and Industry . . . during the 17th and 18th Centuries **1950** The Bannisdale Press, London.

Industrial Archaeology: an Historical Survey **1972** Eyre Methuen, London.

DYNASTY OF IRON FOUNDERS

THE DARBYS AND COALBROOKDALE

ARTHUR RAISTRICK
PhD, MSc

Sessions Book Trust
in association with
Ironbridge Gorge Museum Trust

First published 1953

Reprinted 1970

Revised 2nd Edition 1989

ISBN 1 85072 058 4

Printed by William Sessions Limited
The Ebor Press
York, England

To the

many generations of

Coalbrookdale men and boys

who have laboured

in these works,

1708–1951

Preface to the First Edition (1953)

In the year 1699 Abraham Darby established an iron works in Bristol and in the years 1707 and 1708 he transferred his plant and interests to Coalbrookdale. The iron works in Coalbrookdale were managed by five generations of the Darby family, and the Darby interests remained in the works until recent years. Without any break in production, though with many changes in the nature of the products, and some marked fluctuations in output, the Coalbrookdale works continued operative through nearly two and a half centuries and are today active and an important productive unit. Such a record of two hundred and fifty years' duration covers the whole history of iron founding and the development of foundry practice, of the invention of the steam engine, of electrical machinery, and in short, the whole technical background of our present-day industries. The first eighty years of the firm's work include such pioneering achievements of first magnitude as Abraham Darby's application of coke as fuel in iron smelting, the substitution of cast iron for brass in the early steam engine cylinders, the introduction of cast iron tram rails, and the first cast iron bridge ever built, and so well built as to be still standing as a public monument to the skill and enterprise of the Company. The later years were no less productive, and the Company can claim to be pioneers in plate and bar rolling, in high pressure boiler and engine work, domestic stoves, early electrical machinery, and above all in the use of cast iron in art and structural castings.

These major advances of the earlier period have secured a prominent place for the names Darby and Coalbrookdale in all the literature of economic history, and from the time of Samuel Smiles, the main heads of the Darby story prior to 1790 have been told and retold. More recent and more critical appraisals of their work have been made by Ashton, Hall, Davies and Norris, but all these have still been directed almost entirely to one or other of the technical aspects of the Darby story prior to about 1790.

It is felt that with the completion of two hundred and fifty years of progress (1699–1949) it is fitting that an attempt should be made to present a more complete story, in which some attention can be paid to the personality and character of the people associated with the works, to the everyday life and organization of such an enterprise, and to a fuller documenting of the many high lights that have already been acclaimed in outline. A works which has weathered all the vicissitudes of two and a half centuries, that has maintained a steady flow of pioneer advances, that has claimed the respect of the whole world through all that long period, must have a character and be actuated by principles well worthy of exposition.

This is a task from which one might well shrink, as being beyond the capacity of a single individual. The author is acutely conscious of lack of equipment for undertaking such a full study, but can claim two assets which may enable a little new light, however dim, to be shed on this long history. The Darbys and their managers, until the end of the nineteenth century, were Quakers, active in the affairs of the Society of Friends and motivated by its principles. As a Friend and a student of the history of Friends, particularly their attitude and contribution to industry and technology, it may be possible to present a wider picture of the background and guiding principles of this industrial group than has been previously available. In the second place the desire of the present Coalbrookdale Company and the Allied Ironfounders group, to have some record and appreciation of the inheritance which is theirs, has made available a mass of material, and a wealth of warm and friendly co-operation and encouragement, that will go far to offset some of the author's shortcomings.

The principal printed sources used in this book are as follows, but many others will be acknowledged in due place, by footnote references.

Smiles, S., *Industrial Biography*, 1863, chap. 5. 'Coalbrookdale Iron-works—the Darbys and Reynoldses.'

Ashton, T. S., *Iron and Steel in the Industrial Revolution*, 1924.

Ashton, T. S., 'The Discoveries of the Darbys of Coalbrookdale,' *Transactions of the Newcomen Society*, V. 1924–5, 9–12.

Hall, J. W., 'Notes on Coalbrookdale and the Darbys.' *Trans. Newcom. Soc.*, V. 1924–5, 1–8.

Randall, J., *History of Madeley*, 1880.

Victoria County History, *Shropshire*.

Raistrick, A., *Quakers in Science and Industry*, 1950.

The manuscript sources are numerous though not very continuous, and are mostly for the earlier period of the works. The following are the principal groups.

LIBRARY OF THE SOCIETY OF FRIENDS, FRIENDS HOUSE, LONDON

Norris MSS. 14 volumes of transcripts made by W. G. Norris, who for a time was manager of the Coalbrookdale works. The manuscripts are mostly transcripts of Quaker records, but vols. viii and x include many papers relating to the Darby family and to the iron works.

Kelsall's Diary. 6 volumes, original diary, and 8 volumes partly typed and partly manuscript. The typed portion is a copy of the 6 vols. original manuscript, and the manuscript part is a copy of two more volumes of the original diary now lost. The whole covers the period 1701–46.

Abiah Darby's Journal, 1744–69.

Deborah Darby's Journal, 1796–1809.

Letters, various letters of the Darbys.

SHREWSBURY PUBLIC LIBRARY

Coalbrookdale Company Papers (*Shrewsbury MSS.*).

MSS. 328 Sales Book commencing 10 April 1679. This old book contains Abraham Darby's accounts for 1708–9.
MSS. 329 Cash Book No. 1. Commencing 5 July 1718.
MSS. 330 Stock Book, July 1718–Feb. 1727.
MSS. 331 Cash Book No. 2. Sept. 1732–April 1749.
MSS. 332 Account Book Aug. 1754–July 1762.
MSS. 333 Wages Book. Horsehay Waste Book.
MSS. 334 Day Book. May 1794–July 1798.
MSS. 335 Blast Furnace weekly accounts. Dec. 1798–June 1807.
MSS. 336 Horsehay Journal. April 1802–Oct. 1805.
MSS. 337 Horsehay Journal. Oct. 1805–1808.
MSS. 337a. Minute Book of the Proprietors of the Iron Bridge, 1774–98.

COALBROOKDALE COMPANY LTD.

Coalbrookdale MSS.

1. Stock Book. Feb. 1728–Oct. 1738. This continues Shrewsbury MSS. 330.
2. Horsehay account book or Settling Journal. Oct. 1798–Dec. 1808.
3. Minute Book. Oct. 1789–July 1796.
4. Valuation and Profit and Loss accounts, 1805–1852.
5. Collection of typescript notes, letters, etc.
6. Trade and drawing office catalogues.
7. Leases, agreements, plans, etc.

MRS. LABOUCHERE, BRIDGNORTH

Darby MSS.

Letters of Abiah Darby. Miscellaneous papers.
Richard Ford's Letter Book, 1739–45.

SHREWSBURY COUNTY RECORD OFFICE

Coalbrookdale papers. Various letters *etc.* relating to Coalbrookdale and Horsehay.

RATHBONE FAMILY

Rathbone MSS.

Diaries of Richard Reynolds for 1762 and 1816.
Letters from William Reynolds to William Rathbone.
Letters of Richard Reynolds to various people.

IRON AND STEEL INSTITUTE

Iron and Steel Inst. MSS.

Several sheets of manuscripts, notes of costs and prices for Horsehay Forge.

The story of the Company propounds many problems to which it may not be possible to give an adequate answer, and there are many important developments within the Company for which there is only sketchy and inadequate documentation. For a period of nearly two centuries the Company maintained a steady contribution of major advances in the sphere of technology and invention. At every point there was the temptation to turn to one side and become a specialist producer of their own new invention, but whatever trade increase followed on one of their achievements, and however much their name became associated with that product, the firm continued in its accustomed trade of pot and grate casting. This basic part of their productivity runs continuously through their story—it is the unvarying, sound and strong warp of their fabric. Many varied strands of weft run through the eventual pattern, but however brilliant or dominating they may seem, the underlying everyday hard-wearing warp is unchanged. It is as though the essential Quaker simplicity of its owners and directors found a satisfaction and outlet in the essentially simple pot and kettle foundry. Their inventive genius was able, generation after generation, to throw off brilliant side-shoots, to open up many pioneering ways, but always the family and the Company were stabilized by this broad foundation of a simple basic trade, from which they never diverged very far, whatever may have been the temptation.

In some respects the Company had more of the characteristics of a group of craftsmen than of a large iron works. Machines, furnaces, tools, and much of the equipment and method, remained for generations simple and even, in time, primitive. Water-wheels, wooden cranes, trip hammers and many other pieces of apparatus that could justly claim admiration as specimens from an older order, were to be seen in place during this present century, and it was with this equipment as a background that work of unrivalled quality was produced. It was the true enlargement into the industrial scale of the craftsman's well-loved and homely tools, fitted to his hands, which tools without his superb skill would be little more than near-antiques. This blend of the soul of the craftsman with the equipment of the everyday foundry, is one of the secrets of the Company's remarkable virility.

The persistence of the same family names through many generations of the Company's records is another factor that will be worthy of comment. Five generations of Darbys can be matched by five generations of several families of workmen, and the feeling of unity and sense of historic continuity within the little Coalbrookdale community is still evident and an asset.

All these and many other problems are presented to anyone who is privileged to dip into the Company's records, and in this history some attempt will be made to express and evaluate them.

My warm thanks are due to a large number of individuals who have helped me either by making material available, or by discussion and advice. It is not practicable to name all these, but the following must be mentioned in this place.

The book was made possible by the interest of the Coalbrookdale Company and of Allied Ironfounders Ltd. and the co-operation of their personnel. In the Coalbrookdale Company the manager, Mr. G. F. Williams, has been an unfailing friend at the works, and has gone to considerable trouble to satisfy my innumerable queries. To his interest we owe the excavation of the Old Furnace and the preservation of many other relics of the Company. Mr. D. S. Storrar has hunted for and secured many business records, while the chairman, Mr. Lander, used his good offices to procure the loan of manuscript material.

To Mr. W. T. Wren of the Allied Ironfounders Ltd. is due the inception of the book, and his keen interest has continued through every stage of preparation and production, bringing into a friendly group all who could in any way forward the work. My hands have been strengthened at every turn by his thoughtfulness and friendship. Mr. F. Oppé has advised on the illustration and to his efforts we owe the colour plates. Mr. W. Mason of Airton has relieved me of many items of business, advising, reading manuscript and acting throughout as a friend, without whose good offices there would have been frequent delays.

For the loan of material I wish to thank particularly Mr. L. J. Hobbs of the Public Library, Shrewsbury, and his committee who allowed me to have the use of material from their large collection of *Coalbrookdale MSS.* Miss M. C. Hill, Archivist of the County Record Office, Shrewsbury, has loaned typescripts and obtained photostats of documents in her care. At the Friends Reference Library, Muriel A. Hicks has searched and provided photostats of some of the Darby letters and has checked genealogical material. Mr. A. H. Simpson of Horsehay has given permission for the reproduction of many documents placed by him on loan to the County Record Office. Mrs. Labouchere of Bridgnorth has loaned and allowed the use of the Ford Letter Book and some letters from the *Darby MSS.* in her possession and Mrs. H. R. Rathbone of Liverpool has similarly loaned the letters of William Reynolds and other material referred to in the book as the *Rathbone MSS.*

Lastly my wife and daughter have read much of the typescript, made suggestions, and borne patiently with a house full of untidy notes and manuscript material that was bound to overflow the narrow confines of a study. In the course of the work many persons have become friends whose friendship will continue after the publication of the book, and this alone is an abundant reward for what in itself has been a very happy task.

Linton,
Skipton, Yorkshire.
1951.

CONTENTS

LIST OF ILLUSTRATIONS

PLATES

All illustrations are from the Ironbridge Gorge Museum Trust collections unless otherwise stated.

ILLUSTRATIONS IN THE TEXT

Chapter One

THE COALBROOKDALE COMPANY: AN OUTLINE

THE Darby story commences at the end of the seventeenth century and continues to the present day, thus including within itself the whole of the period assigned to the Industrial Revolution. Starting in the time of the small charcoal furnace for iron smelting, worked on a scale that can be justly described as domestic, the Coalbrookdale concerns demonstrate the various stages by which such an industrial unit progressed towards integration into a business where the sources of raw materials were owned by the same company that converted them into pig iron, and further used that as the basic material of a varied manufacture. For a century and a half the Darby business remained essentially a family concern, managed and directed by its owners who retained a close contact with every section of the work and workers. The families which are associated with the Darbys, and which from time to time provided managers or superintendents, Ford, Reynolds, Rathbone, Dearman, Dickinson, are all related to the Darbys by marriage and are also drawn together by the bond of their common religious beliefs, all being members of the Society of Friends or Quakers. Many of the families employed about the works for several generations, Rose, Thomas, Luccock, Norris, Cranage and a dozen others, were also Quakers and helped to create a close woven fabric of friendship and loyalty that was one of the firm's greatest assets. This bond was by no means confined to the Coalbrookdale concerns, but spread outward over a wide network of Quaker customers and ironmasters.

It has been shown recently[1] that members of the Society of Friends occupied a prominent position in the iron industry at the end of the seventeenth century, and the Darby family was a grouping concerned mainly with the smelting and foundry section of this trade.

The latter half of the seventeenth century had seen a decline in the manufacture of iron, and particularly of iron bar, in this country and the beginnings of a revival of this trade were associated with a migration of the iron-making centres from the Sussex Weald and

[1] Raistrick, A., *Quakers in Science and Industry*, 1950, pp. 89–160.

the Forest of Dean, to the thick woodlands of the Welsh borders, the South Yorkshire and Derbyshire valleys, and to Furness. The search in all cases was for an abundant charcoal supply within reasonable reach of reserves of iron ore, and water power. All these new areas had an ancient if modest tradition of ironworking in monastic forges, and many of the bloomery sites of the early sixteenth century became, in the seventeenth century, small furnace units. In the Midlands and the Welsh borders there were many men who described themselves as ironmongers, lock and nail makers, smiths and workers in small ironware, and from these many of the early Friends were drawn. The family of Lloyd of Dolobran had small forges which they leased from the landlord to whom they had been appropriated at the Dissolution of the Monasteries, and these lay in rich woodlands within reasonable reach of Welshpool and other centres on the Severn. For some years, into the early part of the eighteenth century, their pig iron or ore was purchased and brought up the river from Shropshire or Gloucestershire, but later they built a small furnace of their own. Other Friends had furnaces in many parts of the Midlands, and in the other new areas of Yorkshire and Furness. These furnaces were subservient to the forges where the iron was refined and converted to rod and bar iron, and so in the end were dependent upon the vagaries of the bar iron trade. This trade suffered many checks in the eighteenth century, due to our changing relations with Sweden, and the incidence of taxation and protective tariffs, and the fortunes of the forges and furnaces fluctuated in sympathy.

Abraham Darby started his foundry career in brass casting and from this was drawn to the study of iron founding. His concern however was not with raw pig iron for the forges but with iron cast direct from the furnace into pots and kettles and other small objects. This sheltered him from some of the worst of the cold blast of bad trade which was experienced from time to time by his friends, and his new business at Coalbrookdale could be built up on an assured home market for his products. Thus the Darby works were far more responsive to the state of the country markets and the small town customer than they were to the price of iron in Sweden or elsewhere. The early stages of the development of Coalbrookdale are therefore closely tied to the salesmanship that could find its outlet in the country markets and fairs, very much a small business, largely retail, and carried through on personal contact between producer and customer.

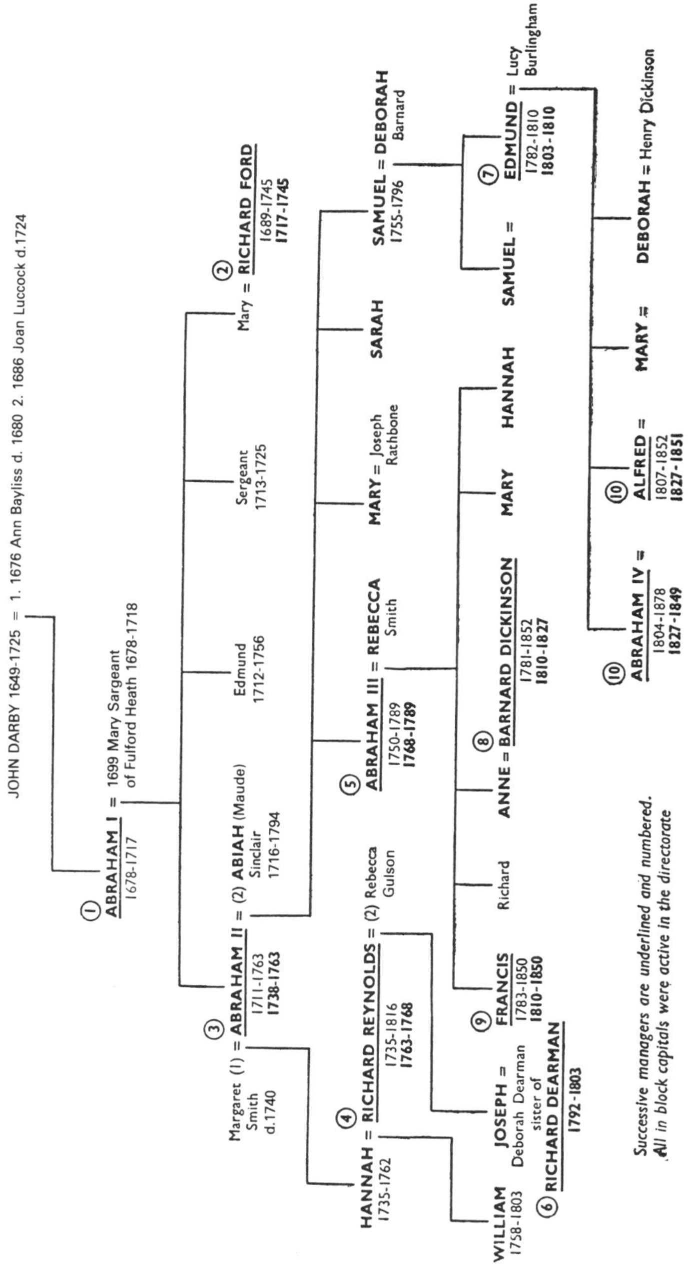

The Darby family connected with the Coalbrookdale Works

The original capital requirements for the lease of the furnace at Coalbrookdale and a minimum of equipment, were largely obtained through partnerships and a mortgage, and the running expenses were paid from the cash received from the customers. It will be worth while to follow out these methods in detail, at least as far as available records go. The nature of these records is such that no continuous account of the financial side of the works is possible, and that what figures are available are in unrelated slabs of a few years at a time. The profits of the Company are only known for two periods, 1739 to 1745, and 1805 to 1851, and in neither case have we more than a very brief and minimum statement. For the valuation of the concerns, there are a few very rare figures, in 1718 and 1796, and partial valuations at one or two dates between these, with an annual valuation for the period 1805 to 1851. In spite of the fragmentary nature of the records, a fairly continuous story can be recovered, but its emphasis and completeness is bound to be greater on the technical than on the economic side, and it is, curiously, more complete before 1805 than after that date.

On the human side of the story, one factor of some importance is the strong religious attitude of the Darbys, as sincere and scrupulous Quakers, and the fact that they drew to themselves families of Quakers both as workmen and as partners and managers. For a hundred and fifty years, the Quakers had strong influence in all relationships in the works, and even later than that, until 1897, the managers were all members of the Society of Friends. During the first century of the works, Friends meetings were held not only on Sunday but on one weekday as well, and for a long time these meetings were held in the offices of the Company, the house of the Darby master, or later in the meeting house built by Abraham II, near the works. In these meetings men from the works would take part on perfect equality with their masters, and the friendliness and fellowship of the meeting was carried forward into the works. With these close relations between the master and men, the Darby concern could fairly be described as domestic in its structure, even if it were growing beyond the limits of the small domestic forge or furnace.

The term 'Coalbrookdale Company' is generally used to name the Darby business in Shropshire from its earliest days, though in point of fact this name was only officially adopted in 1790, up to which time the business was more frequently referred to as the 'Dale

Company'; the longer title was, however, occasionally used even from the beginning. For the first half of the eighteenth century the Dale Company consisted essentially of the iron works in Coalbrookdale itself with, from time to time, other works associated with them such as the Willey and Bersham furnaces from 1732. About the middle of the century the Horsehay and Ketley works replaced these, and Darby began to acquire the ownership of the mines both of coal and ironstone, which supplied his raw material. Richard Reynolds bought a half-share in the Ketley and Horsehay works, so that the 'Dale Company' for the second half of the century tended to be used more specifically for the Darby works in Coalbrookdale, the mines, and the outlying concerns like Madeley Wood furnace, the Bridgnorth forge and the brick yards, while Horsehay and Ketley were referred to by their own individual names. When Richard Reynolds passed over the management of Ketley to his sons William and Joseph, the Ketley works were sometimes called the 'Reynolds Company,' and in 1797 when the shares in Ketley and Horsehay were exchanged, so that all the Ketley shares were in the hands of Reynolds, and Horsehay was entirely Darby, Ketley became 'William Reynolds & Co.' and the 'Coalbrookdale Company' became the official title of all else.

The name Coalbrookdale Company has remained unchanged to the present, though the Company in 1881 became a Limited Company. In 1922 it entered the grouping of Light Castings Ltd., and in recent years became a constituent member of the Allied Ironfounders Ltd. To save confusion in this book, the name Coalbrookdale Company will be used at all times, and before 1790 will imply all the works and/or the managers and owners; after that date it will apply in its stricter sense.*

The first actual reference to the 'Company' is found in 1718 when after the death of Abraham Darby I, Thomas Goldney was at Chester Fair contacting customers and 'collecting money for ye new Company.' In 1738 new agreements were made when Abraham II took a responsible position in the management of the works, and the accounts are drawn to a balance in the cash book, with a note 'Hence Forward the New Company's Cash is Continued.' It is from this date that the references to the Dale Company become common, though in bills and statements sent out by Abraham Darby, *e.g.* in 1748 to the London Lead Co. and others for steam engines, he receipts them almost always 'for self and Company.'

* **See also new (1989) chapters 15 and 16.**

When Abraham I decided to extend his business from Bristol to Coalbrookdale, and took the lease of the old furnace there, he raised the necessary capital by making articles of agreement with James Peters and Griffin Prankard by which he sold them three-sixteenths of his Bristol business and of the newly acquired and established Coalbrookdale foundry. For this agreement the business was valued at £2,804.4.0 and their shares of this, paid to Darby would be £525.18.0. In 1711 the valuation was £2,003.2.7¾ and Abraham had sold a further six-sixteenths share to Richard Champion for £505.7.8 cash, and money already advanced. However by 1712 he was able to afford the repurchase of the six-sixteenths share from Champion, this time for £1,282.1.3, so that the value of the works and stock was then about £3,420.

When Darby entered into the partnerships in the Vale Royal and Dolgyn furnaces, he again raised cash by the sale of shares in Coalbrookdale and also by a mortgage on further shares, but this time with Thomas Goldney of Bristol, merchant and banker. Some time during this early period he also had a loan from his brother-in-law Baylies, which became a source of great trouble and dispute for his widow Mary Darby. These various loans were for capital expenditure as well, as in 1715 he was building the New Furnace at Coalbrookdale, and the new house in Coalbrookdale, near the works. When Darby died in 1717, Goldney through the mortgage and purchases had come to hold a majority of the shares in the Company, and the sons of Abraham I had only three-sixteenths of the shares between them, the whole stock being then reckoned at £3,200, but the valuation made in the inventory of mid-1718 is for £4,200, with the buildings. By 1740 the inventory of the materials at the works, without any buildings, amounted to £7,553, and with the debts owing to the Company and cash paid out at a dividend, the total value for that year was £21,323.

The working partnership of the New Company in 1718 was between Ford and Goldney, who held two-sixteenths and eleven-sixteenths of the shares in it, with three-sixteenths in the hands of Mary Darby, which on her death in the same year, passed in trust for her children. Ford who was Darby's son-in-law acted as clerk and manager at Coalbrookdale, and Goldney as principal agent and financier in Bristol. Joshua Sergeant as trustee for Abraham and Edmund gave some help in the works, but held no position in respect to the management.

The position of Willey and Bersham furnaces from 1732 was a peculiar one. Ford suggested their purchase to Goldney, to enable them to meet an anticipated increase in the demand for cast iron for steam engine parts, and he and Goldney raised the money, Goldney providing the larger portion. When a heavy debt was accumulated on Bersham in 1735, Abraham Darby raised one-third of the required money to clear the position, and thus came in and continued to act as a partner. The two furnaces were managed from Coalbrookdale by Ford, and were visited regularly by Ford and Darby, and the produce of the furnaces was used to satisfy the Coalbrookdale Company's customers at Bristol and Chester. The accounts however were returned separately from those of the Dale, and profits and losses appear to be shared by the partners and not returned into the Dale accounts. Nonetheless these furnaces were an integral part of the working and the trade of the Dale Company.

The Letter Book of Richard Ford, for these furnaces from 1732 to 1737,[1] gives a clear insight into the financial workings both there and at the Dale, and these are confirmed as being applicable to the whole conduct of the business during the first half of the eighteenth century, by a large number of items in the records which remain from the parent Company.

The fragments of Abraham Darby's accounts which survive for 1707 to 1709 show that he was selling his produce of pots and kettles, in small quantities, to customers whom he met in person at the fairs and country towns, and usually the cash settlement was made at once, with very little call for credit. When Ford and Goldney became virtually the owners of the business in 1718, this method of sale was modified in detail, and the sale of pig iron was added to it as an important second string. Goldney and Ford jointly visited the great fairs at Chester, Stourbridge and many other towns of similar regional standing, and there took orders for pots, kettles, and other produce. At the same time the bills for previous purchases had been sent out as invoices with the goods, and the customers attended the fair to settle these in cash. Thus the fair became the normal place both for seeking orders and for receiving cash payment. It was Ford and Goldney, and later Abraham Darby who attended in person, so that dealings were directly with the head of the

[1] This is in the *Darby MSS.*, and contains a transcript of about 130 letters from Ford to Thomas and Gabriel Goldney, mainly on the production of the furnaces and the disposal of the pig iron sent to Bristol.

company, and customers in many cases were or became, personal friends.

For a short time only, Goldney attended fairs, and then settled down in Bristol as agent to the Company. He was already established there as a merchant, and through his various connections received many orders for pig iron and for cast goods. These were sent by barge to Bristol, and for a time his brother Gabriel Goldney acted as receiver and dispatcher, being instructed by Ford that certain cargoes had been loaded and sent off to him, containing the following parcels for various customers, according to orders received from his brother. Gabriel Goldney saw to the distribution to customers, and Thomas Goldney was informed of the amount of goods sent and their agreed price. He then looked after the account and collected in the money and put it to a fund sometimes referred to by Ford as the 'bank.' At the Coalbrookdale end, Ford made fairly regular journeys to the country to collect cash when certain periodic payments were becoming due. Thus we find him telling Goldney that he has been to the fairs to collect cash ready for the yearly payments to the royalty owners of the mines and collieries, or that monthly or quarterly settlements with miners and ore suppliers are coming due and he must visit several markets to collect sufficient cash. When the cash collected fell short of needs, and frequently he complains to Goldney that there is little money about and many accounts must be held over to the next fair or market, he makes the major payments by a bill drawn on either a London or a Bristol business house, usually at twenty-eight days. He at once informs Goldney of the drawing of this bill and asks Goldney to meet it from the money he has received for pig iron and pots, or from 'our bank.' Goldney at regular intervals informs Ford of the money paid into this account from sales and of the balance remaining in it, and at the year's end they decide on the division of the profits and the dividend to be paid on the shares. There is no case traceable of Goldney sending cash to Coalbrookdale. The current needs for wages and raw material payments are all met from the cash collected and by bills drawn against the balance in Goldney's hands, so that Goldney is in effect the Company's banker. Any bills paid in to Ford in settlement of accounts are forwarded to Goldney to be dealt with.

When Bersham and Willey furnaces were in production, Ford wrote a weekly letter to Thomas Goldney, listing the pig iron and pots sent to him, and identifying certain consignments kept separate in the loading, as being from these furnaces, and their price to be placed to the Willey or Bersham credit; similarly the others were to be credited to 'the Dale Company.'

The young Abraham Darby on entering the works in 1732 was very soon initiated into the work of collecting money and getting orders at the fairs, and in 1733 began to take over much of the travelling.

Typical entries in the cash books are as follows.

1733.

Mch.	14.	R Ford & A D at Wrexham & Chester	3.13.8
	19.	R Ford at Stourbridge 3 Days	1. 2.6
Apl	11	A Darbys Exp Collecting ye Contra Cash	1.19.8
Jun	26.	A D & R F Exps with Chaps & Collecting ye Contra Cash	3.19.0
Aug	6	A Darbys Exp in Derbysh 58/9 Gave Biggs ye Engineer 2/6	3. 1.3
	27	Pd Exp collecting ye Contra Cash	1.14.6
Sep	18.	R F Exps to Stourbridge Hampton etc.	6.0
		A D Exp into Wales 39/6 Gave T Brights wife 2/6 Wm Brights Maid 2/6 James Bakers Men 1/6	2. 6. 0
Oct	1	R F & A D Exp at Chester Fair £5.5.6 Gave Wrights wife & son for Fairings 19/6 Gave Bradburns maid & Apprentices 3/6 Remittance of £82 8/-	6.16. 6

Such entries occur quite regularly throughout the available books, though Richard Ford's visits become fewer as Abraham Darby takes more of them on himself.

In 1745 Edmund Darby appears as incurring expenses on journeys to Birmingham, and two new individuals are introduced to the fairs and gradually relieve Darby of these, L. Perry visiting Wrexham and Chester fairs, and John Pearce taking over the Welsh journey and a Staffordshire journey. These 'journeys' were longer than the fair visits, and consisted in travelling a large amount of country, calling upon customers at their homes or shops.

In the accounts quoted there are one or two items of special interest. Ford and Darby sometimes stayed in the homes of Friends, and during their visit would attend the Friends meeting. On such occasions they usually made presents to the servants or apprentices of their hosts. Abraham Darby's journey into Derbyshire was to meet a customer to discuss the performance of one of the Coalbrookdale steam engines, and from time to time on the journeys, Darby called in upon steam engine users to see that all was well, and in this way frequently collected an order for a further engine. Ford has detailed expenses occasionally for entertaining the 'chaps' but sometimes records that he obtained orders from the 'chaps' while at the inn or hotel, *e.g.*

'Met a Mr. Ed. Oliver at Stourbridge Fair and over a glass of wine booked order for 5 or 6 tons of pots.

At Bristol the Champion family stood in a special relation to the Coalbrookdale Company. They were actually the largest customers for pots and kettles, and sent in an order of several hundred pounds' value, two or three times a year. They were in effect warehousemen, as they resold these pots, largely for export, to their own customers, or, as we learn from the Rawlinson and Spencer accounts, they supplied Darby pots or pigs to customers who supplied them with pig or bar iron from other parts of the country. The Champions, first the father then the two sons, were very large merchants in bar iron and pig iron, taking large quantities from Spencer in Yorkshire, Rawlinson in Furness, Darby in Shropshire and the Lloyds on the Welsh borders. They also dealt a little in foreign iron and sometimes provided small quantities of American pig iron to the English iron masters. Comparable with the Champions, but on a smaller scale, were a few other customers in Manchester and Liverpool, and one in London. When Abraham Darby took over the whole management of the works on the death of Ford in 1745, he arranged with the Liverpool customer, Charles Craven, to open a warehouse there, again for the supply of possible exporting customers, as well as for the Liverpool district which was difficult of access from Coalbrookdale. This warehouse became part of the Coalbrookdale Company's assets, and later was followed by others in Cornwall and in the North. The Liverpool warehouse accounts were for a time discussed at a meeting at the time of Wrexham Fair, and one of Abraham Darby's accounts for this visit will illustrate this and also the nature of the business done at the fair.

Cash Recd at Wrexham Fair	
Henry Kynaston	2. 0. 0
William Bickerton	15. 6
Rich Ford acct of Wm Bickerton for Frying pans	18. 6

Randle Bingley	4. 5. 0
Jos Clubb	4. 0. 0
Jos Chamberlain	20. 0. 0
William Wright	4. 2. 0
Edward Griffin in full	5.10. 0
do on account	10.10. 0
Liverpool Warehouse by Chas Craven	680. 0. 0
John Beckett Middlewick	4. 1. 0
Richard Podmore	6. 1. 6
Lawrence Skeel	4. 8. 0
James Eaton	15. 6. 0
Walter Unett	9. 9. 0
John Hand	8. 6. 0
Richard Higginston	2.15. 0
Randle Keay	2.17. 0
John Hassall	3. 5. 0
John Wicksteed	5.10. 0
	793.19. 6

The expenses of the journey and some other items were paid out of this cash and the final account is

By Abm Darby for Rich Ford Cashier to the Company.	
By Rich Ford Payed Thomas Gosnell	754.18. 2
General charges paid.	
Abm Darby & Jno Goslings Exps 18 Nights chiefly staying for cash in Liverpool	1.19. 0
By A D John Pearce	6. 0. 0
By Edmund Darby paid Wm Kerry	3. 2. 6
By Abm Darby pd himself	27.19.10
	793.19. 6

The date of this account is 29 January 1748, and Richard Ford is the son of the first Richard Ford, and he took over the job of cashier to the Company on his father's death in 1745. This was the first separation of the work of the 'clerk' from that of the manager, who formerly had included the cashier's work with the general management.

In the many examples of similar accounts it is striking how many small amounts are concerned, and in fact the vast majority of the Company's customers are of this small type. Large customers are limited to a few merchants like the Champions, and to the people who were buying steam engines and pipe work, who generally paid their account with bills drawn on various people. As late as 1815 there is a complaint from the shopkeepers and warehousemen of the Shrewsbury district, that the Company will sell a single article to any customer who asks for it, at the same rates as they sell larger amounts to their largest customers, and they ask that goods be sold to the shops, and the direct sale at the works be terminated.

The period from 1739 to 1744, during which Abraham II and Richard Ford shared the management of the works, is one for which a note of the profits and losses is available, along with the details of income due to Abraham from his salary and from the Malt House, which was carried on as a family business until well into the nineteenth century. In this period his income was just over £950 in 1739 but between 1740 and 1745 it averaged about £1,800, with a rapid rise in the later years. The Malt House profits rarely reached £100 a year, and his salary from 1740 was £100, so that his income from the two and a half shares in the works which he held was about £1,600 a year at that time.[1] Actually by 1745 his total income from the works and the Malt House had reached £2,650 and if the same rate of increase was maintained, must in the next year have approached £3,000. In the same proportion, the heirs of Thomas Goldney must at that time have been getting from Coalbrookdale profits something in the neighbourhood of £10,000 a year.

From 1745 to 1763 Abraham was the sole manager and the works were considerably extended under his planning and direction. After the building of Horsehay and Ketley furnaces, with the acquisition of the manor of Madeley and the royalties of the mines of ore and coal within it, which were a main source of raw material for the Company, the increase of business brought a great increase of profits to Abraham, though of course the greater share went to the Goldney family. Some of this wealth was used by Abraham II to repurchase shares in the Company, and this repurchase from the Goldney children was completed by Abraham III. At his death the whole of the shares were in the hands of the Darby family with the exception of the part share in Horsehay and Ketley which was owned by Richard Reynolds. It was probably this extensive purchase of shares at the same time as the initiation of such large works as the Iron Bridge and the canals, which created the debt of approximately £54,800 which Abraham and his brother Samuel contracted to the Company,

[1] For more detail see Appendix 1, p. 278.

and which was, a few years after Abraham's death, liquidated by Rebecca and Sarah Darby.

We thus see the business dominated by Thomas Goldney and his family from 1718 to about 1770 so far as the actual shares and profits were concerned, but the Darby family, with the assistance of Ford and Reynolds, controlled all policy and the actual conduct of the works. Richard Reynolds was connected with many other concerns, particularly the South Wales tin plate industry, and the Bristol merchant trade, and he became a man of considerable wealth. Thus when Darby was feeling the burden of debt and the necessity for more capital, Reynolds bought from him the manor of Madeley, and became the landlord of the Coalbrookdale works, in which capacity he was very generous in all arrangements of rents and royalties. From about 1780 we can say that Reynolds acted as banker to the Company, advancing loans and transacting much of their financial business. This continued until the early part of the nineteenth century when his son Joseph established a bank in Wellington and became the Company's banker. It was not until 1845 that the Company purchased the last portion of the Coalbrookdale property from the Reynolds descendants and became their own landlords in all departments.

A change in the structure of the Company is seen soon after the death of Abraham III, when for a time Richard Dearman was the appointed manager. Though not a son-in-law like Ford and Reynolds, he was a connection of the Reynolds by marriage. When he took the management, the Company was being guided by a group consisting of the brother Samuel, though he died within a year or two, the widow and two children of Abraham III, Rebecca, Sarah and Mary, and William Reynolds. The Company was now departmentalized with foremen or managers over separate parts, and the general manager reported regularly to the meetings of the Darby owners. A little later Edmund, and later still, Francis, Abraham IV and Alfred Darby became managers, but maintained and extended the departmental divisions with the delegation of some parts of the work to under managers. In this way the nineteenth century is essentially modern in the structure of the works with the family and domestic element receding.

The first great change in the early sales structure of the Company had come with the development of the steam engine castings trade, which brought with it a new type of customer who was not normally an attender at the local fairs and markets, but who had to be contacted at his mines. For this trade the Company developed agents, though at first they were only lightly and incidentally linked to the Company, Abraham Darby and Ford making contact personally with some of the mining fraternity. An agent was established first in Truro, and at one time, Hornblower was sending orders to Coalbrookdale and advising of materials which would be needed in Cornwall for the mine pumping. Proper agencies were operating in the Northumberland and Durham mining area, from Newcastle, before the middle of the century, and from the letters of William Brown it is evident that the agent was paid by a commission on the sale. In 1768 Abiah Darby writing to her sister says that she is pressing Thomas Goldney to consider supplying Coalbrookdale goods to the agent on a 'sale or return' basis, allowing him to take profits instead of or in addition to a slight commission.[1] The further development was the later establishment of warehouses at London, Bristol and Liverpool, where stocks of goods were carried and direct sales were made. By this time the journeys to fairs and to the country were being made by persons employed specifically as travellers, and Darby and Reynolds attended only the meetings of ironmasters at Stourbridge and at Stourbridge Fair, which developed into a central iron market for the Midlands and south-west.

The opening years of the nineteenth century were marked by keen price competition on the part of the South Wales ironmasters, whose industry was experiencing a rapid expansion, and the struggle of the Midland Ironmasters' Association to formulate a policy for its members by which they could meet this competition. Under the stimulus of this struggle, price lists were issued[2] and as the Company embarked upon the new branches of art castings and more varied foundry work, the preparation of catalogues and the registration of designs were begun. Thus by the middle of the century, standard lists of products were available and goods could be bought from warehouses in London, Bristol, Liverpool, and some other places, which carried a large stock for inspection, or could be ordered from lists direct from the Company or through almost any ironmonger.

The great boom in trade that followed the Great Exhibition of 1851 caused such a multiplication of designs in every department of foundry product that the Company was compelled to expand its

[1] Letter in *Darby MSS.* 26th 9 mo. 1768.

[2] *e.g.* County Records, Shrewsbury; *Coalbrookdale papers*, No. 16, 71.

lists and in 1875 published its huge two volume catalogue from which anything from the smallest pot up to the largest public statue or building could be ordered. At that time this must have been the most varied foundry in this country if not in the world, its products to be numbered in thousands of designs, ranging from pure art to the most modern steam engines and machinery.

This first half of the nineteenth century was one of considerable expansion in spite of several periods of acute depression, connected with the Napoleonic wars. In 1798 the total capital of the Company was a little over £95,000, with Coalbrookdale foundry and forge representing the larger part of this. In 1810 the capital value of Coalbrookdale dropped to under £30,000 and Horsehay furnaces and forge, and the other furnaces and collieries assumed the leading position. From about 1835 both Coalbrookdale and Horsehay began to increase in value, fairly rapidly, and the Company's total capital valuation, which had reached £125,000 in 1830, rose steadily to £365,000 in 1851 after five years of decrease, 1830 to 1834.

The year of the Great Exhibition, 1851, marks another change in the constitution of the Company, when the members of the Darby family ceased to take any direct interest in it, and it is managed by a salaried staff without any other financial interest in the Company than their salary. The shares gradually concentrated in the hands of Abraham and of Alfred's sons, and when the Darbys finally left the Company in 1922 and surrendered their shares, the principal shareholder was Alfred Edmund William Darby, of Little Ness, near Shrewsbury. There were many minor changes in the works at the beginning of the twentieth century, when the engineering section was given up, and the mines relinquished. In 1922 the Coalbrookdale Company united with the Planet Foundry Co. Ltd., of Guide Bridge, Manchester; Messrs. M. Cockburn and Co. of Falkirk; and Messrs. McDowall, Steven and Co. Ltd., of Falkirk, to form Light Castings, Ltd. The Horsehay works had been re-established by an independent company for bridge and structural iron work, and the Ketley works site was developed by Mr. Sinclair, one-time manager of the Coalbrookdale Company, as the Sinclair Iron Company. The final change was the transition about 1930 to the larger grouping of the Allied Ironfounders Ltd., of which group the Coalbrookdale Company is still a constituent member.*

This brief outline of the changes in the Company and in its methods of dealing, now remains to be filled out in detail, and the

* **See also new (1989) chapters 15 and 16.**

following chapters will follow the fortunes of the Company and those who guided it, through this long period of two and a half centuries, and will look in some detail at the major contributions which it has been the fortune of the Company to make, to the techniques of iron founding and engineering construction. The arrangement is chronological, though for convenience the more technical aspects have been brought together in chapters which span a technical epoch, rather than trying to keep them within the life span of one of the long succession of managers, in the manner in which the more straightforward story of the Company is arranged.

Chapter Two

ABRAHAM DARBY I, 1699–1708
THE BRISTOL COMPANIES

ABRAHAM DARBY is one of those tantalizing persons who from time to time emerge from an obscure background and by their life and actions attain a position which commands the interest of succeeding generations. Of Abraham Darby's background as of so many others, there is little to be learned beyond a very generalized picture of the life of the class from which he emerged. The only direct manuscript evidence available has been frequently quoted and requoted in part, although only the first short paragraph refers to his earlier years. It is the paper headed 'Some account of the Family of the Darbys; being what Hannah Rose has heard her Parents, John and Grace Thomas, say concerning them.'[1] John Thomas was closely associated with Abraham Darby, as a workman at Bristol and at Coalbrookdale, for the greater part of his life. His daughter Hannah was born on the 15th of 10th month (December) 1818 at Coalbrookdale, the year after Darby's death. Her story can therefore be taken as first hand, preserving as it does the account spoken by her father, Abraham's most trusted workman and intimate friend. The opening paragraph of the account is but a skeleton statement of bare bones, for which a clothing of flesh must be sought elsewhere.

> John Darby was a farmer—lived at a house called Wren's Nest near Dudley in Worcestershire. He had by his first wife one Son and Daughter named Abraham and Esther. . . . He put his son apprentice to Jonathan Freeth, a maltmill maker at Birmingham who was a 'public Friend,' and while he was there, Abraham Darby and one or two of his master's sons had a gift in the Ministry. I think I have heard there were four of them in the same shop that worked together all public and used to sit together one evening in the week. After he was out of his time he married Mary Sergeant.

All other accounts of John Darby describe him as a nailer and locksmith, as well as a small farmer, and for the time of which they

[1] This manuscript is in the Friends Library, Friends House, under the title of "J. T. Dickinson's account of Abraham Darby's life," and is also transcribed in full in the *Norris MSS.* vol. x, pp. 121–31. These are both recent transcripts of the original document.

are speaking these are by no means irreconcilable terms. Defoe, speaking of the Dudley district, says,

> Every Farm has one Forge or more; so that the Farmers carry on two very different Businesses, working at their Forges as Smiths, when they are not employed in the Fields as Farmers. And all their work they bring to market, where the great Tradesmen buy it up and send to London. ... We cannot travel far in any direction out of the sound of the hammer.

During the seventeenth century there was a considerable traffic in pig iron, between the furnaces of the Forest of Dean and the forges of the upper Severn and west Midlands. In these forges the pig iron was converted into bar iron and then slit into nailer's rods, processes calling for a greater amount of power and fuel than was available in the furnace areas. The many streams of the Welsh borders, and of the hilly country of Shropshire and Worcestershire, were all utilized by scattered bar iron forges, most of which found an immediate market for their bar and rod iron among the population of farmer-smiths and nailmakers, who were a rapidly increasing section of the local population. As this trade expanded after the Civil Wars, a number of warehousemen who were prepared to deal with a multiway traffic, pig iron to the forges, bar and rod to the smiths and nailers, and finished goods to the Bristol and London merchants, found a satisfactory opening for business on or near the Severn. Such warehousemen, buyers and sellers, founded businesses in Welshpool, Bridgnorth, Bewdley and Stourbridge, and even in many smaller places. It was among the increasing population of nailers that the elder Darby, like most of his neighbours, found it natural and economic to set up his own small forge at which his son would frequently help. Thus young Abraham, even before his apprenticeship, would be familiar with the working of the forge, and would also have some knowledge of the general trade in and demand for iron of various kinds.

The increasing burden of the prosecutions and of the distraints for tithe levied against the Quakers,[1] would have influenced John Darby in his decision to put Abraham as apprentice to a trade, in a free, non-corporate town like Birmingham, in which there was already a considerable body of Friends at work. Among the Friends there were several who were engaged in some branch or other of the

[1] This question is discussed at length in Raistrick, A., *Quakers in Science and Industry*, 1950, chap. 2.

iron trade, and John Darby chose from among them Jonathan Freeth, who was a 'weighty' Friend. The term 'weighty' has for a long time been used within the Society of Friends to indicate a person whose spoken contributions in the meetings and whose council and conduct are such as to make his words and advice carry weight. The term 'public' Friend current in John Darby's time though possibly not identical in meaning was very similar. It implied a Friend active in the affairs of the Society, whose words and ministry were acceptable. Hannah Rose assures us that Jonathan Freeth was such a public Friend and there are other testimonies among the records of the Birmingham Meetings to the same effect. In the business of such a Friend, Abraham would have a strict training in his craft, but with the affairs of the Society of Friends, mid-week, monthly, quarterly and other meetings, all duly attended to. The thoughts and ministry expressed at these meetings would be kept in mind, discussed, and would form the basis of much of the conversation in the workshop. Thus Abraham, during his apprenticeship, not only acquired his knowledge of iron casting but took a serious concern for the work and ministry of the Society of Friends, which remained a chief activity of his life. Secular and religious activity were never separated into closed compartments, but were combined in an integrated activity which gave power and direction to the whole of his life.

At the end of the apprenticeship, on the 18th day of 7th month (September) 1699, Abraham Darby married Mary Sergeant at a Friends meeting held at Dudley.

Mary Sergeant's parents were bleachers of linen yarns, 'and by some accident she [Mary] fell into the Furnace when it was boiling and when taken out they thought her dead or near it'; however she recovered, but was left with a serious asthma, and we have a touching picture of her condition in Hannah Rose's narrative. 'Before this accident she was a very strong hearty young woman but after she was married she was troubled with an asthmatic complaint and if her husband was from home, she would sit up all night and sleep by the fire.'

Abraham Darby left Birmingham on the completion of his apprenticeship, and set up in business as a maker of malt mills. His new business was founded in Bristol, with a large body of Friends in business, among whom were many connected with the iron trade. Nehemiah Champion was one such Friend, already acting as agent and warehouseman for some of the Yorkshire ironworks, while there were relatives and associates of the Lloyds, Harfords, Goldneys and other Quaker merchant families.

Hannah Rose is again the principal authority for this early period and her brief statement is that 'while Abraham Darby was at Bristol he went to Holland and hired some Dutch workmen and set up the Brass Works at Baptist Mills. His partners were Edward Lloyd, Benjamin Cool, Arthur Thomas, and John Andrews. Abraham Darby was the acting man, began in 1706.' The Bristol Brass Wire Company was formed in 1702 with the partners mentioned, to whom were added before long John and Thomas Coster and Nehemiah Champion. Abraham's journey to Holland was probably in the year 1704, and it is generally believed that while there he studied the methods employed for casting brass pots, which at that time were a considerable item of import into this country. Hannah Rose continues:

> After some time he had a mind to set the Dutchmen to try to cast Iron Pots in sand. They tried several times but could not do it, so he was at a great loss in paying Wages, for no result. At length, John Thomas, my Father, then a young man who came on trial to learn the trade of Malt Mill making, seeing the Dutchmen try and could not bring to perfection, asked his master to let him try, so with his leave he did it, and afterwards his Master and him were bound in Articles in the year 1707 that John Thomas should be bound to work at that business and keep it a secret and not teach anybody else, for three years. They were so private as to stop the keyhole of the door.

There is a second much longer manuscript by Hannah Rose, which begins with a very modest justification and apology.

> I have had it on my mind for some years past to leave behind me something concerning my ancestors as far back as I have any account from my Parents. Some may object and say it is pride for thee to write of thy ancestors who were all poor people, but as they were honest and sober, and my parents brought me up to read and write, I ought to employ my pen in their behalf for the Scripture says the Righteous shall be had in everlasting remembrance.

According to this account, John Thomas was born near Welshpool in 1679; his mother was Priscilla, daughter of Edward and Katherine Evans who had been convinced and had become Quakers in 1662.

They suffered many persecutions and imprisonments, and Edward Evans died in prison. John Thomas's father died when John was about eleven years old, and he was put out as a shepherd lad to a relation, Thomas Oliver, who later went to Pennsylvania. John then found work with Charles Lloyd of Dolobran, the farmer and ironmaster. Edward Evans had been a fellow prisoner with Charles Lloyd the elder, so that young John would find a warm place in the Lloyd household, for his father's sake.

Hannah's narrative says:

> After my father had lived for some years with Thomas Oliver, he went to live with Charles Lloyd of Dolobran, where he continued till near 18 years old; and then he had a mind to go to Bristol and bind himself apprentice to some trade, but it being in Queen Anne's war he was afraid of being pressed for a Soldier if out of a place. So he got his master Charles Lloyd to recommend him to some friend: and he did so to Edward Lloyd, a Wine Merchant, a relative of Charles Lloyd till he could get a place to his mind. In about two months he went to Abraham Darby, a smith, thinking to be a Malt Mill maker.

Again follows the story of the Dutchmen's efforts to cast iron pots and John's eventual success. The dating of Hannah's story offers some discrepancies. If John was 18 when he went to Bristol, that would be the year 1697 but Abraham Darby did not go there until 1699. John Thomas would serve a seven years' apprenticeship and this would agree with the bond of 1707, between him and Darby, made when he was out of his time and a free man.

In 1707 a patent was granted to Darby for his method of casting pots, so that the experiments on which it was based were probably completed during the later years of Thomas's apprenticeship. We have no technical knowledge of the methods used by Thomas and Darby in their many experiments, and the patent itself tells us very little except in the most general terms. The pot which became the typical Darby product was the three-legged cauldron, the typical 'bellied' pot with the largest diameter at the middle. One problem was to mould such a shape in a way that would enable the pot to be freed from the mould without the mould's total destruction. It was also necessary to use a dry moulding material which would not generate steam on contact with the hot metal, since the steam would either disrupt the mould or spoil the casting. Possibly the patent was double—for casting in pure, dry sand, without loam, and for the use of a special mould box and core.

There is no doubt that Darby realized from the first the importance of finding such a method of casting. The demand for pots was increasing and import was becoming more and more difficult. The statement of Hannah Rose, that during the experiments the keyhole was stopped, to prevent spying, is only one sign of the acute commercial rivalry which made a firm bond with Thomas necessary. She says in the longer account of her father, that he 'was offered double wages to leave his Master Darby, but would not do so.' The articles of agreement between Darby and Thomas, signed in January 1707, follow the usual lines, with three principal clauses.

1. It is agreed John Thomas consents to work and labour faithfully for Abraham Darby in the art and mystery of casting and moulding of Iron Potts from the day and date for the term of three years.

2. Abraham Darby agrees to pay John Thomas £7 per annum for the first two years and £8 for the last year of the agreement, and to provide for John Thomas, good and sufficient meat, drink, washing and lodging.

3. John Thomas in consideration that the making and casting of iron pots is not a trade which he was employed or brought up in, doth covenant that he will not at any time hereafter serve any other person whatever on or about the casting of iron pots in sand nor will he disclose the method to anyone.

Seven years later a similar agreement was made with Thomas Luccock, but the wages were 6/– a week without lodging, and there was a clause adding a fine of '£5 for every pot or kettle he shall cast for anyone else.'

The patent, No. 380, was signed on 18 April 1707, and its preamble tells us that

our trusty and well beloved Abraham Darby, of our city of Bristol, Smith, hath by his petition humbly represented vnto vs that by his study and industry and expence he hath found out and brought to perfection 'A NEW WAY OF CASTING IRON BELLIED POTTS, AND OTHER IRON BELLIED WARE IN SAND ONLY, WITHOUT LOAM OR CLAY, BY WHICH IRON POTS, AND OTHER WARE MAY BE CAST FINE AND WITH MORE EASE AND EXPEDITION, AND MAY BE AFFORDED CHEAPER THAN THEY CAN BE BY THE WAY CŌMONLY VSED, AND IN REGARD TO THEIR CHEAPNESSE MAY BE OF GREAT ADVANTAGE TO THE POORE OF THIS OUR KINGDOME, WHO FOR THE MOST PART VSE SUCH WARE, AND IN ALL PROBABILITY WILL PREVENT THE MERCHANTS OF ENGLAND GOING TO FORREIGN MARKETS FOR SUCH WARE, FROM WHENCE GREAT QUANTITIES ARE IMPORTED, AND LIKEWISE MAY IN TIME SUPPLY FOREIGN MARKETS WITH THAT MANUFACTURE OF OUR OWN DOMINIONS,' and hath humbly prayed vs to grant him our Letters Patents for the sole vse and benefit of the said Invention for the terme of fourteen yeares. . . .'

This petition was granted and the patent duly signed.

Darby's interest in iron casting was evidently not shared by his partners in the Brass Company; this decided him to leave them and set up a new works. 'After a few years Abraham Darby wanting to enlarge the Brass Works and his partners not being willing, he drew his share out of it, and hearing of an Iron Work at Coalbrookdale in Shropshire went and settled there about the year 1709 or 1710.'[1] In 1709 he made an agreement of partnership with James Peters and Griffin Prankard, and the preamble to this confirms that for some time he worked alone at the trade of iron founding, without any partners.

The capital expenses of taking and refitting the Coalbrookdale premises were probably financed by the sale of his share of the Brass Company.

The removal from Bristol to Coalbrookdale was a momentous change which must have been decided upon only after considerable thought. One is impelled to ask what factors influenced the choice of this locality in preference to any other of the several districts which were then producing iron in large or small quantity. Darby's foundry work at Bristol had been, like all others at that time, dependent upon charcoal fuel, and any expansion of his works would have called for greatly increased quantities of charcoal at a time when supplies were not easy and when competition for what supplies were available was becoming keen. It is likely that the difficulties of securing adequate charcoal supplies had already turned his mind towards the possibility of some other fuel, and being brought up in the Dudley district he must have been familiar with the story and claims of Dud Dudley to have produced good iron with coal.[2] His practical experience in the Birmingham and Bristol districts would convince him that whatever the merits of Dudley's claim, good iron had not yet in fact been made available except such as was produced by charcoal furnaces.

Darby was apprenticed and set up in trade as a malt mill maker, and it is significant that in the malting industry coke had been made and had been successfully used in the malting kilns from the middle of the seventeenth century.[3] Patents had also been granted to several

[1] Hannah Rose's narrative. Actually Darby went to Coalbrookdale first in 1708, but continued to hold part of the Bristol works until about 1710.

[2] Dudley, D., *Mettallum Martis*, 1665. For discussions of Dudley's claims see Ashton, T. S., *Iron and Steel in the Industrial Revolution*, 1924; Mott, R. A., 'Dud Dudley and the Early Coal-Iron Industry,' *Trans. Newcomen Soc.* XV. 1934–5, pp. 17–37; Lones, T. E., 'A Precis of Mettallum Martis and an Analysis of Dud Dudley's Alleged Invention,' *Trans. Newcomen Soc.* XX. 1939–40, pp. 17–28.

[3] Neff, J. U., *The Rise of the British Coal Industry*, 1932, vol. I, p. 216.

persons for making iron with 'charked coal,'[1] though these had not been carried to a practical success. It is certainly true that, among the many coals available in the Bristol market, some of the Shropshire coals were far more suited for coking than any from other fields. Whether this was known or determined by Darby we cannot be certain, but of the areas supplying Bristol, Coalbrookdale was the greatest. This coalfield lies athwart the river Severn which cuts through it in a deep gorge at Ironbridge; the tributary stream of the Coalbrook also makes a deep gorge-like valley roughly along the axis of the field, so that the Coal Measures are abundantly exposed and easily accessible along the margins of the two valleys.[2] This factor stimulated the early exploitation of the area.

[1] The earliest is Patent No. 15, granted 25 April 1620 to Sir William St. John, Sir Giles Mompesson and others, to 'charke' pit coal and to 'use and ymploye the said fewell soe charked in anie open or plaine furnace' for casting and refining iron.

[2] The productive measures are of Middle Coal Measure age and contain a large number of workable seams of coal, with many beds of ironstone closely associated with them; in fact the total thickness of the various beds of coal and ironstone at Lightmoor, immediately east of Coalbrookdale, is respectively 40 feet and 24 feet. The section of the Measures, worked out by the Geological Survey, is as follows—

Measures with Chance Pennystone Ironstone	84 ft. 0 in.
FUNGUS COAL	3 ft. 0 in. to 3 ft. 10 in.
Measures with Ballstone Ironstone	90 ft. 0 in.
TOP COAL	4 ft. 0 in. to 5 ft. 6 in.
Measures	30 ft. 0 in.
DOUBLE COAL	3 ft. 0 in. to 6 ft. 0 in.
Measures with Yellowstone Ironstone	6 ft. 0 in.
YARD COAL	3 ft. 4 in.
Measures with Blue & White Flats Ironstone	29 ft. 0 in.
BIG FLINT COAL	3 ft. 0 in. to 6 ft. 0 in.
Measures with Penny Ironstone	30 ft. 0 in.
SULPHUR or NEW MINE COAL	to 7 ft. 0 in.
Measures	20 ft. 0 in. to 40 ft. 0 in.
TWO FOOT or GANEY COAL	to 2 ft. 8 in.
Measures	to 20 ft. 0 in.
BEST COAL	
RANDLE COAL	8 ft. 0 in. to 15 ft. 0 in.
CLOD COAL	
Measures	to 30 ft. 0 in.
LITTLE FLINT COAL	to 3 ft. 0 in.

This section is elaborated in *Geological Survey Memoirs*. Sheet Memoir 153, 1928.
See also Birch, T. W., 'The Development of the Coalbrookdale Coalfield,' *Geography*, XIX. 1934, p. 119.

In the early seventeenth century Coalbrookdale was raising about 95 per cent. of all Shropshire's output of coal, and the Broseley and Benthall areas came into production not many years later; the Madeley pits were greatly increased in number soon after the Civil War. A manuscript report to the Treasury[1] discussing the possible taxation of coal says that such a tax would be easy to collect as the coal was nearly all produced by the three great collieries of Madeley, Benthall and Broseley. Each of these groups of pits produced about 30,000 tons of coal yearly, while the total output of the whole district would be around 130,000 tons.[2]

At that time the Severn was possibly the most important waterway in the country, and its traffic linked together into a remarkable unity a number of very rich markets, from Welshpool and Shrewsbury down to Gloucester and Bristol, so that corn and coal were cheaper here than anywhere else in Britain. In 1678 coal in Tewkesbury cost only 6/– a ton, less than half its price in London, but the extra river freightage increased the price in Bristol, where also there was keener competition for the supplies.[3]

If Abraham Darby was finding the development of his iron founding business hampered by the rising cost of charcoal, it would be natural for him to revert to the many suggestions that had already been made for the use of coal as the fuel in iron working. He may even have made experiments and been baffled by the sulphur and other volatile constituents of the coal, and then called upon his wide experience of malting kilns and furnaces where coke, a coal purged of these very elements, was generally used as the fuel. The failure of his partners to respond to his desire for expansion was the trigger which released the determination to start out afresh in some new place. That decision being taken, and some idea, however vague, of experimenting with coal or coke fuel having formed in his mind, Coalbrookdale and its vicinity would offer many attractions. It lay near the centre of adequate coal supplies, in an area which was still well wooded so that supplies of charcoal would be available for as long as he needed it. The swift running stream and the nature of the valley offered good prospects of an abundant water supply for power,

[1] Treasury Board Papers 34/51.

[2] Neff, J. U., *Rise of the British Coal Industry*, 1932, vol. I, p. 361.

[3] Neff, J. U., *op. cit.* I, p. 96, says that at the end of the seventeenth century there was more traffic on the Severn than on almost any river in Europe, except the river Meuse between the Namur-Liége coalfield area and the plains.

for either furnace or forge bellows. Coalbrookdale was an old established iron making centre, and premises were available, and to be had on a short lease.[1] If necessary, a good business could be built up on the old methods, with cheap and abundant supplies of ore and charcoal; the presence of an excellent coking coal, of which he would know from his malt mill customers, offered the ideal conditions for his experiments. The disposal of his finished goods would be no more difficult than at Bristol, as there were important markets at Bridgnorth, Shrewsbury, Bewdley, and Welshpool well served by river transport, and many other inland towns within easy reach. Friends were busy in that area with the Lloyds of the Dolobran forges trading into Welshpool and Bewdley, the Milners already established as iron dealers at Bewdley, and such families as the Crowleys of Stourbridge and Osbornes and others near Wolverhampton and Shrewsbury; Birmingham and Dudley were within reasonable reach. In 1707 Darby had been admitted a freeman of Bristol, without the payment of a fine, by favour of the mayor, so that he could assume a secure position as trader in the Bristol market.[2]

The partnership agreement with Peters and Prankard, 8 February 1709/10, by which they took one-sixteenth and two-sixteenths respectively in the Cheese Lane works and Coalbrookdale, gives a little information on the capital, which was then taken to be £2,804.4.0.

The partnership was made when Darby had already settled into the Coalbrookdale premises, and brought his furnace into its first blast, and was just launching out into his trade with the Midland dealers. The work of establishing first the Cheese Lane foundry and then the Coalbrookdale furnace had been carried through single-handed by him, and at that time he may have intended to supply the Cheese Lane foundry with its pig iron as well as establishing a separate pot casting trade at Coalbrookdale. By mid 1709 the furnace and casting floors at Coalbrookdale were established in a steady production, and materials, patterns, and men had been moved there from Bristol. Some time after this and before 1711, Darby gave up all his interests in the Bristol Company, and for a time Coalbrookdale became his only concern.

At the time when Darby was establishing his Coalbrookdale

[1] Coalbrookdale already had a furnace and forges in it, the forges being documented as far back as the Caldebrooke Smithie where iron was made in blooms in 1544. This was on the site later to be known as the Lower Forge, and a hundred years later an Upper Forge was also at work.

[2] *Victoria County History. Shropshire*, vol. I, p. 461.

venture, the iron industry in South Yorkshire had already begun to shape its organization under the influence of Cotton, Dickin, and Spencer, while the iron producers on the Welsh borders were well settled to a regular pattern of trade. In Yorkshire there was a belt of furnaces for producing pig iron, largely located on or near the outcrop of the Tankersley or other good Coal Measures ironstone seams. This grouping was on the whole concentrated between Wakefield and Sheffield, but was linked both in diverse partnerships and by direct trade with a series of forges scattered over a much wider area. The furnaces made heavy demands on the local timber supplies around them, and in fact drew on the country for almost twenty miles around for charcoal. It is certain that the resources of the country were fully taxed by the furnace demands. The forges were of necessity removed to other areas where they could have independent supplies of charcoal, along with good water power for their hammers. Thus forges were again from ten to twenty miles away from the furnaces, and were each centred on an area of woodland only just sufficient for its own needs. The pig iron from the furnaces was apportioned to the various forges which produced bar and rod iron, and this in turn was disposed in two directions. Some part went to nailers and other consumers direct from the forges, through the interests of some of the partnership in these secondary trades, while the rest was sent to be marketed by agents or through warehouses in various parts of the country, a moderate amount finding its way into the Severn area through Nehemiah Champion and other dealers. The effective pattern of this industry was therefore a wide network of furnaces and forges spread over an area at least forty miles by twenty miles, with a very heavy transport problem for charcoal to each member, and for pig iron between furnaces and forges.

In the Welsh borders, we have such groups as that of the Lloyd forges, buying their pig iron at Welshpool warehouses or at Bewdley, and having it carried up the rivers and then overland to forges which were located on a strong stream within a suitable charcoal area. Again there was a large transport problem of pig iron and charcoal to the forges and bars and rods back to the distribution centres. Many of the Midlands forges took their pig iron from the Forest of Dean, until the Staffordshire furnaces came into prominence at a little later date.

Against these common patterns, Darby was instinctively moving towards the creation of a new type. His furnace and its forges (although the latter did not come into operation till much later,

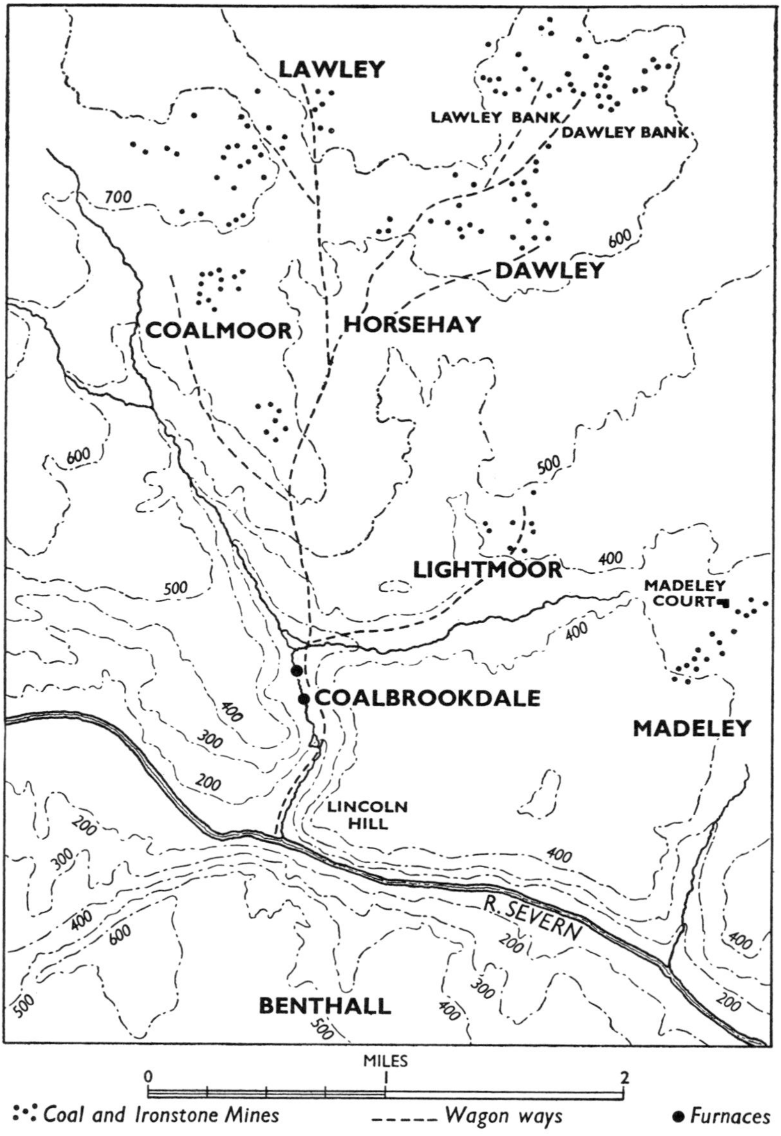

Map showing relation of Coalbrookdale Works to Mines, about 1760.

they were already there with their potential) were located side by side on a stream where the construction of furnace and forge pools, in a series one below the other on the quickly falling stream, enabled the same water to serve all of them one after another. At first there was enough charcoal for his needs, and as soon as he developed his method of using coke in the furnace, he was released from one of the great tyrannies, that of the transport of a very large bulk of charcoal from a wide district; coal seams were to hand within less than a mile of his works. A second problem, that of the use of coal for the refining of pig iron in the forges, was not urgent, as he had based his trade upon total or almost total consumption of the pig iron produced in direct castings from the furnace. The geography of the site he chose approached an ideal gravity-feed system. The highest ground around the valley edges produced coal and ironstone, with the best possible facilities for the drainage of the pits. A downhill run brought the material to the top of the furnaces which could be built against the steep slope of the valley. Iron castings were made at the foot of the furnace, and a short run of a few hundred yards, still downhill, delivered these on the wharf of the Severn, the greatest commercial highway of the iron trade at that time.

If too much is being credited to the foresight and deliberate planning of Abraham Darby, then we can truly say that he builded much better than he knew. In either case, his works broke free from all existing patterns and approached very near to a forecast of modern rationalization. The advantages of this lay-out were sufficient to over-ride many difficulties of his early years, and remained throughout the eighteenth century a definite and valuable asset of the Company.

Only south Yorkshire and Wales have been quoted as examples of the general dispersed pattern of development, but if the young and vigorous industry of the Rawlinson groupings in Furness be examined, the same dispersion is visible and persistent. Their furnaces and forges were widely scattered, location being largely determined by the supplies of charcoal and water power, and long journeys of ore being taken for granted. In the extreme case, as charcoal became scarce, some of the Furness ironmasters found it expedient to ship ore to the Highlands of Scotland, in order to smelt in a centre where charcoal was cheap and abundant.

The location of works made by Abraham I therefore takes on extra significance as soon as his experiments with coke smelting promise success.

Chapter Three

COALBROOKDALE WORKS, 1708–1717

ABRAHAM DARBY's first Coalbrookdale furnace was not a new one, but was the blast furnace that had been in use for a long period. It was built by Basil Brooke, and carries over the tapping arch a cast iron beam with the date 1638.[1] In 1685 a lease of coal and ironstone mines, in Lawley, carried the condition that the operator was 'to convey yearly ten dozen Strike of Ironstone to be carried to the ffurnaces at Cawbrookdale or Leighton or one of them at the option of Thomas Burton,' and in 1698 the lease was renewed and extended, and included the same conditions to carry ore to Coalbrookdale and Leighton. Abraham Darby took the reversion of a lease of the furnace and forge granted in 1696 by Basil Brooke, late of Madeley Court, to Shadrack Fox. The manuscript account of the Darby family, by Hannah Rose, says

As to affairs about the Dale before A Darbys time I know but little but have heard that Wolfe of Madeley carried it on before Fox. . . . The Furnace was blown up by the Pool Dam breaking and blew a great piece of Iron into the Timber Coppice. There were two men asleep in the Cabin but not hurt. I believe it was in Fox's time he made Cannon Balls, hand Grenades, &c for the Government. He went over to Russia with the Emperor called Peter the Great but left his wife and children to suffer great poverty, although it was reported he had with her a fortune of £10,000. Mary Ford was very kind to her and employed her in sewing and she taught a few children to read.'

When Darby took occupation of the furnace it was of course blown out and his first task was to overhaul and repair it ready for blowing in. The largest repair was to the hearth and bellows, jobs which were done usually after each blast. In the first account book[2] there are several items relating to this reconditioning, and although they are not perhaps complete, they are sufficiently so to make possible a direct comparison with the completely detailed accounts for Yorkshire furnaces in the same year. From a run of nearly sixty

[1] Illustration. Randall says this beam was brought from Leighton Furnace but this is most improbable.

[2] *Shrewsbury MSS.* No. 328.

years of furnace accounts for the many furnaces in the Yorkshire Ironmasters' group,[1] the general procedure before a blast and the pattern of the accounts become clear. The blast usually lasted from twenty to thirty weeks and the rest of the year was spent in accumulating the stock of charcoal needed for the next blast. When Darby introduced coke smelting, one of the greatest advantages was the possibility of running successive blasts at an interval only long enough to allow of remaking the hearth and reconditioning the furnace. In the Yorkshire accounts, each blast account includes the same items usually in the same order and they reflect a routine procedure which was carried out at the end of the blast, and which generally occupied the summer months of each year. The items of expenditure include most of the following, and in the order here given.

Hearth	to breaking up the old hearth
	getting and leading a new hearthstone
	getting and leading clay for boshes
	getting and leading a new dam stone
	getting and leading sand
Bellows	pulling down old bellows and taking off ironwork
	unnailing and other small jobs
	buying hides
	buying sheepskins
	oil, tallow, glue and rye meal bought
	new bellows boards
	carpenter's work
	smith's work or purchase of iron work

There are many other items which generally come under the heading 'Mixt disbursements' and which include renewals of the furnace linings, strappings, bridge and other general structural repairs, and there are still further items from time to time for the repair to goits, water wheels, and dams.

In the Darby accounts for 1708 the following items fit into this general pattern and show that furnace procedure was following the conventional lines of general practice.

[1] The *Canon Hall (Spencer) MSS.*, Cartwright Hall, Bradford. These have been analysed in Raistrick, A., 'The South Yorkshire Iron Industry,' *Trans. Newcomen Soc., XIX*, 1938–9, pp. 51–86, and in Raistrick, A. and Allen, E., 'The South Yorkshire Ironmasters (1690–1750),' *Economic History Review, IX*, 1939, pp. 168–185.

8th mo. 28.	By Cash pd Wm Plomer for Breaking Down ye old hearth	5. 0
30.	By John Litellhales to whom pd for getting ye furnes harth	5. 5. 0
	& for labor & ale &c for landing harth	9. 0
	By Cash pd Benj. Daws labor about ye harth	1. 0
9th mo. 12.	By Cash pd Jno Tyler for making ye herth	1. 0. 0

This compares well with an average account from Yorkshire at the same period.

Hearth:	Breaking old one	5. 0
	Getting new one	1. 0. 0
	Leading hearth	3. 0. 0
	Making £2, and Labourers, 10*s.*	2.10. 0

the comparative costs being £7.0.0 and £6.15.0.

The bellows accounts follow on those of the hearth, and in passing it is perhaps amusing to note in how many ways the clerk has spelt his word for bellows.

9th mo. 12.	By Cash pd for ye long belos bords	15. 0. 0
	By cash spent looking after caridg for ye bellos bords	16. 0
	By Cash pd Benja. Daws for Caring Belo bords	6. 6
13.	by Cash pd for ye carridg horses & 2 nights & sundry other charges about ye long bely bords	2.19.11
22.	By Cash pd Adm Ware for caridg of Bords	1.10. 0
	By cash pd for greese	1. 0
	By Cash pd Andrew Bowdler by his father for 2 Hides	4.10. 0
	By cash pd ye men	1. 8. 1
	By Cash pd Jno Dodal carpenter	1. 0. 0
	By cash pd for a peck of meele	1. 2
	Sundry expenses on ye forgemen & about ye ironwork of ye belos	9. 3
	a sheet of irn for ye Balys	2. 2
	for ye windfall bords	1. 9

This account totals £28.5.10, while a comparable Yorkshire account has a total of £12.16.10, but does not include new bellows boards. If £15 is added for the cost of boards, then the Yorkshire account would be £27.16.10, and agrees very closely with Darby's costs.

These comparisons justify us in thinking that Darby's furnace and its equipment followed standard lines and differed in no important aspect from those in use in the north.

In late December there is an item—

By Cash pd for meete &c warming ye furnes   14. 0

so that presumably it was well on towards completion, and in the 11th month (January 1709) the wages of a founder are paid for the first time.

Abraham Darby not only brought workmen from Bristol, but also got a certain amount of ironwork for the Coalbrookdale plant from there. There was a close connection with the two works in the early stages, and among the first furnace accounts there is the following.

11th. mo. 15th. Abram Darby furnes & Iron work at Bristol   Dr.

	T. c. q. lb.	*£. s. d.*
To a parsell of Broken ironston bought of R Corfield & Compy	2.10.0.0	43.15. 0
to a parsell of new pigs	4. 5.2.0	25.13. 0
to a parsell of old iron that came from ye Ragmen	1. 6.0.0	2.12. 0
4 Backstones	3.10	7. 7
		72. 7. 7

It would seem from this that the first batch of new pigs was run at Coalbrookdale about the beginning of the month, and sent along with scrap iron and ore to the foundry at Bristol.

The wages for the first week of blowing are as follows

11th. mo. 17th. By Cash pd	Jno Tyler founder	10.0	
	Jno Felton keeper	8.0	
	Richard Hart filler	7.0	
	Edwd Bear mine burner	6.6.	
	Rich Knowles stocker of ye bridge	6.6	1.18. 0

There is a note in this account book, against a few items, that these were separated out in Abraham Darby's 'own book,' and among the *Norris MSS.* there is the transcript of a page 'from a supposed Cash Book of Abraham Darby.' It carries all the items above given, though not in the same order, and has a few additional ones not itemized in the *Shrewsbury MSS.*; these include a note of the work at the furnace.

1708. 11. mo.	Paid ye men for a weeks work.	2. 3. 0
	Cartboxes, Furnace grates, Hatters irons	9. 0
	John Ffelton and Jno Tyler in full for castings T4.12.0.0	3. 8. 0

Connected with the taking and fitting out of the furnace, there are three items of interest;

1709. 5thmo. 11. Sundry expenses two journeys to take ye Furniss before our take	8.17. 6
6mo. 20. John Williams a Workman spent on a Journey to Bristoll on bringing up some of ye men	3.15. 0
My Landlords Richard Corfield and Thomas Dorsett by Cash paid them for ernest at taking ye Furness	1. 1. 6

The dates are not very helpful in determining just when the lease was taken, but the payment of the first half-year's rent on 20 April 1709 shows that the nominal date of entry on the furnace premises was the end of September 1708.[1]

Darby's removal from Bristol to the house called White End was made about the middle of 1708 and furnace equipment came in various instalments after that; these materials are not itemized in the accounts but appear in one distinct entry.

A. Darby & the Bristol Iron Work
By Sundry Boxes Patterns and other
Utensils as p note from 4mo. 1. 1708
to 9mo. 9. 1709 337.10. 0

The work of preparation had gone steadily on so that in December Darby paid 14/- for 'meat etc. at warming ye furness,' and early in January 1709, it was brought into blast.

It is not possible from the scant references in the accounts to determine the length of the first blast with any accuracy, but an indication is given in the payments made to Tyler, Felton, Hart, Bear and Knowles, who formed the furnace crew. Their first pay day was the middle of January (17th 11th mo.) and similar payments

[1] April 20th. 1709. My Landlord Richard Corfield & Thomas Dorset.
By Cash pd Tho Dorset in full for ½ a years rent ending on Ladyday last for ye ffurnis & White end. £20.0.0.

continue until June 1709. The materials used for the blast are also not very specific, as fuel and ore would be accumulated on the furnace site for as long as convenient before the actual blowing in, and the life of the stock pile is no real indication of the length of the blast. The supplier of ore was Gabriel Cleeton and Company, who directed payments to be made each month to various individuals and companies.

Two varieties of stone, Baull stone and Flat stone, appear at prices which range between 4/4 and 4/10 a Dozen. The first month of supply is October 1708, as follows

> 8br. 23. Gabrell Cletone & Comp.
> By Cash pd by his Order to Joseph Carter for getting 10 Doz. flat ston 2. 3. 4

and following on in the same form—

Jno. Bear & Co	10 Doz Baull ston	2. 3. 4
Wm. Booth	8 Doz Baull ston	2. 0. 0
Jos Forrydy	7 Doz flat ston	1.11. 6
Richd Tranter	6 Doz Baull ston	1.10. 0
Richd Tranter	12 Doz Baull ston	3. 0. 0
Joseph Carter & Co	6 Doz flat ston	1. 6. 0
Jno Hide	8 Doz flat ston	2. 0. 0
G. Hide	8 Doz Baull ston	2. 0. 0
Philip Jones & Co	14 Doz flat ston	3. 0. 0

This is a total of 89 Dozens of ore at a price of £20.14.2. The other items can be summarized, though twice a payment for ore is made without the quantity being stated.

November	96 Dozen	(49 Doz. and a parcel at £11, say about 47 Doz.)
December	106 Dozen	
January	53 Dozen	
February	91 Dozen	
March	56 Dozen	(approximate—payment of £15)
April	12 Dozen	

This is an approximate total, for the whole of the period, of 503 Dozens of ore.

The Dozen is actually a measure of volume and it is difficult to assess an equivalent weight which can be used with any certainty. It is most probable that the measure is one of an actual Dozen of loads, and if so it could vary, with the customary load of pony or horse, between $2\frac{1}{4}$ and $3\frac{1}{2}$ cwt. each load, and 28 and 42 cwt. in the Dozen. A figure that has been quoted in connection with Coalbrookdale is that the pack horses carried $3\frac{1}{2}$ cwt.[1]

The fuel accounts give no measure of quantity since only cash payments are recorded for the mined coal provided by Richard Hartshorne, the lessee of the Madeley Wood collieries.

July 2. 1709. Lawrence & Weling Downs	
By cash pd him in part for Coles & Iron wheald ye first blast	£30. 0. 0
July 22. Richard Hartshorne	
By Cash pd E Dorrell for their Order in part for coles	8. 4. 6
By Cash pd Edward Dorall for getting Coles by theyer order	11.19. 6
By Cash pd Edward Dorrell for Coles	5.18.11
Richard Hartshorne	
William Garbit for getting Coles	3.19. 0
Ed. Dorall for getting Coles	5.16. 4
	65.18. 3

Charcoal is nowhere mentioned in the account of the first blast, but later there are two small items which may relate either to charcoal or to coke.

Nov. 1708 By Cash pd Richard Dorrall for Charking coles	6. 0
April 1709 By Cash pd for Charking Coles	1. 3

In October 1709 the fuel and ironstone accounts begin again presumably in preparation for the second blast; in October and November Richard Hartshorne receives £81.5.7 for Coles, but only £2.7.6. has to that date been paid for ore.

These accounts continue into 1709, still rather mixed and not yet settled into a regular form, but they are sufficient to give the outlines of a general picture. Ironstone was mined at several small pits by miners who were paid individually by Gabriel Cletone & Company, the lessees of the pits. The terms Baull stone and Flat stone continue in general use and refer to the seams of ironstone lying above the Top Coal and the Big Flint Coal seams, which outcrop near the Dale. There is no indication of which coal was used, but it

[1] *Coalbrookdale MSS.* A typescript headed 'Notes on the origin and development of the British Iron and Steel Industry—the Coalbrookdale Co. Ltd.' Printed in *Iron & Steel Times*, I, No. 34, 1909, pp. 293–300.

PLATE I *This painting was specially commissioned for the 1959 Coalbrookdale Museum, and represents the first attempt to reconstruct the Furnace as it was when Abraham Darby I started smelting in the Dale.*

PLATE II *The Old Furnace photographed between 1880 and 1900, showing the cast-iron lintels added by Abraham Darby III when the structure was enlarged to provide the metal for the Iron Bridge. The 'B' on the lower lintel is a rebus for Brooke, the family who operated it when it was a charcoal furnace.*

PLATE III *Following demolition of the buildings above and around the Old Furnace, the author and G. F. Williams took the opportunity after the Second World War to excavate the site. This was the scene in 1951, eight years before the area was 'landscaped' and opened to visitors along with the Allied Ironfounders museum in an adjacent building. When this photograph was taken the Furnace was still under threat, only the cast-iron lintels thought worthy of preservation.*

PLATE IV *As visitors to the Furnace Site increased in the 1970's and its importance became more widely appreciated, the need to preserve the Furnace against the elements, and interpret it to the public provided the momentum to have this 'cover' building erected. It was financed by the National Heritage Memorial Fund, the National Coal Board and the Department of the Environment, and was formally opened by HRH The Duke of Gloucester on 27th July 1982.*

was all got by colliers working for Richard Hartshorne in the Madeley Wood and Benthall areas.

There would be constant streams of pack horses carrying fuel and ore down to the bank above the furnace, where the bridge keeper regulated its use. We know that a little later the coal was burned to coke in large heaps set out on a piece of ground very near the bridge head of the Old Furnace, and probably these smoking heaps were a part of the picture from the earliest days. Below the furnace there was the sand floor where much of the smelted iron was cast into pigs, run in open trenches in the sand, and the rest was cast into pots and kettles and other small ware.

The first account book only carries us as far as the autumn of 1709, but it is sufficient to show the Coalbrookdale works with the furnace in condition, and casting proceeding in a routine manner. The products are mainly pots and kettles, but there are also a number of 'furnaces' being made, a 'Furness patern containing 24 Galls' being one item paid for in the November of 1708. These furnaces, which became one of Darby's regular products, were like our 'set-pot' or 'copper,' large boiling pans with a fire grate, bars, door and door frame, varying in capacity but commonly containing 20 to 30 gallons. Hatters' irons and cart boxes or bushes were among the 4 tons 12 cwt. cast in the first week. In the next month a furnace of 74 gallons weighing 4½ cwt., and 45 cart boxes, 2 cwt., were cast; succeeding accounts include backstones (fireback plates) at 10/- a cwt.; furnaces at 16d. a gallon, cart boxes at 10/6 a cwt., pots, pans, grates and pig iron. The customers to whom goods were sent include Darby and the Bristol Ironworks, who were by far the largest at first, Henry Paton, ironmonger of Dudley, John Adams of Shrewsbury, and Thomas Milner of Bewdley.

The first few years must have been a time of constant experiment and anxiety, with a good deal of success in the casting of pots and small ware, but with a real difficulty of making a pig iron that would be acceptable to the forge men for reworking. The temperatures of a coke blast furnace would make a very fluid iron, of advantage for casting thin ware, but would make the pig iron hard and intractable in the forge. The inventory of the works made in 1718, after the death of Abraham Darby, includes 70 tons of sculls valued at £140, and these represent spoiled iron waiting for recasting, and may have been the product of less successful experiments, or ill-regulated blasts. Abraham's daughter-in-law, Abiah Darby, recapitulating some of the works of Abraham I, says that at first he smelted iron ore with charcoal, and a little later discovered the use of coke. We can now feel more sure that the charcoal smelting was mainly limited to the Bristol period, and that coke superseded it at an early date in the Coalbrookdale works. Abiah Darby's letter was not written until about 1775 but includes information gathered from an old workman and associate of Abraham Darby.[1]

After expressing her regret that the Destroyers of mankind are recorded and remembered while the Benefactors are unnoted and forgotten, she gives some account of her father-in-law, along with many other things relating to the works at various periods.

I now make free to communicate what I have heard my Husband say, and what arises from my own knowledge; also what I am inform'd from a person now living, whose father came here as a workman at the first beginning of these Pit Coal Works.

Then to begin at the original. It was my Husband's Father, whose name he bore (Abraham Darby who was the first that set on foot the Brass Works at or near Bristol) that attempted to mould and cast Iron pots &c., in sand instead of Loam (as they were wont to do, which made it a tedious and more expensive process) in which he succeeded. This first attempt was tryed at an Air Furnace in Bristol. About the year 1709 he came into Shropshire to Coalbrookdale, and with other partners took a lease of the works, which only consisted of an old Blast Furnace and some Forges. He here cast Iron Goods in sand out of the Blast Furnace that blow'd with wood charcoal; for it was not yet thought of to blow with Pit Coal. Sometime after he suggested the thought, that it might be practable to smelt the Iron from the ore in the Blast Furnace with Pit Coal: Upon this he first try'd with raw coal as it came out of the Mines, but it did not answer. He not discouraged, had the coal coak'd into Cynder, as is done for drying Malt, and it then succeeded to his satisfaction. But he found that only one sort of pit Coal would suit best for the purpose of making good Iron—These were beneficial discoveries, for the moulding and casting in sand instead of Loam was of great service, both in respect to expence and expedition. And if we may compare little things with great—as the invention of printing was to writing, so was the moulding and casting in sand to that of Loam. He then erected another Blast Furnace, and enlarged the Works. The discovery soon got abroad and became of great utility.

This Place and its environs was very barren, little money stirring amongst the Inhabitants. So that I have heard they were Obliged to

[1] This letter is reproduced in full in Ashton, T. S., *Iron and Steel in the Industrial Revolution*, 1924, pp. 249–52. Original in *Darby MSS.*

exchange their small produce one to another instead of money, until he came and got the Works to bear, and made Money Circulate amongst the different parties who were employed by him. Yet notwithstanding the Service he was of to the Country, he had opposers and illwishers. . . .

After the closing of the old account book in 1709 we have only very fragmentary material from which to fill in the story of the works, but by 1711 the new fuel had proved satisfactory and the need for capital was being felt by Darby.

Smiles has some references to this early period which cannot be overlooked although they do not help in fixing the date when coke-smelting of iron was brought to a satisfactory method. He says that:

It appears from the 'Blast Furnace Memorandum Book'[1] of Abraham Darby, which we have examined, that the make of iron at the Coalbrookdale Foundry, in 1713, varied from five to ten tons a week. The principal articles cast were pots, kettles and other 'hollow ware,' direct from the smelting-furnace; the rest of the metal was run into pigs. In course of time we find that other castings were turned out: a few grates, smoothing-irons, door-frames, weights, baking-plates, cart-bushes, iron pestles and mortars, and occasionally a tailor's goose. The trade gradually increased until we find as many as 150 pots and kettles cast in a week.

The fuel used in the furnaces appears, from the Darby Memorandum-Book, to have been at first entirely charcoal; but the growing scarcity of wood seems to have gradually led to the use of coke, brays or small coke, and peat. An abundance of coals existed in the neighbourhood; by rejecting those of inferior quality and coking the others with great care, a combustible was obtained better fitted even than charcoal itself for the fusion of that particular kind of ore which is found in the coal-measures. Thus we found Darby's most favourite charge for his furnaces to have been five baskets of coke, two of brays, and one of peat; next followed the ore, and then the limestone. The use of charcoal was gradually given up as the art of smelting with coke and brays improved, most probably aided by the increased power of the furnace-blast, until at length we find it entirely discontinued.

Smiles does not give 1713 as the date of the introduction of coke-smelting, but uses it as an example of the normal activity of the furnace, and to that extent we can assume that it is later than the experimental period. By 1711 Darby was thinking of extending his interests, and although he eventually had shares in Vale Royal and

[1] Smiles, S., *Industrial Biography: Iron workers and Tool makers*, 1863, p. 82.
The Blast Furnace Memorandum Book of Abraham Darby has not been traced, so we have no idea of its scope or contents, beyond this one quotation.

Dolgelly furnaces, both of which smelted with charcoal, their situation in relation to the supplies of wood or coal amply explain their use of charcoal, and throw no disparagement on his experiences with coke at Coalbrookdale. In 1712, as we shall see later, he offered the method of coke-smelting for the consideration of one of the Furness ironmasters, and, again, the fact that the Furness trade kept to the use of charcoal is no reflection on the process, but is due to the marked preference the nail trade had for charcoal iron. The effect of these references is to strengthen the case for a date not any later than 1711, and probably a few years earlier than that, for Darby's success in coke-smelting.

In contemplating wider interests, Darby's first effort to secure some fluid capital is probably seen in an Indenture drawn on 28 February 1712, between Abraham Darby and Richard Champion of Bristol, merchant. This deed states that an earlier indenture of assignment had been made between them on 21 September 1711, reciting that Abraham Darby and his partners (James Peters and Griffin Prankard) carried on the trade at Coalbrookdale and had a stock amounting to £3,534.11.4¼, but that there was a debt owing on that stock of £1,531.8.8½ so that the clear value of the Coalbrookdale concern was £2,003.2.7¾. Richard Champion had agreed to buy six-sixteenths of this stock for £500. This new indenture of 28 February confirmed that purchase and for another payment of £5.7.6 he bought a six-sixteenths interest in the original patent which Darby had secured. Since Champion had become interested he had advanced £200.5.0 but Darby was now in a position to buy back the whole of Champion's shares with the interest in the patent and to repay the advances made, for an overall sum of £1,282.1.3.[1] The fact that Darby was in a position to do this within five months of their sale argues well for the success of his efforts at smelting with coke.

Three months after this repurchase, when thirteen-sixteenths of the total shares were in his own hands, the condition of the works was such that he opened up negotiations to take up interests elsewhere. At the same time he visited William Rawlinson in Furness, and evidently had it in mind to discuss the matter with him. A letter written to Rawlinson when Darby returned from the visit, has recently come to light, which makes this possibility clear. Rawlinson was a Friend and for many years the Rawlinson family had carried on an iron

[1] *Norris MSS.*, VIII, pp. 41–4.

industry in Furness, and lately had founded the Backbarrow Company[1] through which they were in close touch with some of the Midland dealers such as Milner and Champion.

The Backbarrow Company of course were smelting with charcoal and were feeling the pinch of the rising price of wood due to the increased demands and the local competition of the other companies. These difficulties with some others had been the subject of conversations between Darby and Rawlinson, and gave rise to this letter.[2]

For Mr. Wm. Rolleson, near Kandale, Westmorland, these for his owne hand.

Esteemed friend Wm. Rawlinson,

Madeley Court, the 12th of the 5th mo. 1712.

This will informe thee that wee came well home on the 6th day after wee left Kendall, and in complyance with my promes, I have hear inclosed the Swedish way of making iron, which, though it may not agree in all parts with owers, yet it may be some light in ower British improvements on thathead. I had some other things in vew in youer parts moore than making iron in the common way and with common fuell, but did partly forget it at coming away, and partly the seson, being first day, was unfit for buisnes of that nature, and, to dell plainly, I had some hesitations about communicating that new method at this time, but rather did intend to defer it for 2 or 3 years longer, and then thought I might dow something, either with thou and Compa, or with ower intrest seperatly in youer parts, for which i had sundry resons, such as being fixed at this furnes for 5 years and could not well draw out stock in this place to put in with you, but must stie on the work hear, and as the matter proposed is very much a secrit, so I was willing to be at the head of that buisnes to be a shaerer in the advantidg, which, if well managed, will be no trifle, but upon farther considerations I intend to comunicate the afaer to thy thought, which yet must be kept close, as thou willt see by the nature of the buisnes when proposed, and I am apt to think if I am duly advised how the work goes, that I can give such instructions by post as may answer the end, though I dow not see it moore the one or 2 times pr, anum. and whether or no wee are consernd in this new buisnes, yet if you will advise me how the work is when out of order, I will redyly give my thoughts upon a fot of publique good, as respecting the iron trade in Britain, but if we shall think proper to prosecut what is in my thoughts

[1] Fell, A., *The Early Iron Industry in Furness*, 1908; and Raistrick, A., *Quakers in Science and Industry*, 1950, pp. 95–107.

[2] The letter is in photofacsimile in the National Library of Wales. N.L.W. MS. 10823, E. and has been printed by W. H. Chaloner under the title 'Further Light on the invention of the process for smelting iron with coke.' *Economic Hist. Revue*, 2nd ser. II, 1949, pp. 185–7.

for such alterations as hinted above, then I must confes I shall incline to tast the profet.

Nor wilt thou grudg to part with one 8th part of the profets that shall arise by such management, nor will I expect aneything from it unles it is plainly to the good of said work, as I think thear is not the lest dought but by it you may save £700 pr. anum., and when I began this letter I did intend to have sent the mater by this, but sending it by Maybery's son to save postidg, being double, I thought it best to send the mater pr. post, lest it should by any chance miscary.

The rest of the letter relates to a dispute between Rawlinson and Hall, in which Abraham Darby tried to act as mediator, calling on Hall on his way home, and sending advice to his friend on how to act. The matter in dispute was settled later in a way which showed the wisdom of Darby's advice. The letter is signed

Thy asuered friend, Abra^m^ Darby.

Nothing came of Darby's proposition, as the Backbarrow Company continued to smelt with charcoal fuel, and in 1727, when the supplies were becoming very difficult, they even ventured on a furnace at Invergarry in the Scottish Highlands, for the sake of the more abundant wood available in that remote district.

The next venture in expansion was Darby's interest in the Vale Royal Furnace, near Oulton, Cheshire. Here again we have only indirect material for the story of the venture, drawn from the accounts of Darby's affairs just after his death in 1717. The matter arises in a claim made by Thomas Baylies for a debt said to be owing to him from the estate of Abraham Darby. The statement is that

In the lifetime of A. D. he was often solicited by Charles Cholmondeley of Vale Royal to enter into partnership with him for ye carrying on Vale Royal Furnace and A. D. seeing the affair likely to be advantageous communicated it to Thos. B(aylies) and Jno. C(hamberlain) who all went together to C. C. and entered into articles of Partnership under ye penalty of £1000 in ye following terms viz—C. C. obliged himself to deliver as much charcoale as should at any time be wanting for carrying on ye sd furnace at his proper cost and charge and A. D., J. C. and T. B obliged themselves to find mine Ironstone and Workmens wages for carrying on ye furnace at their proper costs and charges; and what Pigg Iron was made at ye sd furnace was to be equally divided every Monday morning: one moiety to C. C. ye other moiety to A. D., J. C., and T. B.'[1]

[1] *Norris MSS.*, VIII, p. 134. 'Paper in the handwriting of . . . .' This blank is in the Norris transcript. The articles of partnership were signed on 25 April 1716, and later were cancelled in a new partnership, made 11 March 1720.

Thomas Baylies who came to Coalbrookdale as a clerk in 1714 was the brother-in-law of Abraham Darby, his wife being Hannah Sergeant. Hannah Rose says that 'he proved to be a very bad man: borrowed money in A. Darby's name and my Father was cheated and some other of the workmen by him. Richard Ford being a clerk and marrying A. Darby's daughter and buying a share in the works got authority to turn him out. He afterwards went over to America, set up Iron works there and called them Coalbrookdale, but did not behave well there.' The new agreement for Vale Royal furnace made in 1720 notes that Baylies has not paid his share of the partnership capital, and so is excluded from the concern.

Very soon after the Vale Royal agreement of 1716, an indenture was made with William and Pitchford Corfield on the one part, and Darby, Chamberlain and Baylies on the other. The sub-lease of Coalbrookdale had been taken in 1708 from Richard Corfield who held the reversion of the original lease granted in 1696 to Shadrack Fox. The death of Richard Corfield made necessary the renewal of the sub-lease by his heirs, William and Pitchford Corfield, and in this renewal Darby, Chamberlain and Baylies share, as partners in Coalbrookdale ironworks, forges and furnaces. It is nowhere stated how Chamberlain and Baylies come into the possession of shares in Coalbrookdale but, as Peters and Prankard have dropped out, it may be that Chamberlain and Baylies had bought their shares.

In 1721 Baylies had an account of his grievances privately printed, 'The Case of Th-m-s Ba-l-s in relation to his affairs with Ab-h-m D--by and family before and since their deaths.' In this pamphlet he says that Abraham Darby had an ironwork with Charles Cholmondeley as partner with a share purchased for £330, that A. D. offered him, T. B., a share for £300 but Baylies declined the offer and A. D. instead offered him a clerkship of the works at £60 per annum with a good house, horse and cow. Baylies accepted this offer and in April 1714 removed from Stourbridge to Coalbrookdale and spent the summer in getting acquainted with Darby's customers and dealers, by travelling round the fairs and markets. He also spent some time preparing for erecting a new works in Merioneth where Darby had taken a lease. In November or December Darby went to London to renew his lease of Coalbrookdale for Michaelmas 1717, for twenty-one years. The lease for Merioneth, and one for Vale Royal with Cholmondeley and Chamberlain, were both made with Baylies as a partner. Baylies tells us incidentally that

Darby shortly after this started to build the new house and also a new furnace to cost £1,500.

The Merioneth scheme mentioned by Baylies is that of the Dolgyn furnace, near Dolgelly. The story of this furnace is contained in the diary of a noted Friend, John Kelsall, who for many years was associated as clerk and manager with Darby, Milner, Lloyd and Paton, all ironmasters or ironmongers on the Welsh borders. Kelsall came to North Wales in 1701 as schoolmaster at Dolobran, the home of the Lloyds, but later left schooling for the management of iron forges and furnaces. He was a zealous minister in the Society of Friends and a great traveller in their concerns.[1]

The notes in the diaries, which relate to his service with the Coalbrookdale Company, are very sparse.

> In the latter end of the year (1713) an offer was made me by Ab^m^ Darby of a clerkship under him, who designed to build a new iron furnace near Dolgelly, £25 per annum with house room and firing. Upon the 3rd of 3rd mo. we left Dolobran and settled in the town of Dolgelly where we stayed one year and in 3 mo. 1715 moved to Dolgynele near the furnace.

In 1715 in preparation for this move, Kelsall had spent three weeks of January at Coalbrookdale, for instruction in his job. In 1717 he was again in Coalbrookdale in 3rd month :

> Dined at the Dale with John Chamberlain and Thos. Gouldney & son of Bristol. Abraham Darby was ill and died on the 5th. 25th Th Baylies, Thos Chamberlain & T Gouldney came on to Dolgyn. 4th mo. 11th. Began to set out the foundations of the furnace.

The furnace was situated three miles from Llyn Hir which was the upper limit of navigation on the river Mawddach, just beyond the head of the estuary from Barmouth. It lay two miles east of Dolgelly town. It was intended to use the interbedded iron ores of Cambrian age, from the Cader Idris range, which could be worked near Aran Mawddwy. The decision to try these ores may have been helped by the experiments which Darby had made with the somewhat similar Cumberland ores which were supplied to him by Rawlinson. The building of the furnace was delayed and it was not actually brought into blast until the year after Darby's death.

[1] For a general account of Kelsall, see Raistrick, A., *Quakers in Science and Industry*, 1950, pp. 112 ff. The diary is among the Friends House MSS.

The original lease of Coalbrookdale included a furnace and forge, but of the forge activities there is little evidence. In the Inventory of 1718 the 'Old Forge' makes very little show, having only a beam and scales, a forge hammer and odd things, an old wrought iron cannon, and 'centres,' and no stock of any kind; the total value was only £14.10.0 and we must presume that for some time before 1718 the forge was very little used.

During the last eighteen months of his life Darby was a sick man, dependent upon his clerk and employees for most of the conduct of the business, and many of the schemes for expansion lacked his driving power and insight to bring them to maturity. Thus at his death he left the works burdened with some mortgages and debts, but still with a valuation, according to the inventory, of £2,957.15.0 and a further £1,242.5.0 for the buildings, a total of £4,200. The Old Furnace was in steady blast, producing about five tons of iron a week, and the New Furnace was well equipped and in production. There were two Air Furnaces, moulding shops, stores and the old forge, with a wide connection of good customers in most of the Midland markets and towns.

The Air Furnaces were used for remelting some of the pig iron for such casting as was not done directly on the furnace floor—probably this was mainly a matter of room for moulding the very large numbers of pots that were cast as small ware. These huge numbers of pots would take a far greater area of moulding space than ten times their weight of pigs or heavy castings. The air furnace or reverberatory furnace was already in wide use by the Quaker Lead Company who had built several at their smelt mills in North Wales,[1] and attempts had been made to use it for iron and other metals. During Darby's life the pot and kettle trade, with the sale of pig iron to Bristol, was quite sufficient to account for the full production of his old furnace, so that the conversion of the pig iron into bar in the forge was not necessary. Later when the second furnace was in full blast, about and just after the time of his death, an outlet for some of the pig iron in the forges, and the great demands being made round about for the bar iron, would be more of a temptation towards using the forges than any which Abraham I experienced. In most other furnaces in the West Country, as in south Yorkshire, the output of charcoal-smelted pig iron was easily absorbed by the forges which were feeding the nail trade and the wire drawers, and

[1] Raistrick, A., *Two Centuries of Industrial Welfare*, 1938, p. 101.

in many cases there was a direct link between furnace and forge. Darby stands almost alone in not having a direct customer in the forges, and in having created or discovered for himself a new and sufficient market for all his output in the casting of pots and small household ware. This domestic market was for a time almost insatiable. His cast iron pots, kettles, furnaces, firebacks and small ware, were within the financial reach of the majority of the population, where before his time household pans of brass and copper had been things of great price, largely imported from Holland, and of such value as to be specified individually in wills and used and treasured by several generations.

It cannot be too much stressed that by his basic method of an efficient process for casting better and cheaper pots and kettles, Darby had in fact divorced his furnace from the demands and dictates of the forge masters, and secured for himself a period of independence in which he could use the iron produced by his experimental furnaces and find a ready sale for its products.

Chapter Four

RICHARD FORD, 1717–1745
ABRAHAM DARBY II, 1732–1738

THE death of Abraham I on 5 May 1717 brought the first period of the works history to a close. He had been ill for over a year but had been able to continue some of his work and to attend the meetings of the Society of Friends. Hannah Rose says:

When A. Darby first came into the Dale he and my Father used to go once a month to Newport and meet William Osborne from Wolverhampton, and hold meetings near an Inn, I think, the Swan, and many of the inhabitants would come and behave sober and attentive. The last meeting he was at was in the new house which he built in Coalbrookdale. It was not quite finished so not inhabited. The meeting was held in the room now called the best parlour and he was greatly favoured in prayer. My Father and Mother said they never heard him so fine but he was too ill to sit the Meeting out. He died not long after. He died at Madeley Court and was brought to the new house to be buried from there at Broseley.'[1]

The minutes of Friends Monthly and Quarterly meetings were frequently signed by Abraham Darby as Clerk, and they provide abundant evidence that whatever may have been the pressure of business affairs he never ceased to be active in the work of the Society of Friends. 'My Husband's Father,' Abiah Darby says, 'died early in life; a religious good man, and an Eminent Minister among the people called Quakers.'

Hannah Rose continues her narrative of Abraham Darby:

His widow did not live long after him. Thomas Baylies would not let her go to the new house, but went there himself and family; but put her in the old house formerly belonging to Lawrence Willington. She being ill went down to Bewdley, and died there. About this time the late Thomas Goldney came up and went into the old house and he and Richard Ford, when they got T. Baylies out of the new house went and lived there. Then my parents went into the old one.'[2]

[1] This was in the Friends Burial Ground attached to the Friends Meeting house there.

[2] When Abraham Darby first came to the Dale he paid rent for a year and a quarter for the house called White End, the house which was later called Sunniside, and which keeps that name to the present. This is the house referred to by

Abraham and Mary Darby had a large family, five sons and six daughters, though some of the children died young. The eldest son Abraham was born in 1711 and a brother, Edmund in 1712, these being the two who eventually entered the works. The eldest daughter was Mary, and another son, Sergeant, was born in 1713. At the death of Mary Darby, Trustees had been appointed to take all responsibility for the education of her children, of whom Joshua Sergeant was the most active. The Trustees seem to have been Goldney, Ford and Sergeant, and their accounts occur in the ordinary books of the Company, with payments on behalf of the children made by any of the Trustees, though mainly by Sergeant.

The boys Abraham, Edmund and Sergeant, and their sister Sarah were sent to school with Gilbert Thompson at Penketh, Lancashire. This was a well-known Quaker school, probably recommended by John Kelsall who had been a pupil there. Gilbert Thompson's son carried on the school after his father, and during the son's mastership John Coakley Lettsom was a pupil. Thompson became interested in medicine and was associated with Fothergill, and the curriculum and discipline under both father and son seems to have been very enlightened. The accounts show that Abraham and Edmund stayed at the school until about 1730, the payment made to Gilbert Thompson being about £30 a year for the two.

The boys would be dressed in the plain but substantial clothes approved by the customs of Friends, and these were made for them at home, with the expenses appearing in the works accounts. We find that Edward Caldwell was paid £7.16.3 for making two suits, and Ann Hower charged 8/– for making shirts; these were of Irish Holland for which £2.11.0 had been paid. There are numerous small sums disbursed for the boys, both at school and in preparation for returning each year; one year they include 'hats 12/–, stockings 4/–, knives 4/–, and given in pockets 4/2'; two years later Abraham and Edmund are provided with wigs costing £2.12.0 for the two, two fustian frocks 18/–, and boots at 12/– and 13/– a pair. In 1730 the Trustees gave Abraham a watch for which they paid £5.5.0 and about that time Abraham and Edmund were taken

Hannah Rose as the old house. When the works were well established Darby moved into part of Madeley Court but finding it rather remote from the works, planned and built his own house. This stood between the Upper Forge and the Malt House but it was removed in 1939 in the course of a County Council road improvement.

into the works, Abraham to become a partner on attaining his majority, and Edmund in a position which would best compare with that of a pupil apprentice. In 1734 Richard Ford received £52.10.0 'for Ed. Darby's Board and Instruction.'

Of the other children who went to Penketh, Sergeant died in 1725 and Sarah in 1726, there being an entry in December 1726, 'Thomas Ford for gloves at Sarah Darby's funeral.' Hannah was for a time sent to Bristol to be trained in service, and all mention of her in the accounts relates to her preparation for being away, until 1727, when her funeral is noted.

It is perhaps of interest to note what the Trustees considered as reasonable preparation for Hannah in the way of clothes. In May 1724 they purchased for her

a calamcer gound	15. 7
a hat & silk gound	8. 3
stockings	7
flannen [flannel]	9. 2
shoes	15. 0
a pair of shoes and cloggs	5. 0
paid Thomas Morton for 21 yards of cloth for shifts	1. 7. 0

Items of clothing were renewed regularly for three years, then her death is recorded with details which give at least a glimpse of the sad occasion of her burial.

1727.3.7mo. Sundry Expences at Hannah Darby's Funeral.

Thomas Corser for Shroud and Sheet	1.10. 0
Samuel Bowdler for Buscuits	2.10. 0
Widow Clarke for Wine	3.14. 6
John Bayley for Gloves etc.	8.18. 0
John Fosbrook for a coffin	15. 0
for a drink	12. 0
for ye grave	1. 0
Sundry women for attandance	13. 0
Dr. Wykes bill	1. 4. 4

With this account we lose all record of the children of the first Abraham Darby, except Abraham and Edmund, and the two married daughters, Mary and Anne. The childhood complaints seem always to have been very serious among the Darby children, while the parents did not reach what could be called old age. Abraham I died at the age of thirty-nine, Abraham II at fifty-two and

Abraham III at thirty-nine. Edmund, the brother of Abraham II died at forty-four, but this by accident, being killed by a fall from his horse. Finally, Samuel, the brother of Abraham III, died at the age of forty-one.

Abraham Darby I had died intestate when his eldest son was a child of six, so that the continuance and management of the works presented a serious problem. His widow, Mary Darby, took out letters of administration by which she was allowed possession of the works. Almost the last piece of business which Abraham had completed was the renewal of the Coalbrookdale lease for a period of twenty-one years from 9 September 1717, in which lease he had associated with his own the names of John Chamberlain and Thomas Baylies, the partners with him in the Vale Royal Furnace. To raise capital, probably for the building of the New Furnace, which Baylies said cost £1,500, Darby had mortgaged half of the works to Thomas Goldney of Bristol, as security for a loan of £1,600. 'At ye death of A. D. Thomas Goldney made a demand of his money and ye widow Darby not having a conveniency of advancing such a sum it was agreed to by Mary Darby Jno. Chamberlain Thos Baylies Thos Goldney to divide ye sd Works into 16 equal parts or shares each share valued at £200 so that the whole stock was then allowed to be £3,200':[1]

Mary Darby then assigned eight shares to Goldney and sold two more to her son-in-law Richard Ford. Baylies claimed that he had an outstanding debt of £1,200 owing from Abraham Darby and suggested that he should take Darby's share of the Vale Royal partnership as a settlement of this debt. This agreement was not kept and after much hesitation and dispute, Baylies took six Coalbrookdale shares from Mary Darby leaving her with no further interest in the works. He also obtained the transfer of the letters of administration to himself. Baylies soon got into financial difficulties and after a short while some of these shares were purchased by Thomas Goldney and his son. Mary Darby survived her husband by less than a year and when she died the position of her children appeared very inauspicious. Joshua Sergeant was much concerned for the well-being of her seven orphan children and for the way in which they seemed to have forfeited all interest in the works, so 'out of tender love and regard for 'em he came over to ye Dale and finding there was likely to be but little left for their maintainance and bringing up in ye world, did of his own accord and by and with ye consent of Thomas Baylies ye Administrator make an offer to Thos

[1] *Norris MSS.*, VIII, p. 134. 'Paper in the handwriting of . . .'

Goldney purely in ye behalf of ye children of paying him £400 and security for £100 being ye £500 the 2 shares were mortgaged to him for, provided he would deliver ye Mortgage up all wch Thomas Goldney readily consented to.'

The net result of these many complicated transactions was that in 1718 the works were continued under a new ownership of the shares, which were then held as follows: Thomas Goldney 10, Richard Ford 2, Joshua Sergeant (for the children of Darby) 3, and Thomas Goldney 1. In 1723 Joshua Sergeant assigned over to the children two of his shares in the Dale works, in return for £700, part of which he accepted in bills paid to the Company by its customers. Three years later he made an indenture with Richard Ford, to make some further provision for the children, handing to him his remaining share in the works in return for £50 for himself and a payment of £100 each to Abraham and Edmund Darby and £100 to Levey Perry. Following this arrangement Abraham and Edmund were entered in the Company's books as holding two-sixteenths and one-sixteenth interest in the works, respectively, and these remained their shares for many years.

In the early part of 1718 Ford, Goldney and Sergeant took control of the works and Ford became the manager though still retaining the title of Clerk. For a short time Goldney assisted him by accompanying him to most of the markets and fairs in which Darby had sold his products. They found everywhere that the reputation of the Dales works was excellent, and all the customers were anxious to continue their trade with the new company. After a lengthy tour in July, which included Nottingham, Manchester and Chester fairs, Goldney went to Bristol and he and Ford more or less divided the country between them. Goldney soon slipped into the position of financial agent and banker and combined with this the selling agency for Bristol and the South-West. Ford continued to visit the fairs of the Midlands and North and to look after the technical side of the works at Coalbrookdale.

A new account book was opened in 1718 and its first few pages are occupied by a carefully written summary under the title 'An Inventory of Quick and Dead Stock in the Iron Work at Coalbrookdale taken in ye Begin^{g} of July 1718,'[1] and from this we get the first complete picture of the works and their equipment as Abraham I

[1] As this is the first complete view we have of the whole works and their contents, it is printed in full in Appendix 2, p. 279.

had developed them. There are two blast furnaces, the Old Furnace which he rented at first, and the New Furnace built by him, each with a Bellows Room and with a stock of utensils and materials at the Tunnel Head. There are three Mould Rooms, Daniel Richardson's and John Thomas's at the Old Furnace, and one at the New Furnace not named. John Thomas will be recognized as the original moulder who shared the patent with Darby at Bristol, and who remained all his life at the Coalbrookdale works. The stock in the mould rooms is largely a miscellany of patterns, utensils and sand, with 'A New Air Furnace with Utensills at the New Furnace Mould Room,' valued at £40. The Upper Air Furnace with its utensils is valued at £50 and the stock with it is largely made up of kettle patterns, so that by comparison with the Blast Furnaces, it would appear that the Old Furnace cast most of the larger goods, furnaces, large pots, kettles and firebacks, while the Air Furnace cast some of the smaller ware. At the Old Furnace Door there is a stock of large patterns for 20 to 50 gallon pans, and at the Tunnel Head (top of the furnace) a good stock of fuel, ore, limestone, and tools. Within the works there is a Smith's Shop with tools in which new pattern boxes are being made; a Dressing Room at the upper Forge contains patterns and various stores but no tools, and a building called Samuel Roden's Shop is evidently the carpenter's shop. There is a Warehouse with a large stock of finished goods ready for sale, and near it a Dark Store Room with a stock of heavier ware, and another Warehouse at the New Furnace. Raw materials are dealt with in a Coal Yard, on which there is a stock of brays, wood and turf, Coal Hearths with a stock of coke, and a Mine Yard where the iron ore is stored and prepared. The Pigg Yard, besides stores of pig iron, has a large amount of odds and ends, patterns, castings, bricks, moulds and 70 tons of sculls or spoiled iron. There are two buildings called the Copper and the Copper House Warehouse which contain two Air Furnaces and an Old Air Furnace, and a stock which includes a number of grate and fireback patterns with grates, firebacks and bakestones in the warehouse, from which it appears that most of the stove and fireplace work was done here. The Old Forge is included but is evidently unused, with no tools and very few stores in it. Finally there is the office, in which the more valuable items are pot and kettle patterns mainly of brass. Of office furnishings as such, the only items are a writing desk, two tables and shelves, four reams of paper and a spring lock on the door.

Such in very brief, is the survey of the works, and the impression given by almost every portion of it is that of a foundry in which pots, pans and kettles dominate the scene, and in which the variety of size and kind is far more extensive than anyone could ever expect. The grate and fireplace work is fairly obvious, but takes a very secondary place. There is very little to suggest that pig iron was produced in any quantity for sale, but it appears that most of the blasts were cast direct at the furnace mouth into pots and kettlės, except for what iron was needed for the air furnaces.

The accounts of the new company are kept to a rigid pattern with a basic four-week period for the reckoning of production, consumption of raw materials, labour and carriage. All cast goods are credited to the Warehouse and the pig iron to the Pigg Yard, and from these the goods are sold or the pig iron issued to the air furnaces for remelting and casting.

Abraham Darby had not developed the forges which were part and parcel of his lease, but Richard Ford soon turned his attention to them. The iron made with coke as fuel was not liked by the forge-masters and Abraham probably spent all his efforts on improving his foundry practice for which coke-iron was well suited. By September 1718 Ford had put the Old Forge into working condition as items appear in the new account book generally in the form

To Making 9 Ton of Blooms att 11/– . . .

In 1719 Ford sent some of his pig iron to a forge for a proper trial of its nature, and this is recorded in the accounts:

Trial of pigs in making bar iron etc. Mch. 26–31

By Pigg-yard Sundry Expences in mak^{g} a Tryall of our Piggs.	
Pd Cap^{n} Stanley's man mak^{g} a Ton of Barrs from em	1. 4. 0
Pd Thos Brindley Slitting it & for carriage	2. 2. 6
Gave ye Slitters 5/– Expences to Stourb. 15/–	1. 0. 0
	£4. 6. 6

From this we can gather that not only was the iron drawn out in a finery and chafery but was put through the slitting mill probably for nailer's rods, and that the trial was carried out at Stanley's forge at Stourbridge. The trial must have appeared to give satisfactory bars, for almost immediately Ford opened up negotiation and by 1720 had taken over the Middle Forge in Coalbrookdale from Thomas Stanley, and bought Stanley's stock of tools and iron; items appear in the account book for timber for the forge buildings and payments are made for the labour of reconditioning the forge. When this got to work the production of wrought iron assumed larger proportions, and William Crannage was made forge-master.

> 1722. June 11. By ye Forge pd Wm. Crannage draweg out 175c. of Blooms at 9/– per ton makeg 72c. 15 over yield 7/6. 3 Tue irons 18d. fillg ye Coals 4/6. for 8 Days work 8/–. gave 9d. £5. 1. 0

The above note, one of many such, shows that the forge was now working on a fairly large scale, though in the general scheme of the Coalbrookdale works it occupies only a very minor position. It was not until the steam engine trade increased that the forges were all fully occupied. In fact for the twenty years to 1738 much of the forge work needed in the Coalbrookdale trade was bought from their neighbour Cornelius Hallen of the Upper Forge, who forged tools and made most of the handles and rings needed for the iron weights and irons made in the works.

When the forge was regularly making bar iron, parcels of scrap and of charcoal iron were bought in addition to the smaller quantities of pig iron taken from the furnaces. This is a strong indication that the Coalbrookdale pig iron was not yet really suitable for forge work.[1]

In 1724 the forge had a new tilt-hammer and paid £2.6.0 for the freight of the hammer beam from Bewdley, and a gratuity of half a crown was given on putting it in. The work of the forge only averaged from five to six tons a month in 1730 and much of this was sent away as bar iron, being mainly traceable by the payments to Richard Ford for his carriage of the bar iron from the forge to the river Severn. Working parts for the steam engines made up the rest of the output of the forges at this time.

[1] An example of the general form of these accounts is the following.

From 12th. Dec. 1721 to 27th. Mch 1722.

Middle Forge Dr to Sundry Accts. for Piggs.

Pigg Yard for 2 tns 4 cwt. deld. at £7	15.	8.	0
To Boulden Company for 78 cwt. 0. 7. neat at £8	31.	4.	6
To Vale Royal Company for 5 ton at £8	40.	0.	0
To Richard Baldwin & Compa. for 5 ton at £7.12.6	38.	2.	6
	£124.	15.	0

Forge Warehouse Dr to ye Forge for Barr Iron made by Jno France & William Crannage from x.12.1721 to Mch. ye 26.1722 102c.3.9. at 19/–	97.	13.	9½

The Boulden Furnace belonged to Edward Knight.

It is very evident from the material which has survived for the period from 1718 to 1730, that Richard Ford was a most capable man of business as well as one who was very much aware of the trend of things in the technical sphere. Trained under Abraham Darby I, he seemed to have much of his spirit of invention and his willingness to explore new avenues of trade and manufacture. Goldney had relieved him of most of the financial management of the Company, and this seemed to leave him free to work up the commercial side of the business by repeated visits to customers and constant attendance at the markets and fairs. At the same time, like the Darbys he did not neglect the meetings of the Society of Friends, but from time to time is noted in their records in connection with various of their activities.

The trade of the Company was developed under Ford's management in three directions. The pot and kettle trade had a very long list of customers starting in 1718 with forty, all of whom were old customers of Abraham Darby. In the first two years Ford more than doubled this list and extended the range of towns and villages served, by a wide area, reaching north to Cumberland and Northumberland, and south to London and Cornwall. The largest individual customer was Nehemiah Champion of Bristol who took over a thousand pounds' worth of pots and evidently developed a large export business. By 1730 his orders, which had been given steadily at regular intervals, varied from twenty to thirty tons at a time. A typical shipment to him was '2,370 Pots & Kettles, 550 Small Ware, approximately 29½ tons, £360.' Another order in the following month was for 2,255 Pots & Kettles, 620 Small Ware, and 228 Backstones, a total of a little over twenty-seven tons. In the same year there was still another of these wholesale orders, 2,775 Pots & Kettles and 800 Izops, again about twenty-seven tons. Nehemiah Champion, and after 1730 his sons, Nehemiah and William, were the only customers on this scale, but there was another exporter, John Ives at Gainsborough. He maintained, the whole time, a steady order of a few hundred pounds a year, taken almost entirely in pots and kettles. The firm of William Jukes & Co. of London took each year some nine or ten tons of pots and kettles and other occasional goods, but there is no indication whether these could be absorbed by the home market or were also being partly exported. Many of the larger kettles and 'furnaces' were the familiar three-legged cauldron,[1]

[1] The Inventory includes sets of legs and ears, patterns for the three legs and two ears for the handle of these cauldrons.

which was the special Darby product for more than two centuries, and it is said that Africa proved to be an almost insatiable market for these. A little later in the eighteenth century large numbers of sugar boiling pans were exported to the Americas, but so far as can be traced, always through the wholesalers or larger merchants.

Another group of customers included the larger ironmongers in towns like Shrewsbury, Birmingham, Chester, Manchester and Liverpool, who kept a stock of Coalbrookdale goods or forwarded special orders for unusual articles. Some of these customers appear regularly in the books for more than twenty years; among these are Samuel Yates of Welshpool, Edward Griffith and Nathan Wright of Chester, Abraham Freeth of Birmingham, Arthur Ikin & Company of Manchester, Andrew Shakeshaft of Wellington, Thomas Milner of Bewdley, and John Adams of Shrewsbury, most of whom had been customers of Abraham Darby before 1717. While these were regular customers, there were many others who purchased goods at intervals over the whole long period. The mainstay of this trade was of course the pots and kettles with larger pans or furnaces and purgatories; in addition to these were some other goods in constant demand, cart bushes, bakestones, fire backs including special Dutch fire backs, furnace grates and doors, smoothing and sad irons and heaters, weights, pestles and mortars and 'small ware.' Less common articles were rollers, hatter's basons and pitch pans, and one customer, William Rutter of Stafford took 'chymical pans' from time to time. A certain number of pig moulds were supplied to mines and Griffiths of Swansea, and from time to time special plates or other articles were cast to order.

The second direction in which trade was developed was that of cast iron sold in pigs. This trade was largely carried on through Thomas and Gabriel Goldney of Bristol, who carried a large stock and accounted at frequent intervals for their sales. Milner of Bewdley and Nehemiah Champion also took some share in the trade in pig iron, and in the case of Champion the flow was reversible, as sometimes he bought pigs from Goldney and sometimes sold them to him, but at other times he took them direct from the Company.

Finally, from 1722 there was an increasing interest in the casting of steam engine parts and in pipe work, and though in bulk this never became a major part of the work, it soon assumed a position of great importance and served to extend the reputation of Coalbrookdale castings over much of the country.

Early in the period of Richard Ford's single management, the Company began to cast iron railings, a trade which a century later was to become one of the great interests of this foundry. There were many small consignments of railing parts but the first large job came in 1731, when John Smitheman of Little Wenlock ordered 128 Palisadoes, 6 Pillars, 10 Rails, 6 Scrowls and 134 Spear Heads, 57 cwt., 2 qr. 3 lb. at 17/- a hundredweight, and paid for their carriage to Preston Hospital.

An invention which proved to be of great importance to many of the rapidly developing hardware trades in Birmingham and the Midlands, was that of the screw-press, used for stamping buttons, medallions and many other small articles. The main part of the press was a heavy iron frame fitted with a nut through which a heavy screw could run, the screw being rotated by a powerful lever arm. In the early years of Ford's management, the accounts include a note of several press plates and screws, and before long this developed into quite a steady product of the foundry.

When Ford had had the management of the works for twelve years, Abraham Darby II had reached the age of nineteen and was being trained in and around the works. In 1732 he was given a regular position as assistant to Ford, and in a letter to Goldney early in 1733, Ford says:

> Ye country Journeys are pretty considerable though not above 2 or 3 in a Year more yn wn yee was here & wch Abraham wd manage besides keeping ye Books very readilly, he does not anyway complain about it neither does he know anything I have wrote yee on this Head, but my time being taken more yn usual in ye above articles, I cannot so constantly attend ye Waying & Sending out of Goods as I ought to do, wch adds to his Business & I presume 'tis more yn he can regularly go through with.'[1]

Soon after the sending of this letter Ford sent Abraham to Chester Fair by himself, to meet customers and to collect money; he was also instructed to call on his return journey at Bersham furnace where he was to report on its working and to make a valuation of the stock. The fact that he was entrusted with these responsibilities is the best evidence of the thorough training he had received, and it was greatly to Ford's satisfaction that Abraham collected an encouraging amount of money at the fairs, and also made an excellent report on the condition of Bersham. Other journeys followed this one, both

[1] *Darby MSS.*, Ford's Letter Book. Letter to Thomas Goldney, 23 April 1733.

with Ford as companion on some of the longer ones, or by himself to many places in the Midlands and Leicestershire. When Ford was away by himself on longer journeys, Abraham was left in charge of the furnaces, office and warehouse, and in a relatively short time was able to take in hand any of the duties fulfilled by Ford. In addition to the normal work of the place, Abraham took a special interest in the transport of the heavy cylinder and engine castings, and in this connection was a prime mover in the application of wooden railways in and around the works, a few years later.

In view of the large responsibilities which Abraham was now sharing with Ford, a new tenancy of the works was obtained in their joint names and this was signed in June 1734.[1] In March the following year Ford and Darby agreed that Ford should receive three-quarters and Darby one-quarter of all rights, privileges and advantages that arose from this new tenancy. It is probable that in these two agreements Ford was acting largely on behalf of Goldney who still held the majority of the shares in the works.

With Abraham admitted to a proper partnership in the works, his particular genius soon expressed itself in a close attention to the furnaces and the foundry side of the work, while Ford gave more of his time to the selling and correspondence side of the business. In fact it is not long before we find that Abraham has quietly assumed the direction of the technical side of the business and is busy making experiments and improvements in all branches of the works.

In 1732, Richard Ford and Thomas Goldney were making changes to meet a changing market. The Old and the New Blast furnaces were both in good production making about five tons of iron each per week, which was divided between the pot trade, the pig iron trade, and the larger castings. The sale of pig iron was carried on mainly through Thomas and Gabriel Goldney and a large part of the pot trade was in the hands of Nehemiah Champion. The demand for pig iron was increasing in Bristol and at times Ford found it difficult to meet all these orders without delaying his make of pots. Some time in 1731 Ford and Goldney took over Bersham furnace from John Hawkins, husband of Anne Darby, leaving Hawkins to manage it, and relying on it to serve a good part of the pot trade which centred round Chester, thus relieving Coalbrookdale furnaces to that extent. Bersham furnace had been built by Charles Lloyd in 1717 and was brought into blast in 1719. Kelsall's diary has an entry

[1] See Appendix 3.

1721.3.12mo. 'I understood Bersham furnace ceased this day blowing with charcoal, and went on blowing with Coakes for Potting.' In 1727 the furnace was sold to John Hawkins who was a little later involved in legal difficulties and then transferred it to Ford and Goldney. In 1732 the furnace was in good condition but the preparations for a blast were held up for a month through Hawkins's difficulties; at the same time the stock of ironstone was thought to be not quite sufficient for a full-length blast. Ivie is the person quoted as having a process out against Hawkins but it is also noted that Ivie, while managing Bersham furnace before Hawkins, had had poor blasts making scarce three tons of iron in a week and that the iron was as white as silver so that it could hardly be got out of the hearth. Ford put this down to Ivie's lack of skill and was sure that Hawkins could do better. In February 1733 Ford, replying to demands for pig iron from Bristol, says that the furnaces at Coalbrookdale cannot keep up with the demand, but will send more pigs as quickly as they are made.

It was about this time that Ford began to anticipate a rapid expansion of the steam engine castings demand, when the Savery patent expired. He proposed to meet the increase by putting Bersham furnace in blast and by taking over a furnace at Willey, on the Severn bank near Coalbrookdale. This furnace he would put in order and get into production with little trouble, as it was near both coal and ironstone. In a letter to Thomas Goldney[1] he says:

> Ye Business in Castings of one kind or other is Enlarged pretty much here and as ye Patent for ye Fire Engine is now Expiring that Business will consequently Increase more & where these Furnaces to go on to our Satisfaction, ye Piggs produced (besides other Castings) would not be sufficient for ye Bristoll Demands, & as they can't well do without 'em & we should not have 'em to Supply, it may put 'em upon further Experiments wch may be of bad Consequence So that a Blast once in a Year at Willey for Piggs will be a Fortification against their Attempts. I could have sold a Pretty many Piggs to Birmingham & Wallsall had we had 'em to Spare, but I was willing to supply ye Bristoll Chaps wth what we had, but hereafter their Markitts may be supplied.'

Neither Bersham nor Willey had a very good start, though from different causes. Bersham was at times badly managed through Hawkins's preoccupation with his personal difficulties, though the difficulties were more those of finance than of smelting technique.

[1] Ford Letter Book, 1732–7. *Darby MSS.* Letter 16 March 1733.

At Willey, the furnace was old and not well designed, and like Coalbrookdale had an insufficient water supply. There were good ironstone and coal to be had near the furnace, and as they were mined close together the ore was burned at the mine bank to save the carriage of coals. Low water delayed the lighting of the Willey furnace until 12 November 1733; but it was making iron in December, though it is noted that it did not make iron so hot and grey as was desired. The occurrence of some showers of rain made it possible to blow a little faster and get a better iron.

It was unfortunate that the year in which both Bersham and Willey were being brought into production was one of exceptional drought so that what little iron they could make hardly offset the losses of iron at Coalbrookdale through the same lack of water. Ford's expectations of an increased trade in heavy castings looked at first like being realized, as orders for iron and for engine cylinders and pipe work came in. This made it doubly irksome to have to report that he sent '145 piggs (5 ton) all we have and unless we have rain soone 'twill be a Considerable time before we have any more for we are Obliged to Blow so Softly that we cannot make Iron sufficient for Potts & Castings etc. & must waight wth Patience though greatly to our loss till raine does come.'

During the five years from late 1732 to 1737 Bersham was able to make three long blasts, as it had no shortage of water, and generally made just over five tons of iron a week of very good quality. An air furnace and a moulding room were built for the pot casting and there is a note that the pig iron is good and 'the potts exceed ours at Dale in colour & lightness—down to 5 lbs p gallon. May spare 50 or 60 ton of Piggs at 29/– a ton for Bristoll.' In 1736 Bersham found that its iron was good enough to make a saving in cost by ladling direct from the hearth for pot casting, so cutting out the air furnace and the cost of remelting.

Technically Bersham furnace was a success, but financially it was a constant worry, making so many demands for advances of money that Ford and Goldney frequently discussed the advantage of disposing of it. Hawkins, deeply involved in his law suit, had used advances of money made for the furnace for his own purposes, not by any wrong doing, but by failing to keep any clear and separate accounts of his own affairs. However, he did know how much he was in debt to the Coalbrookdale accounts and was prepared to repay this debt when it became possible. In spite of difficulties a slight profit was made on the first blast and with larger sales and a reduction of dead stock this profit could be increased. Ford made a practice of calling at Bersham on his way to and from Chester fair, and Abraham Darby also made several visits; with Goldney they felt that a close oversight and better management could convert this into a valuable asset. They received a shock in January 1735 when Hawkins informed them that the land and lease of Bersham furnace had been used by him as security for a loan and that the loan was being called in on 10 February. To keep Bersham this loan must be paid and Ford, Goldney and Darby raised one-third each. A valuation of the furnace showed pigs and castings in stock £1,114, allowing £7 per ton for pigs and £10 per ton for castings; boxes and patterns, £50; buildings and repairs, £120; coke, baskets, and tools and odd things, £140; total £1,328. There are several more items which add up a little, and 'when the pigs are recast into pots and sold, and John Hawkins repays what he has used, there wont be much loss against the money, upwards of £1,500 already advanced.' Hawkins had half a share in Coalbrookdale, through his wife, and agreed that all the profits on that share should be retained against his debt. Later he offered to sell the share and it was bought by Ford, as Abraham and Edmund Darby declined it.

With the closer oversight the Bersham furnace worked well and made small profits, but its chief value in Ford's estimation was that it kept alive the country trade around Chester and also reached several areas in Wales which could not easily be reached from Coalbrookdale. Transport to the Chester and Liverpool markets had been difficult for a long time and as Bersham could serve them more easily it was hoped this would lead to an expansion of their trade. When Coalbrookdale extended later, towards Ketley and Horsehay, Bersham furnace was sold to Isaac Wilkinson and became his principal furnace from 1753 until his failure in 1795.

The Willey furnace in some ways offers a sharp contrast with Bersham, as it was in good management but encountered many technical difficulties. It was an old furnace and during its first blast Ford realized that the water wheel and bellows were in a very bad condition so that almost half of the blast was lost. Like Coalbrookdale, Willey had only a marginal water supply and could ill afford to have inefficient use made of this in a year such as 1733 and the winter following it, which were marked by unprecedented drought. When the furnace was blown out after a relatively short blast, the lining or 'in walls' built of sandstone were found to have failed, being badly attacked by the hot metal and in parts fused and fluxed, so as to be in a dangerous condition. These were rebuilt and the opportunity taken to reproportion the furnace which had been three feet higher and six to nine inches narrower than those at Coalbrookdale. With this rebuilding, and the reconstruction of the wheel and bellows, a pool dam was also constructed, so that the furnace came into its second blast in very good condition. It is regularly reported as making excellent iron. The furnace made only pig iron, which was sent to Bristol along with the Coalbrookdale pig, and as they were made from the same ironstones, they were usually indistinguishable in quality. If the water had been in sufficient supply, Willey furnace would have been a source of large profits. As it was, it paid its way and in the later years made a profit, but it was not able to keep in blast for more than about forty weeks in the year. Eventually this furnace was sold to Wilkinson and was later taken over by his son and partners in 1759 as the New Willey Company.

The scale of working was not very large and is clearly indicated by the accounts of the blasts. In October 1734 the first blast was summarized, with a note that no profit had been expected as the raising of a pool dam for the bellows wheel had been a heavy expense. The position was stated in brief as—£585 received for pig iron sent to Bristol and £45 more owing for iron, which would represent a make of 90 tons. The stock of ironstone, limestone and coke, with the new hearth and various oddments, are valued at a further £188, a total of £813 which is a little more than the money that had been advanced for this blast. In 1735 the blast made 92 tons of pig iron on which there was a total profit of £213.10.5, or £2.6.5 per ton of iron made. Of this profit £157.8.4 was spent on repairs to buildings, new in-walls to the furnace, and other work which would not recur for many years and which was a definite asset for the future blasts. We have only one more year of accounts for Willey furnace, 1736, which show a profit of £234.16.3¾ on a make of 209 tons, *i.e.* £1.2.5 per ton.

The venture at Willey furnace was carried on by Ford and Goldney who provided all the money and took the profits, but the Coalbrookdale works received an indirect benefit in so far as the iron from Willey helped to satisfy and retain their Bristol customers during the years when Coalbrookdale was finding it difficult to meet the demands for pig iron.

Through all the vicissitudes of the Bersham and Willey furnaces Abraham Darby was meeting similar difficulties at Coalbrookdale, and along with Ford was applying his experience in various practical experiments at one or all of the furnaces. In this way he became an expert foundryman with many ideas on the design and operation of furnaces, and this experience enabled him to carry all the responsibilities of a managing partner when in 1738 he was included in a new partnership agreement.

The contribution which Abraham was making to the running of the works was recognized in 1734 by giving him a salary of £50 a year in addition to any return he got from his share in the works capital. Until the partnership in 1738 Abraham's cash was handled by the Trustees and is usually noted in the books of the Company in this manner

May 1735. Trustees Dr. to Abm. Darby for £66.13.4 being so much cash paid said Abm. Darby on Acct. for his Share in ye Works & tis charged to his Acct. of Sallary.

When Abraham was taken into full partnership, the occasion was taken to bring all accounts in the Company to a balance and to carry this forward as the commencing item of what is called 'the New Company.'

folio 84. Nov. 1738

To Ball: as pr Contra being Cash in Rich[d] Ford's hands Recon'd in the Inventory as a Bank for the New Compa: and is Carry[d] into New Comp[as] Cash Book Accordingly

£1050.16.1¾

Hence Forward the New Company's Cash is Continued. . . .

folio. 1.

To a Ballance of Cash by Preceeding Company's Cash Book fol. 84. See this Book 2 Folios Back £1050.16.1¾

4th. 9mo. To Ballance by Preceeding Company—New Company Accounts continue.

Preceeding Co. Loss in bad money in 17 yrs. £1.6.6¾

On the next accounting at the end of the first four-week period, there is an item which completes the new arrangements, 'pd. H. Rainsford for a Copy of a Deed of Partnership 9/–.,' and the accounts then resume exactly according to the former pattern, being still kept by Richard Ford acting as Clerk.

From the commencement of the New Company Abraham assumed a position not distinguishable from that of works manager, but with Goldney and Ford still holding thirteen-sixteenths of the shares and thus largely determining the commercial policy. Thomas Goldney died in 1738 and his death was one contributory influence towards the new partnership. His shares were left to his children and to his brother, and on 30 October, Abraham Darby and Richard Ford entered into an agreement with Goldney's son Thomas, approving the redistribution of Goldney's shares. For the purpose of this agreement the works were valued and a figure of £16,000 accepted, making £1,000 a share. The new holders of the Goldney shares were Thomas Goldney junr. 3, Gabriel Goldney (his uncle) 1, John Ball (husband of Hannah Goldney) 1, Martha Vanderwall (Goldney) 1, Mehetable Goldney 1, Anne Goldney 1 and Elizabeth Goldney 1. In matters of policy, Thomas Goldney junior acted for all the group, but was by no means such an outstanding man as his father had been.

Chapter Five

ABRAHAM DARBY II, 1738–1763

THE first venture which is associated directly with Abraham Darby II is the attempt to improve the furnace performance by improving the blast, and particularly its regularity throughout the year. Ford had already made pumps which were operated by horses, to pump the water from the lower pool into which it ran from the tail race of the bellows water wheels, back into the upper furnace pool, to be used again and again. In 1742 Abraham began to replace Ford's pumps by a set driven by a steam engine, thus getting a much quicker return and circulation. Fortunately we have Abiah Darby's note on this scheme and some details of the actual engine are preserved in the Company's books and are discussed in the chapter on the Steam Engine.[1]

My Husband Abraham Darby was but Six years old when his Father died—but he inherited his genius—enlarg'd upon his plan, and made many improvements. One of Consequence to the prosperity of these Works was as they got very short of water that in the summer of dry Seasons they were obliged to blow very slow, and generally blow out the furnaces once a year, which was attended with great loss. But my Husband proposed the Erecting a Fire Engine to draw up the Water from the lower Works and convey it back into the upper pools, that by continual rotation of the Water the furnaces might be plentifully supplied; which answered Exceeding Well to these Works, and others have followed the Example.

There is no doubt that this scheme was very successful, as the furnace records show that variations between summer and winter blowing were considerably smoothed out, and the frequent rests of six weeks or two months, which were a regular feature of the earlier years, were cut out altogether.[2]

Darby, Ford and Goldney were all Quakers, and Darby was very active in the work of the Society of Friends, attending First day and mid-week meetings, acting as Clerk of Monthly Meeting, and frequently travelling in the ministry. It is therefore very difficult to understand how the new Company came to enter into the gun

[1] Chapter Eight, pp. 138–9.

[2] For a fuller account of this see Chapter Seven, pp. 108–3.

trade from 1739 to 1748. It is possible that the Goldney holding of nine-sixteenths of the shares of the Company, and the death of Thomas Goldney senior in 1738, gave Thomas Goldney junior the opportunity to press this very profitable trade upon Richard Ford. As a body the Quakers had been very consistent in their testimony against war and against the use of all armed force, most of the Quaker merchants even refusing to have their goods carried in ships which were armed for defence. The Peace Testimony of the Society had been formulated as early as 1660 and Friends had suffered many persecutions for their refusal to bear arms or to pay levies for militia or other military purposes. It was this objection to war which had kept Friends out of many profitable businesses, and Abraham Darby I had followed true to the pattern of the Quaker industrialists in his refusal to enter any part of the armament trade. After the reorganization of the Company in 1738, Abraham and Edmund Darby had only a three-sixteenths interest in the works, and Richard Ford had four-sixteenths, while Thomas Goldney and his relations held nine-sixteenths and thus were the dominant partners. The Goldneys were merchants and bankers as well as being partners in the Coalbrookdale works, and were already committed through their connections to trading ventures to the West Indies. Our relations with Spain were marked during the later 1730's by increasing tension and a growing threat to our trade with the Spanish colonies in America; this culminated in 1739 in the war with Spain. The years of this accumulating tension were marked by the heavier arming of merchant ships, and the fitting out of privateers, and it seems most likely that the Goldneys were drawn into this arming through their wide trading connections. Thomas Goldney was the Company's agent in Bristol and was responsible for shipping much of their pig iron at least to London, while he and his brother Gabriel were merchants with interests in many ships. They may have first accepted the arming of some of the ships in which they had interest, then found it easy, as times got more difficult, to take the next step of seeking to share in the large profits to be made by supplying arms to the merchant ships. However it came about, in January 1740 the Coalbrookdale Company paid £1.5.8 for the carriage of cannon patterns up the Severn from Bristol, and in April they built a new boring mill. The first guns are mentioned in November the same year when Cornelius Hallen is paid £3.9.0 for 'dressing' 33 guns. The output increased and by 1748 over 2,000 cannon and guns had been dealt with as well as 182 tons of 'guns, heads and fittings.' The descriptions of the guns range from $\frac{1}{2}$ pounders to 9 pounders, and after 1745 all sizes were being turned; as the accounts include payments for dressing, boring and turning, but the casting is included in the general amounts of 'cast goods' without itemization, it is not possible to arrive at any accurate estimate of total production. No single parcel of castings can be traced through all the stages of dressing, boring and turning, and as each account mixes numbers and weights, the possibility of reaching any accurate estimate seems remote from the records now available.

During the time in which guns were being made at Coalbrookdale, the works were visited by the Reverend M. Mason, who sent an account of his visit in a letter to the President of the Royal Society[1] describing what he had seen. In this letter he said 'Mr. Ford, from iron ore and coal, both gotten in the same Dale, makes iron brittle or tough as he pleases, there being cannon thus cast so soft as to bear turning like wrought iron.' The books of the Company afford ample confirmation that the guns were turned.

In 1745 Richard Ford died and the complete management of the works devolved upon Abraham Darby, while Richard Ford's son, Richard, took over the clerkship of the Company. Richard Ford left three sons, Richard, Edmund and Abraham. Abraham Ford became a traveller for whom there are many expense accounts at fairs in Staffordshire, Gloucestershire, on the 'Welsh Journey,' at Birmingham, Manchester and many other towns. The third brother, Edmund, was associated with the Leighton furnace and only occasionally finds any place in the Coalbrookdale records, chiefly when making payments to his brother Richard on behalf of the Leighton Company. Richard gave up keeping the books of the Dale Company about 1748, but continued his interest and activities in the works, though at the same time entering into other business ventures with his brothers. The youngest brother, Edmund, had gone to Lancaster to promote the business of making iron pipes and pumping machinery. Richard Ford had taken up an interest in several small iron works in which William Hallen acted as manager. These various ventures came to an end in 1764 when Edmund and Richard Ford became bankrupt. The *Norris MSS.* include a mention of the bankruptcy of Richard Ford but date it to 1758: 'There is money supposed to be due to R. Ford from Caynton, Sawbrook and Ibberton Ironworks wch cannot

[1] *Phil. Trans.*, 1747, p. 382.

be set forth, not having been able to get the Accounts belonging to the sd Works settled by Wm. Hallen, Manager of the sd Ironworks.' Caynton and Sawbrook will be the two Shropshire forges Kaynton and Sambrook. Kaynton had been a good customer for Coalbrookdale iron until 1756 in which year both Kaynton Forge and William Hallen drop out of the accounts. This probably marks the beginning of the trouble in Richard's concerns and as Richard is not mentioned again in any of the records, it is likely that this was the occasion when Abraham Darby bought the Ford shares in Coalbrookdale.

After the death of Richard Ford senior, it seems to have taken Darby a year or two to get rid of the gun trade, and to develop his own plans for the works. By 1748 he began to alter and extend their activities in many directions, and one of the incentives that must have influenced him was the great demand then being made for pig iron suitable for forge uses. The nail and small ironware trades of the Black Country and indeed of all the Midlands was increasing at a rapid rate, and the supplies of charcoal iron were heavily taxed to keep up with the growing demand. There had been considerable difficulty experienced when attempts were made to refine pig iron made by coke smelting, and to convert it to a malleable bar iron which could be slit for nailer's rods. As the greatest demand for iron was for the use of nailers it was obviously to Darby's advantage if his projected new furnaces could supply an acceptable iron for this purpose. After a long series of experiments, Darby succeeded in producing an acceptable pig iron, but unfortunately we have no detail of the actual technique by which he achieved his aim. Abiah Darby wrote a letter, which though undated, can be localized to 1775, in which she gives some account of her husband's trials. She says they were carried out about twenty-six years previous to her writing, and this would make the date about 1749–50.

But all this time the making of Barr Iron at Forges from Pit Coal pigs was not thought of. About 26 years ago my Husband conceived this happy thought—that it might be possible to make bar iron from pit coal pigs. Upon this he sent some of our pigs to be tryed at the Forges, and that no prejudice might arise against them he did not discover from whence they came, or of what quality they were. And a good account being given of their working, he errected Blast Furnaces for Pig Iron for Forges. Edward Knight Esq. a capitol Iron Master urged my Husband to get a patent, that he might reap the benefit for years of this happy discovery: but he said he would not deprive the public of Such an Acquisition which he was

Satisfyed it would be; and so it has proved, for it soon spread and many Furnaces both in this Neighbourhood and Several other places have been erected for this purpose.

Had not these discoveries been made the Iron trade of our own produce would have dwindled away, for woods for charcoal became very scarce and landed Gentlemen rose the price of cord wood exceeding high—indeed it would not have been to be got. But from pit coal being introduced in its stead the demand for wood charcoal is much lessen'd, and in a few years I apprehend will set the use of that article aside.

There is an oft quoted story which tells how Abraham Darby at one time stayed six days and nights on the bridge of the furnace, watching the experiments, waiting to see the result of a particular blow. When at last he saw the metal run from the tapping hole, and found the iron to be of the quality he was hoping to get, he collapsed and was carried to his home by his workmen. There may be a good deal of addition and dramatization in the many versions of this story, but none the less it probably preserves the record of a real incident. Darby *was* successful about this time in producing a pig iron which was acceptable for use at the forges, and a large trade in this new pig iron soon developed with the forge masters of the Midlands.

There is a gap in the records now available from 1748 to 1754 but during that short period there was a significant change in the location of the Company's larger customers. Up to 1748 the principal sales of pig iron had been to Thomas Goldney, acting as agent in Bristol, who shipped a good deal to London for the use of foundries there. In 1754 the largest purchases of pig iron were being made by the leading makers of rod iron situated in the Midlands, who found their market among the nailers, locksmiths, chain makers, and other users of good wrought iron, whose demands previously had been solely for bar and rod made from charcoal iron. Edward Knight, the 'capitol Iron Master' of Abiah Darby's letter, was one of the first and largest customers for the new iron, his purchases between 1755 and 1761, the years for which there are detailed accounts for the Coalbrookdale furnaces only, omitting the Horsehay and Ketley furnaces, are 366 tons, 405 tons, 465 tons, 275 tons, 412 tons, and 464 tons in the respective years. Another large customer was the forge master, Lord Foley, who took in the same period a total of 1,188 tons of pig iron.

The success of the new furnace method and the great increase in demand for pig iron encouraged Darby to take steps towards a considerable expansion of the works. The first stage in this enlarging of interests was the leasing of coal areas in Ketley Manor from the Earl of Gower, and the reorganization of the fuel and ore supplies. New pits were sunk and the wooden railway which already connected the works with the wharves of the Severn, and extended up the Dale as far as Lakehead, was planned to extend to Ketley and to include collieries and furnaces which Darby proposed to build there. In 1753 the lease of minerals, both coal and ironstone, in the Manor of Dawley, was taken from Plowden Slaney and the Horsehay works and furnaces were begun. Two furnaces at Horsehay were built and were blown in in 1755, and the following year two at Ketley came into production, each furnace having a capacity of about twenty-five tons a week.

The five years from 1750 to 1755 were years of revolution and change in the Coalbrookdale Company. The old furnace methods on which the Company had built its reputation and position were changed, and a new trade in pig iron suited for the forges and refineries was developed on a considerable scale, although the original basic trade in pots and kettles and general cast ware continued unaltered. The steam engine was applied to the furnace blast through water wheels and improved wooden bellows, and furnaces of greatly increased capacity were built. The production of both coal and ironstone was taken over to a very large extent by the Company, though the demands of their increasing output still allowed them to use all the coal and ore which were provided as a condition of their lease of the old furnaces. In this very extensive building programme, the Company were able to supply practically all their own materials. They had established brick and tile works for their own use which later were to develop into an important commercial unit. Timber was felled from their own woods and coppices and sawn in their own saw mill, for all purposes. Much of the labour, both in the mines and the woods, was still provided by workmen who in small companies or partnerships contracted for getting or preparing raw materials or timber, for sinking pits, driving soughs, or doing various other kinds of work. Outside Shropshire the Company had for a short time an interest in foundries in London, Bristol and Liverpool and also kept agents for their steam engines in Truro and Newcastle-on-Tyne.

The Dale and the country round about must at this time have presented a busy spectacle. The glare of the furnaces and casting floors would light up the place at night, while during the day the constant rumbling of waggons with their loads of coal and ore, timber, bricks and iron ware of all kinds, must have given a permanent air of bustle and movement. In 1753 Hannah Darby, Abraham's daughter, wrote to her aunt, Rachel Thompson

> . . . Methinks how delightful it would be to walk with thee into fields and woods, then to go into the Dale to view the works; the stupendous Bellows whose alternate roars, like the foaming billows, is awful to hear; the mighty Cylinders, the wheels that carry on so many different Branches of the work, is curious to observe; the many other things which I cannot ennumerate; but if thou wilt but come, I am sure thou would like it. It's really pleasant about our house, and so many comes and goes that we forget it's the Country till we look out at the window and see the woodland prospect. . . .

The development of the works had been confined to the bottom of the valley, in the rather narrow areas in the bends of the Coalbrook. Here every yard of level ground had been utilized; the stream was dammed to form first the Upper Furnace Pool, above which the house of the later Darbys, White House, or Sunniside, stood in its wide grounds. Below the great dam of the pool, on the flat ground alongside the stream, there stood the Old Blast Furnace, with its accompanying moulding shops, blacksmith's shops, boring mills, Air furnace, Old Forge and many other buildings. From the water wheels the tail race water was carried into the Lower Furnace Pool, and drawn from there for the Lower, or New Blast Furnace, around which were the principal moulding shops and the great warehouse. Below this again was the Upper Forge Pool leading to the Upper Forge and smith's shops, and just below the Forge, Darby's old house. Still further down stream, at the mouth of the valley, was the Lower, or Hallam's Forge, and, along the banks of the Severn, Nailer's Row and the Ladcroft wharf. From the Upper Furnace Pool to the cottages below the upper forge was a distance of about a thousand yards and the valley bottom was about a hundred and fifty yards wide. This area was entirely occupied by a mass of buildings, railway lines, and crowded machinery, confined by valley sides which rose very steeply, in parts almost precipitously, and which were shrouded in woods and coppice. The valley slopes rose to a general plateau of cultivated land, part of which was obscured by the numerous mine workings for coal and iron. The general effect was that of a narrow belt of crowded industry deeply set within a finely wooded and hilly landscape. This aspect of the scene, with the striking contrast which is still a feature of the Dale today, deeply impressed Arthur Young when he visited Coalbrookdale in 1776.[1]

> Coalbrookdale itself is a very romantic spot, it is a winding glen between two immense hills which break into various forms, all thickly covered with wood, forming the most beautiful sheets of hanging wood. Indeed too beautiful to be much in unison with that variety of horrors art has spread at the bottom; the noise of the forges, mills, &c., with their vast machinery, the flames bursting from the furnaces with the burning of the coal and the smoak of the lime kilns, are altogether sublime, and would unite well with craggy and bare rocks, like St. Vincent's at Bristol.

There are two engravings by T. Vivares after drawings by Thomas Smith of Derby and George Perry, one of the engineers at Coalbrookdale.[2] The 'View of the Upper Works at Coalbrookdale' 1758, gives an accurate impression of the situation of the works below the Upper Furnace Pool. Darby's house and the Friends Meeting House are seen across the pool, on a steep hillside of farm land. The square top of the furnace is very inconspicuous but can just be discerned among the chimneys and buildings of the works. On the right foreground there are four heaps of smoking coal, where coke is being made on a piece of ground which was rented for that purpose in the very early days of the works. The road detail in the foreground shows a large engine cylinder being transported on a six-horse waggon, and as this is proceeding not down the Dale to the Severn but up the Dale road, it will be one of the cylinders for the Horsehay or Ketley furnace engines. A view of the Dale drawn many years later as a bill-head for the Company gives an even better picture of the way the works crowd in the valley floor, between steep, well-wooded hills.

We must now give a short space to a consideration of the more personal and social aspects of the life of Darby and of events in the Dale. Some time after his entry into the works and probably in 1734, Abraham Darby married Margaret Smith of Shifnal, and occupied the house which his father had built just before his death. By Margaret Smith, Abraham had three children, the eldest being a daughter,

[1] Young, Arthur, *Annals of Agriculture*, 1776, vol. IV, p. 168.

[2] George Perry (1719–71) left Coalbrookdale in 1758 and started a foundry at Liverpool which he called the Coalbrookdale Foundry. This later became the business of Joseph Rathbone and William Fawcett, and kept a close connection with the Coalbrookdale Company.

Hannah, born in 1735. In 1757 she married Richard Reynolds and will enter again into the Coalbrookdale story. The two sons, Abraham and Edmund, born in 1736 and 1738, both died in 1740, on the same day, the 8th of November, probably from some children's disease. His wife Margaret died the same year, 1740, and for five years Abraham was alone to look after his small daughter Hannah, having, however, the help and comfort of his sister Mary, wife of Richard Ford, close at hand. In 1745 Abraham decided to marry again and chose for his partner Abiah Sinclair of Sunderland, a widow.

Abiah was the youngest daughter of Samuel Maude of Sunderland, a member of a Quaker family of several generations. She was born in 1716 and while still in her teens married John Sinclair. She was of very serious mind and became a great Quaker preacher and zealous minister, travelling widely to meetings and on visits to Friends. She had a large family, and when the children were beginning to read she wrote a brief account of her own experiences for their instruction. 'I was born,' she says, 'of religious and honourable parents. My parents had thirteen children, of whom I was the youngest; several died young.' One of her sisters, however, Hannah, born in 1698, married Mark Burleigh of Sunderland, and her daughter Jane became the wife of Abraham, son of Richard Ford of Coalbrookdale, thus making a second link between the two families. Abiah resumes her narrative:

> Soon after my father died I became very serious and could not join with my companions in the innocent diversions we had been accustomed to. I read and searched the Scriptures and valuable books for comfort to my soul. Thus was I concerned till I was nearly sixteen, diligent in attending meetings and exercised the rein.
>
> But now how shall I relate, or in what words set forth my obstinacy and disobedience. . . . Meeting after meeting did I withstand against His holy Will! Thus, for nearly two years, did the Lord vouchsafe to strive with me—once I did stand up but sat down again without opening my mouth.

Here we see her early drawings towards the vocal ministry, but from shyness or diffidence she kept silence, and felt that she was doing wrong in not speaking. About that time she became aquainted with John Sinclair who sympathized with her, and after a time she married him. She had one child, Rachel, who died of smallpox, a little before her husband also died. When Abraham Darby approached her with the desire for marriage she accepted him and found a great happiness in her life.

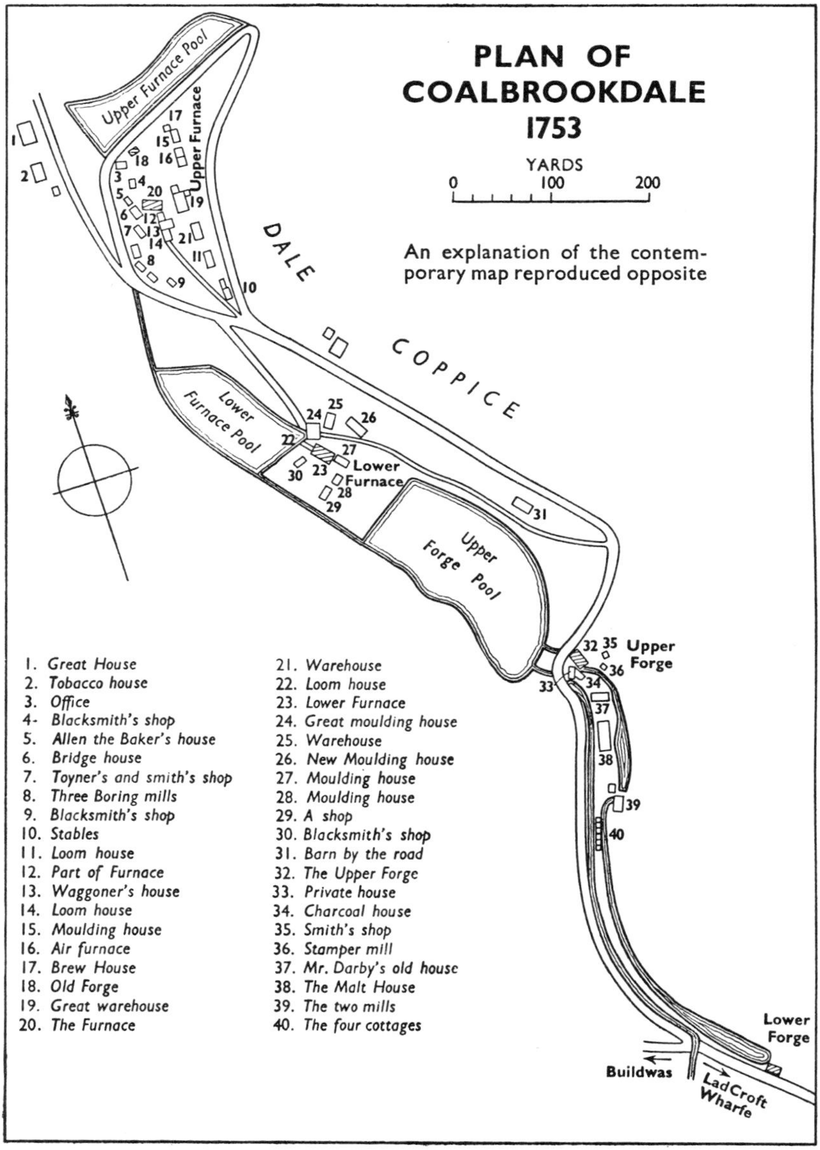
PLAN OF
COALBROOKDALE
1753
YARDS
0
100
200
An explanation of the contemporary map reproduced opposite
Upper Furnace Pool
Upper Furnace
DALE
COPPICE
Lower Furnace Pool
Lower Furnace
Upper Forge Pool
Upper Forge
Lower Forge
Buildwas
LadCroft Wharfe
1. Great House
2. Tobacco house
3. Office
4. Blacksmith's shop
5. Allen the Baker's house
6. Bridge house
7. Toyner's and smith's shop
8. Three Boring mills
9. Blacksmith's shop
10. Stables
11. Loom house
12. Part of Furnace
13. Waggoner's house
14. Loom house
15. Moulding house
16. Air furnace
17. Brew House
18. Old Forge
19. Great warehouse
20. The Furnace
21. Warehouse
22. Loom house
23. Lower Furnace
24. Great moulding house
25. Warehouse
26. New Moulding house
27. Moulding house
28. Moulding house
29. A shop
30. Blacksmith's shop
31. Barn by the road
32. The Upper Forge
33. Private house
34. Charcoal house
35. Smith's shop
36. Stamper mill
37. Mr. Darby's old house
38. The Malt House
39. The two mills
40. The four cottages

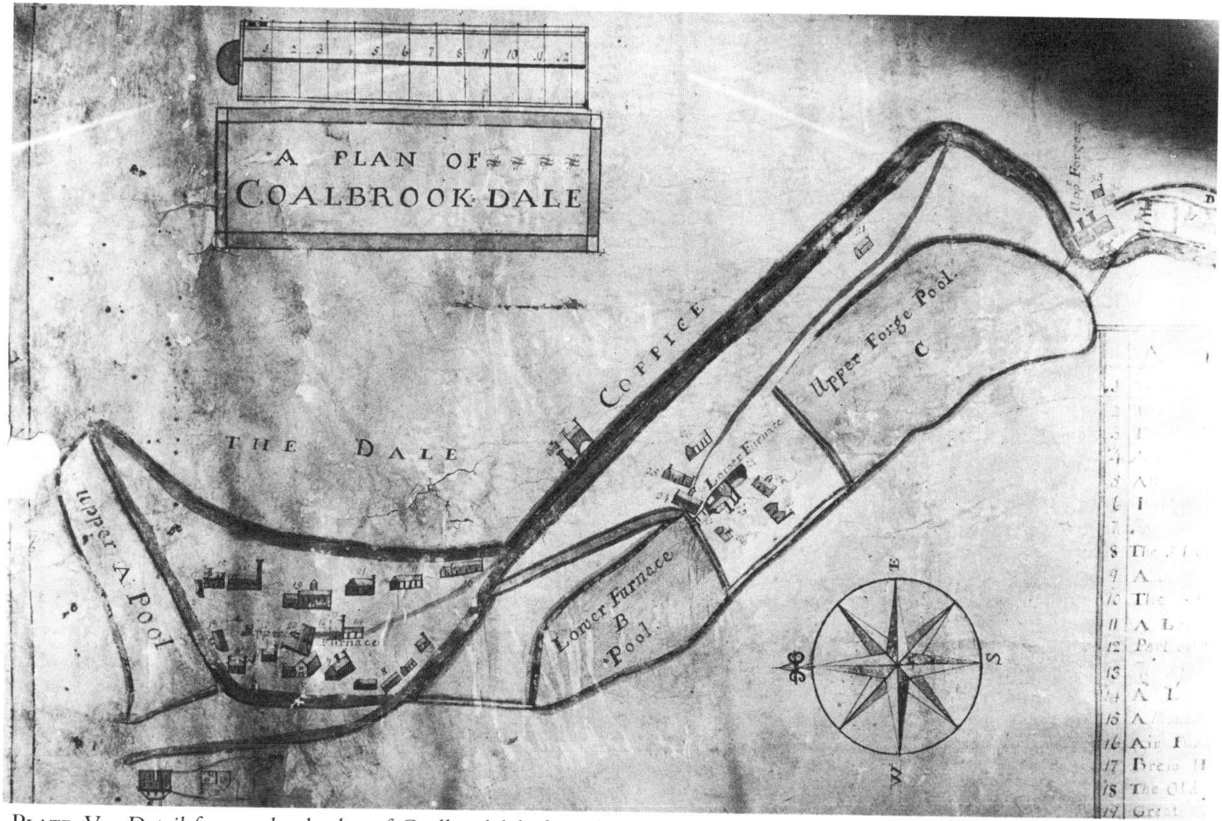

PLATE V *Detail from a sketch plan of Coalbrookdale from the Upper Works down to the Lower Forge near the River Severn.*

PLATE VI *The earliest view of the Upper Works of the Coalbrookdale Company, engraved just five years after Thomas Slaughter's plan outlining the same area. In the middle distance surrounded by buildings is the square topped Furnace, in blast. To the right is the Furnace Pool with coking in progress near by, and above this Dale House and Rosehill House with Tea Kettle Row behind.* (See PLATE XXIV.)

By the second marriage Abraham had a large family—Rachel, the eldest, born in 1746, and Mary born in 1748 who married Joseph Rathbone; Abraham the eldest boy, born in 1750, and Samuel born five years later. Several of the children died in infancy, but Abraham, Samuel, Mary and Sarah survived to adult years. Among the many troubles the children had to face, there was an epidemic of smallpox which swept the Dale in 1758, during which Abiah had the children inoculated. A letter from Abraham Darby to his friend Samuel Fothergill, mentions this and also the arrangements for travelling to the half-yearly Meeting of Friends.

Coalbrookdale 29. 3mo. 1758

Dear Friend
Samuel Fothergill.

I hereby Salute thee and thy Wife with Dear Love, and we are in hopes of being Favoured with thy company here in thy Way to Chepstow, but whether I shall be able to go or not Seems Somewhat uncertain. I have had a Long and bad Cold which I am not yet got free From; And the Small Pox having Many Months been in the Neighbourhood, has kept us under a continual Apprehension on Acco^{t} of our Children So that we have at Length partly concluded to have them Innoculated, and which if it takes place Seems likely to be about the time We Should Set out, & may therefore prevent my going; I believe such as go will Set out on the 7th of Next Month, of which Number I Apprehend Jno Gosling Will be one, and they Will be very glad to have thy company to Get to Gloucester on 7th day Night and be at that Meeting on 1st day I suppose will be very agreeable. I Salute thee and thy Wife with Dear Love in which my Wife Joyns me. From

Thy truely Affectionate Friend
Abraham Darby

There is extant a diary or collection of notes made by Samuel Maude of Sunderland[1] which in some of its entries gives us a glimpse of the state of the works. Samuel had visited the works and in 1751 writes

I see at the Dale a Cast Vessel; 4ft 11in deep: 5 ft 10½ ins over Top & 4ft 6ins at Bottom wt. 24½ Hund: holds 713 gallons also another 7 ft wide and 4 ft high.

It may be that before Samuel was allowed to visit the Dale with its many young 'cousins' of opposite sex, Quakerly caution had

[1] Samuel Maude's MS., *Bevan-Naish Collection*. Woodbrooke Library, Selly Oak. B.N. 2462.

instituted some enquiries as to their standing and prospects. This may be a gross mistake and we may slander the good Friends by such a suggestion. Whatever the reason, Samuel Maude includes in his diary at this time,

> Advices from Jno. Gosling.
>
> Dale Stock about £25,000
>
> Unkle's Share; his income 6 or 700 £ per Ann.
>
> Cos. Fords has ½ share each may give 100£ per Ann: other works about 100£ per Ann. each more, worth about 200£ per Ann.
>
> Cos: Abm about 300£ per Ann
>
> The Lasses: about 200£ per Ann.
>
> Cos. Abm informs me there is 16 Shares Unkle Darby has 3½, Thos: Goldney's family 6; there family 6, y[t] Cos. Edmund Darby has ½ a Share: that ye Shares for this 10 years has given 200£ per Ann; that theres is equally divided among the 7 children; Unkle's Malting he thinks may bring him 200£ per Ann: Unkle Burleigh says Unkle Darby told him he had about 1000£ per Ann.

Thos. Goldney's family	9	Shares[1]
Cos. Ford's	4	do
Unk: Darby	3	do

> That Cos Abrm. Ford is book keeper to some works distinct from ye Dale; and rides: that his income may be about £250 per Ann: or yt way: that ye Coalworks brings in about £100 per Ann: to the family of ye Fords: that ye Lasses is he supposes about 200 per Ann fortune: that there lease of ye Dale is for 21 years, part of wch is gone that they pay about 100 guineas per Ann: for it being ground rent.

The account of the shares and incomes in this diary, is not very lucid; the Cos. Abm. would of course be Abraham Ford,[2] and the

[1] The preceding statement is different—

Thos. Goldney's family	6
Ford's family	6
Abraham Darby	3
Edmund Darby	½

[2] The relations might be clearer from an abbreviated diagram.

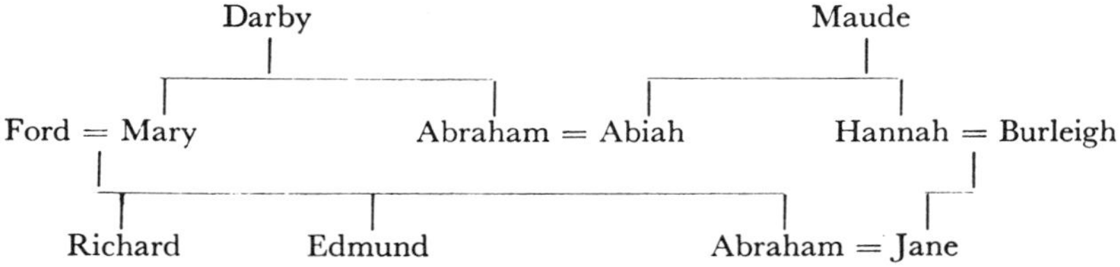

lasses might be Abraham Darby's daughters. In the diary Samuel speaks often of dining with his uncles, and later he goes to London with them, and frequently dines with them and attends Friends Meetings in their company. There may have been some idea of his entering the business as he more than once, while with them, meets the customers and the London agent of the Company.

The Darby home was a place of perpetual hospitality as is hinted in the letter from Hannah Darby already quoted in this chapter. Abiah tells us in her journal that she was often moved to speak words of spiritual comfort and advice to the many persons who gathered at her table, and she and Abraham travelled to most of the meetings in Wales and the borders. In 1754 she notes that 'My Husband, Daughter Hannah and myself set out with several Friends from hence, 14 horses, for our Yearly Meeting at Swansy—hired a guide over the mountains.' The year previously she notes 'went with my Dear Husband to our Welsh Y. M. at Abergavenny, 24. 4mo.' Not only the parents travelled about Friends business, but Hannah, now a girl of eighteen, also made long journeys in the company of Friends. Among some of her letters, there is one in which she describes her journey over the mountains to a meeting at Swansea, full of adventure and excitements, and racy beyond expectation. She must have inherited much of her father's courage and interest in the work of Friends. In the course of the letter she says that when she and her companion arrived at a house, even where people were used to entertaining travelling Friends, they were surprised when she took off her cloak as she appeared so young, but as soon as she mentioned her name, the people, knowing her father, felt that they could not offer her good enough accommodation. Nonetheless, she enjoyed the hardships and the excitements of the road.

It is from another letter of Hannah Darby's to her aunt Rachel Thompson at Newcastle-on-Tyne that we get a glimpse of unrest in the Dale, culminating in 1756 in riots, stimulated by the high price of food. It appears from this letter and from one from Abraham Darby, that the Coalbrookdale men were neither instigators nor leaders in this rioting, but were tempted to join their fellow workers from the surrounding areas.[1]

[1] The letter is among the *Rathbone MSS.*, but has no date; the petition for the four prisoners made during the riots, sent by Darby to Earl Gower, is among the *Friends House MSS.*, Portfolio 38.3. and is dated 23.8.1757 and by reference dates Hannah's letter to 1756.

My Dear Aunt,

Being apprehensive that you may hear of the tumult which hath happened here we are willing to inform you of the particulars, as such things generally gains much by carriage—the affair was this; this day week, the 1st Inst. we were somewhat alarm'd in the morning with an account that the Colliers at Brewsley were rose & consternation was greatly increased soon by fresh accounts that the Madely Wood as well as our own Colliers had joynd them, and we plainly could hear the dismal sound of blowing of horns which is their signal—their pretended reason for rising was to lower the price of corn so accordingly they went in a body to Wenlock market & there gave the farmers two hours to consider whether they would sell their weat at 5s. pr Bushel or have it took from them, some of them refused the first proposition so they took it, but did not comit any great outrage that day, the next morning they went to Shiffnal market & in their way called at an old justice Jourdans & oblig'd him to ride in the midst of them to the market where they commited great outrages they broke open houses barns etc & took anything they could meet with in this days expedition some of our Dale workmen was with them, the next day was Brewsly market where they were if possible worse than ever; they got into the Baker's shops took some bread & some threw it away; here the gentlemen read the Proclamation when they had done the mob gave a loud huzza & told them they neither valued them nor it, & to day they began to visit us both in going and coming; they behaved pretty civil, only asking for meat and drink which we were glad to give them to keep them quiet; they threatened that they would destroy the Dale Works if our men would not join them the next day to go to Wellington market—to prevent which my Father gave one of our Clerks 20 guineas to have given the ringleaders had they offered such a thing, but they did not, he also deputed to stand with money in their hands to give them at our lower gate to prevent them coming up to the house for fear of frightening my Mother—where they were to have drink this did with a few but the numbers increased so fast that they all came running up like wild things where we imploy'd several men in carrying them pailfuls of drink this was as they went to Wellington where they became quite Plunderers they not only took from them that sold any thing, but went into private peoples houses & took away money Pewter Silver plate or anything they could meet with, they also Plunder'd farms houses or any out houses they met with, they came back in droves loaded with booty & I believe moste of them called at our house but did not offer any violence—several hundreds had meat & drink this time—we baked bread three days together and sent several miles for it besides, for there was not a bit of bread nor corn nor flower to be had for money, for some miles about—so that the country was in the greatest distress. The mob gave themselves the title of levelers & so they were indeed—this night the gentlemen muster'd up several hundred men, to suppress them, they were all arm'd and marched up our railway they made a formidable appearance, they met with the mob at Ketley & they stood three fires before they fled; that morning they had agreed to Plunder all our houses they intended to have begun with our house & so have gone quite through, but through Divine favour were prevented—they have took many of them prisoners, & we hope its all over, tho we have had several alarms since. I intend to write again soon for cant say more now, we are pretty well all join me in love to you

post waits H Darby

On 23 October, Abraham Darby petitioned the Earl Gower for mercy on behalf of four of the prisoners—

May it please Coalbrookdale 23. 8. 1757
Earl Gower Shropshire.

The Riots that we have unfortunately had in this County under pretence of the High price of Corn, made it prudent and necessary for Government to proceed with severity against the Ringleaders & promoters of those disorders for the sake of Example and to prevent the like Tumults for the future; with this view several of the Rioters were prosecuted last year two of whom out of the number of 10 were capitally convicted, & have been hanged. The other 8 were repreived till the last assizes, when they were ordered to be transported for 14 years. In the number to be transported are included Rd Corbett, Wm. Cadman, John Cock, & Saml. Barker who till they were drawn into the said Riots at the Instance and threatenings of others, & perhaps with a view to procure sustenance for their starving families, always behaved as honest Industrious and most laborious Workmen; and as such deserve pity and compassion, and the rather as they are truely sensible of the high offence they have comitted and hope his Majesty will extend his Mercy to them for the sake of their distressed Familys.

The characters of these four Men till this unfortunate affair happened, makes me feel greatly for their distress, and solicitous to obtain their pardon, and for that purpose I have presumed to trouble thee with the state of their case, earnestly entreating thee to apply to our king for their pardon.

Examples have been made by hanging two of the said Rioters, and if the King shall be graciously pleased to shew Mercy to the 4 I have mentioned, I am persuaded it will have a good effect upon the minds of the people of this County in general, and be considered as a shining instance of that Humanity Mercy and Compassion which the king always wishes to shew to the moans of his distressed subjects; and thou wilt likewise by thy recommendation of those poor people to the kings Mercy, do a most agreeable act to a great number of thy friends in this County & in particular to with true Submission

Thy Oblig'd Friend
Abraham Darby.

As the situation of these unhappy people requires an immediate application I hope thou wilt have the goodness to represent their case to the king in the most favourable light, as soon as possible.

We do not know what effect this petition had, but hope that it was successfully presented to the king and that his mercy restored these men to their families. In the drawing up of the petition, there is a sidelight on Abraham Darby's strict Quaker manners. The draft of the petition has been drawn in some other handwriting, and then corrected with many insertions in the writing of Abraham Darby himself. The Petition is headed 'May it please thee Earl Gower,' but the 'thee' is crossed out by Darby. In several places the titles given such as your Majesty, his most gracious Majesty, etc., are crossed out and 'the king' or 'our king' substituted. Similarly the subscription at the close of the letter has been crossed out and Abraham's typical Friendly signature added. This is in agreement with all accounts of Abraham Darby, which are unanimous in marking him as a quiet, unassuming, and plain Friend. It is clear from the letter from Hannah, that the source of the unrest was not in the Dale, and this is paralleled by the rioting in Cumberland among the lead miners, where the better wages and the policy of maintaining a good standard of living of the workmen prevented the employees of the London (Quaker) Lead Company from taking part in the riots in surrounding districts, for which the military had to be called out.

Abraham Darby, like his father before him, in spite of the heavy demands that the works made upon his time and energies was always faithful to the meetings of the Society of Friends, and for many years was clerk of the Preparative Meeting in Coalbrookdale, and Broseley, sometimes clerk of Monthly Meeting; he even acted as clerk of the Welsh Yearly Meeting on occasion. In 1745 the meeting which had been held in the Darby's home for so many years was held in a new Meeting House, and the times of meeting were sent to the Monthly Meeting for approval, by Abraham Darby, as the clerk of the local meeting.

There is no need in this place to include such documents; the records of the Friends meetings in the Welsh borders are full of minutes, papers, etc., signed by Abraham Darby in various capacities, and the slightest perusal of them shows him to have been one of the most esteemed, active, and trusted Friends in the area. Broseley Meeting placed its leases and trust deeds in his safe keeping, and there is still extant a paper listing 'Broseley Meeting Writeings in Abraham Darbys keeping.' The most immediate interest of these papers is perhaps the constant association of Quaker family names from the late seventeenth century onwards—Darby, Reynolds, Osborn, Palmer, Griffith, Lloyd, Simpson, Davies and others, all met with again in the records of the early ironmasters of that area.

We left the story of the works about 1755, when the new furnaces at Ketley and Horsehay were being blown in and the Company had begun to implement the policy of owning its own sources of supply for most of its raw materials. In 1756 Thomas Goldney and Abraham Darby each put £1,350 of extra capital into the works, for the development of the collieries, and the production in all departments was rapidly increased. In 1756 Richard Reynolds came to the Dale and the following year married Hannah Darby. He settled at Ketley Bank and says in his memorandum[1] that he had a half-share in the iron and coal works there in partnership with Abraham Darby and Thomas Goldney; in 1762 he also purchased from them a small share in the Horsehay works. Richard Reynolds entered almost at once upon the management of the new furnaces at Ketley and promoted the expansion of these works with his utmost energy.

Nothing has been said yet of Abraham's brother Edmund who, though a shareholder in the Company, enjoyed only a very minor position.[2] Edmund figures from time to time in the account books, generally as a traveller visiting fairs and customers on behalf of the Company. From Ford's letters we learn that in 1733 Edmund, being of age, desired to start in business for himself and, as he supplied many items of grocery and general stores to the warehouse, his chosen trade was probably that of grocer and general merchant. He is often paid for supplies of candles, soap, hops, etc. for the works, and some of the accounts suggest that on some occasions the Company acted as his agent, *e.g.*

[1] Greg, E., *The Reynolds-Rathbone Diaries and Letters 1753–1839*, privately printed, 1905, pp. 171–7.

[2] The Company's capital was still held in sixteen equal shares and a little confusion arises because in the accounts and agreements the portion which Mary Darby left to each of her children is described sometimes as a half-share and at other times as one thirty-second share. If we adhere to the second and more usual manner of expression, then in 1745, Abraham had five thirty-seconds and Edmund one thirty-second interest in the works. As Abraham and his brother and sister had started with equal shares, there must have been some sales and purchases of which no record has been found.

R. A. Slaney, Dr. to Edmund Darby.
Tobacco 20 lbs at 18d. Herring 120 at 5/–. Jamaica
Rum 10 gallons at 10/6. Barrel of Cod at 9½d. 7lbs.

Many such items indicate that his trade was connected with the West Indies, through some of the Bristol merchants.[1] Whatever his position in the works, there are few entries except of this nature or in connection with his journeys. Edmund died in 1756 after a serious accident when riding. It occurred as he was returning from Abingdon Fair at which he had attended many customers and done much business, that he was thrown from his horse, fracturing some ribs and sustaining injuries from which he died soon after.

With the completion of the Ketley and Horsehay furnaces and with Richard Reynolds in charge of them, Abraham Darby gave most of his attention to Coalbrookdale where as well as the general management he was personally responsible for much of the more difficult transport of the cylinders and larger castings. In 1759 (20 June), on behalf of the Company he leased from Richard Burton an area of land in Dawley on which to build houses for his miners, and this estate, on which also a Meeting House for Friends was built, was known as the New Dale Building Lease, and on it houses were built in addition, at later periods.

Abraham Darby died on 6 June 1763, while his son Abraham was still a minor of only thirteen years of age. Richard Reynolds moved to the Dale from Ketley and took charge of the works with full management until the young Abraham reached an age of responsibility.

Of Abraham Darby II there are many testimonies of character to be derived from the writings of Friends, but it is enough to quote his widow, Abiah Darby, who says:

> He was just in his dealings, of universal benevolence and charity, living strictly to the Rectitude of the Divine and Moral Law, held forth by his great Lord and Saviour, had an extraordinary command over his own spirit, which thro' the Assistance of Divine Grace enabled to bear up with fortitude above all opposition: for it may seem very strange, so valuable a man should have Antagonists, yet he had. Those called Gentlemen with an Envious Spirit could not bear to see him prosper; and others covetous, strove to make every advantage by raising their Rents of their Collieries and lands in which he wanted to make roads; and endeavoured to stop the works. But he surmounted all: and died in Peace beloved and Lamented by many.

[1] The mixing of trade in groceries and iron was common to many of the Quaker iron makers and dealers, particularly along the river Severn. See Raistrick, A., *Quakers in Science and Industry*, 1950, pp. 150 ff.

Chapter Six

RICHARD REYNOLDS, 1763–1772 ABRAHAM DARBY III, 1768–1789

THE quiet and apparently casual entry of Richard Reynolds into the Coalbrookdale works in 1756 could not at the time have been recognized, even by the most venturesome imagination, for the revolution it portended. We are generally told, in baldest outline, that Reynolds was sent to the Dale by Thomas Goldney, to carry messages and transact business with Abraham Darby on behalf of Goldney, and that while in the Dale he met and fell at once in love with Hannah Darby, Abraham's daughter, whom he married in the following year. We can at least fill in a few details of Reynolds's background, some of which might remove a little of the appearance of casualness and accident which in such an account surrounds his first contacts with Coalbrookdale.

Richard Reynolds was born in Corn Street, Bristol, on 1 November 1735, the son of Richard and Jane Reynolds, both members of the Society of Friends. His great grandfather, Michael Reynolds, had presumably been convinced by George Fox, and had frequently suffered heavy fines and distraints for his refusal to pay tithes, after his convincement. Richard's father had married Jane Donne, daughter of a sound Quaker family, and his sister was married to Joseph Allen another Quaker. Richard was cousin to Joseph Allen junior, who married Anne Osborne and so brought him in contact with a well-established Quaker family already in the iron trade and general merchanting.

Richard was sent to a Quaker boarding school kept by Thomas Bennet, at Pickwick, Wiltshire, and was there from the age of five to fourteen years. On 18 October 1750 he was bound apprentice with the Quaker William Fry, Grocer, in Castle Street, Bristol. In the Fry family there were several cousins near Richard's age whom he would meet, among whom was Joseph Fry, the founder of the chocolate industry, who set up his apothecary's shop in the year of Reynolds's apprenticeship; there was Joseph's scholarly brother, William Storrs Fry, only a year younger than Reynolds. At the Fry houses and at the meetings of the Society of Friends he would meet and become familiar with the members of many families who were interested in trade and manufactures and also in the iron industry—Champion, Lloyd, Harford, Goldney and others. It must also be noted that Richard Reynolds, his father, was an iron merchant, and, at the time that Richard went to Coalbrookdale, his father's firm of Daniels & Reynolds was a considerable customer, taking as much as twenty tons of pig iron a month from the Dale. The apprenticeship was completed and on 14 May 1757, he became a Freeman of Bristol. It was in October 1756 that Thomas Goldney sent him to Coalbrookdale. Whether his father had hopes of his eventual interest in the iron trade we do not know, and it is just possible that the apprenticeship with William Fry was mainly to secure a training in business methods and to qualify for a Freeman's grant.

On his marriage with Hannah Darby, he acquired a half-share in the iron and coal works at Ketley, becoming a partner with Goldney and Darby. As these works were only just being opened, and considerable capital was involved, it would be a most opportune moment for the purchase of such a share, and this may have been the business on which Thomas Goldney sent Richard to Coalbrookdale, his father providing the capital.

The work at Ketley and Horsehay would be no light task for a young man. Apart from the running of the furnaces and the casting floors, there was all the turmoil of construction of the railway extensions, linking the new works with the old ones in the Dale. Several large steam engines were erected, and the collieries were put in order, with the sinking and fitting up of some new shafts, and the problems of pumping at the old workings properly dealt with.

Richard and Hannah Reynolds established themselves in a house at Ketley Bank, and here they had two children, William, born in 1758, and Hannah born 1761. His wife died 24 May 1762 after an illness of only four days. Richard had important business in Shrewsbury on the day of her death, and in the morning the medical attendant thought her condition so satisfactory that Richard was persuaded to go to Shrewsbury; a little later in the day her condition took a turn for the worse, and a messenger recalled Richard, who only arrived home in time to have a few farewell words with her before her death. So passed Hannah (Darby) Reynolds, a sweet and most generous personality, leaving the young husband with two small children, and, what may have been a great help to him in such circumstances, a business which called for all his attention and skill in its management.

A year later his father-in-law died and Reynolds removed from Ketley to Coalbrookdale to act as manager of the whole of the works during the minority of the younger Abraham. By this time the Company had expanded considerably, under the management of Abraham II, having agencies in many parts of the country. In Shropshire there were the works in Coalbrookdale, Horsehay and Ketley, coal and ironstone mines in Dawley and Lawley and near Little Wenlock, limestone quarries, a forge at Bridgnorth, and partnerships in some other companies such as the Willey furnace. The Company worked its own brick and tile yards and clay pits, and did a great business in timber for all purposes. The great demands upon his time soon made Reynolds conscious that his infant children needed some other care than he could give them, and so he contemplated a second marriage. He chose for his second wife Rebecca Gulson, daughter of William Gulson of Coventry. She was a woman of great piety, an intimate friend of his late wife Hannah, and a strict Friend, adhering closely to their manners of plainness and simplicity in all things. Their marriage was performed on 1 December 1763. In 1765 their first son Richard was born, at which time Jane Reynolds, Richard's mother, took the children William and Hannah to Bath. There is extant a delightful letter from her to Richard, on receipt of the news of the birth of his son, but the letter is almost entirely taken up with an account of the children's activities. She says

> It was with great pleasure we heard of thy Wife's safe delivery and wish to hear of her increase of Health as to little Son, we think it is much if he lives as he's come so untimely. Billie was so rejoyc'd to hear of him his eyes and the flush on his cheeks discovered great pleasure, Moley (Hannah) caper'd and frisk'd about and said she would have a Bro from under the rosemary tree she wonna goe to see him till I goe with her.

In 1766 a second son Michael was born, who died of smallpox in 1770, and in 1768, Joseph was born, who with William became a partner in the Ketley works and had part interest in the Coalbrookdale Company.

During the management of Richard Reynolds, the most noteworthy event was the work done by the Cranage brothers on the methods of preparing wrought iron from pig iron. The conversion of pig into wrought iron had been carried out in the finery at the Forges, using charcoal fuel, and many experiments had been made to find a successful method of employing coal as fuel. George Cranage was a foreman in the Coalbrookdale works and his brother Thomas was in charge at the Bridgnorth Forge which the Company had leased in 1760. They experimented with a reverberatory furnace in which the iron never came in contact with the fuel, but only with the flames from it. Reynolds saw some of their experiments and in writing to Thomas Goldney at Bristol, gives a full acount of the matter.

Coalbrookdale, 25th April, 1766

. . . I come now to what I think is a matter of very great consequence. It is some time since Thos. Cranege, who works at Bridgenorth Forge, and his brother George of the Dale, Spoke to me about a notion they had conceived of making bar iron without wood charcoal. I told them consistent with the notion I had adopted in common with all others I had conversed with, that I thought it impossible, because the vegetable salts in the charcoal being an alkali acted as an absorbant to the sulphur of the iron, which occassions the red-short quality of the iron, and pit coal, abounding with sulphur would increase it. This specious answer, which would probably have appeared conclusive to most, and which indeed was what I really thought, was not so to them. They replied that from the observations they had made, and repeated conversations together, they were both firmly of the opinion that the alteration from the quality of pig iron into that of bar iron was effected merely by heat, and if I would give them leave, they would make a trial some day. I consented, but, I confess, without any great expectation of their success; and so the matter rested some weeks, when it happening that some repairs had to be done at Bridgenorth, Thomas came up to the Dale, and, with his brother, made a trial in Thos. Tilly's air-furnace with such success as I thought would justify the erection of a small air-furnace at the Forge for the more perfectly ascertaining the merit of the invention. This was accordingly done, and trial of it has been made this week, and the success has surpassed the most sanguine expectations. The iron put into the Furnace was old Bushes, which thou knowest are always made of hard iron, and the iron drawn out is the toughest I ever saw. A bar $1\frac{1}{4}$ inch square, when broke, appears to have very little cold-short in it. I look upon it as one of the most important discoveries ever made, and take the liberty of recommending thee and earnestly requesting thou wouldst take out a patent for it immediately. The specification of the invention will be comprised in a few words, as it will only set forth that a reverberatory furnace being built of a proper construction, the pig or cast iron is put into it, and without the addition of anything else than common raw pit coal, is converted into good malleable iron, and being taken red-hot from the reverberatory furnace to the forge hammer, is drawn into bars of various shapes and sizes, according to the will of the workmen.

The patent was secured in the name of the Cranage brothers, almost in the wording suggested by Reynolds in his letter,[1] and when the process was applied at the Dale, much better iron was produced at a lower price than by any earlier process. This discovery encouraged the Dale to extend their forges and to continue the working of forges at Bridgnorth and Liverpool. In 1784, however, Peter Onions of Merthyr Tydfil took out a patent for an improved process, and the next year the vastly improved method of Henry Cort was patented and superseded that of the Cranages entirely.

One of Richard Reynolds's biggest tasks was the completion and maintenance of the railways belonging to the Company, and it was here that he made his unique contribution by the substitution of cast iron rails for wooden ones. This is described in a later chapter but we may note here that, according to the suggestion in Hornblower's letter, there was a serious drop in the price and market of iron in the years 1767 and 1768 and that Reynolds first had the idea that much iron could be stored, until prices rose, in the useful form of plate rails. This is well in accordance with the policy of the Company which tried always to maintain the furnaces in work, even if iron was being accumulated on stock. The importance of the saving and the ease of operation of plated rails was soon revealed to Reynolds, and more permanent rail forms were quickly designed. In a relatively short time the Company had built over twenty miles of such iron railways.

Reynolds provided a link between the Coalbrookdale Company and the iron and tin plate industry of South Wales. Through his father, Richard Reynolds senior, he had connections with forges and plate mills at Carmarthen, Margam and Pontrhydyfen, and in 1762 he entered into partnerships with John Partridge and his son in the Redbrook Furnace and Lydbrook Forge. Reynolds's father, through the firm Daniel & Reynolds of Bristol, had many connections as a customer for Dale pig iron, and as early as 1756, when Richard junior first went to the Dale, they were buying in addition to pig iron fire bricks and other materials from the Coalbrookdale Company.

[1] Pat. No. 815, June 1766, 'Making pig iron or cast iron malleable in a reverberatory furnace or air furnace with pit coal only.'

28.9mo.1756. Daniel & Reynolds Dr. to Sundry Accounts.
To William Lane for Fire Brick 4000 at 40/–
and 500 slanted at one end at 40/–
Do. Brow Brick 200 at 5/– pr hund:
Do. large Do. 50 at 2d each
Do. Common Do cut in two at ½d each
To Fire Brick & Clay Co. for 6 Tons Fire Clay at 10/–
To James Owen for Fre[tt] of the above Brick to
Monmouth £7 & the Clay to D. £3.

There are similar accounts with both the Coalbrookdale foundries and their brick and tile yards for materials needed for the furnaces, and there is an occasional return trade in tin plate, *e.g.*

New Blast Furnace Dr to Reynolds & Roberts for 1 Box Tin Plates £2.13.6 etc.

Reynolds's interests spread over the Monmouth Forges, the Melingriffith tin plate works and many other of the South Wales units in the iron industry. In 1768 he was instrumental in forming the Bristol Company of Ironmasters and entered into the new Reynolds, Getley & Company, and into many other partnerships with Harford, Cowles (his brother-in-law) and others of the Quaker group of ironmasters.[1] Through these connections and his partnership in Ketley and Horsehay, he soon amassed a fortune which he used wisely and generously to help the Coalbrookdale Company over many very difficult years towards the end of the century.

We might at this point note some of the business transactions by which he attained such a powerful position for helping the Company's affairs in later years. In 1775 he bought the Manor of Sutton from Benjamin Allen for £20,800 and in the same year was able to purchase Gabriel and Ann Goldney's shares in the Ketley and Horsehay works. In 1776 Abraham Darby had negotiated with the families of Smitheman and Giffard for the whole manor of Madeley as the end of some of the twenty-one year leases, taken in 1755 and 1756, was approaching, and was able to buy the manor. In 1780 Richard Reynolds bought the manor from Abraham Darby for £30,673, and in the same year, according to his memorandum, he paid R. Darby £5,000 for some unnamed shares. It is not clear who R. Darby was nor what were these shares. A few years later (1787 and 1788) Reynolds bought land from Abraham Darby for £1,300 and

[1] An outline account of some of these many partnerships will be found in Raistrick, A., *Quakers in Science and Industry*, 1950, pp. 146–51.

Stanley's Farm for £6,750. By these various purchases Reynolds became the principal landlord of the Coalbrookdale Company and held the royalties of some of their coal and ironstone mines. He arranged a reasonable rent for these, which included the royalties, and he also continued to make small purchases of property in the district, often as a means of providing cash for the continuance or expansion of the works. In this way Reynolds soon replaced Goldney as the principal figure behind the finance of the Company, acting as a banker, and in the most difficult times advancing money to them, at very low interest or even free of interest.

At the beginning of 1789, the year when Abraham Darby III died, Richard Reynolds resigned his shares in the Ketley and Horsehay works to his two sons William and Joseph, and removed from Ketley to Coalbrookdale. He had given William the management at Ketley many years before, and remained at Coalbrookdale until 1804 when he removed to Bristol for the remainder of his life. From the memoirs and letters of Reynolds, preserved by his descendants,[1] we have a more intimate and personal picture of the man, than we can obtain of any of the Darbys. His relations with the workpeople continued the policy of the Darbys, complete friendliness and care for their well-being; Abraham Darby III was brought into the works under his care and counted him not only his partner, but his dearest friend and adviser. In all the property that he acquired he laid out walks and made access to the woods and hills and encouraged their fullest use by the workpeople. The policy of the Darbys in providing housing for their workpeople was continued by him, and we have the testimony of Plymley[2] to the good effect of this policy in the Dale.

The population of the parish of Madeley, in which Coalbrookdale is situated, has increased very much. In January 1782, it contained 440 houses, 560 families, 2,690 persons; in March 1793, it contained 754 houses, 851 families, 3,677 persons. In viewing this increase it is pleasant to observe that the houses are increased in a greater proportion than either the families or the persons, which bespeaks greater prosperity and comfort than heretofore, and has arisen as well from the benevolence of the lord of the manor as from the works. He has built many comfortable houses for old and distressed persons, and granted a great number of leases of waste land, in the proportion if I recollect aright, of about one-eighth of an

[1] Rathbone, H. M., *Letters of Richard Reynolds, with a Memoir of his Life*, 1852, and Greg, E., *The Reynolds-Rathbone Diaries and Letters 1753–1839*, 1905.

[2] Plymley, J., *Survey of the Agriculture of Shropshire*, 1803.

acre to each person to build on, they paying a fine of five guineas for a lease of ninety-nine years, and five shillings a year ground rent.

The figures used by Plymley are to be found in the diary and note book of Richard Reynolds, and occur with many other notes on the area, which Reynolds supplied to Plymley.[1] In addition to building many houses Reynolds also provided at Madeley a school, and with the Coalbrookdale Company provided schools and Sunday schools in the Dale and at Ketley.

In the Memorandum left by Richard Reynolds there is a very brief note, '1768. 5. 6mo. Returned to Ketley having resigned the superintendence of the Dale works.' Abraham Darby III, still only a youth of eighteen, took over the Dale works, managing them with the constant help of Reynolds and of the older workmen. The two concerns, Coalbrookdale and the Ketley-Horsehay works, were intimately connected, half the stock of Ketley, and a majority of the Horsehay stock being held by the Coalbrookdale Company. In the actual day to day working Coalbrookdale was managed by Darby, Ketley by Reynolds, and Horsehay more or less jointly as far as the running of the works was concerned, but a single agreed policy covered the whole grouping. The books were kept separately at the three works but the accounts were balanced quarterly and brought to a joint discussion from which an annual balance was got. The only surviving book for this period is a Waste Book for Horsehay, 1767 to 1774,[2] from which we can reconstruct a little of the activity of the works.

The book starts in February 1767 and the wages accounts show that a number of men were working on the Bank Railway construction and upon the railways in general, some at 1/6 and others at 1/- a day, while several others were employed in waggoning coal and ironstone from the pits to the furnaces and pig iron to the Severn wharf. Limestone was coming for the furnaces mainly from Buildwas and Benthall and in each case it was delivered at the Severn wharf and waggoned to Horsehay as a return cargo by the waggons which brought down the pig iron. There was a considerable interchange between Horsehay and Ketley, each month, pig iron to Ketley and loads of Ketley sand brought back. Frequently some of the Horsehay pigs were used to make up large orders upon Ketley and, among such,

[1] This diary is among the *Rathbone MSS.*, and has not been published.
[2] *Shrewsbury MSS.*, 333.

figure several orders from Sampson Lloyd of Birmingham. Axletrees, wheels and other castings were frequently bought by Ketley from Horsehay or from the Dale. The railways were still of course, of wood, and large quantities of timber were cut and sawn in the Company's woods.

There is no perceptible change in the accounts when Abraham III took over in 1768. In 1769 the Ketley and Dawley railways were being built and the Lawley and Dawley collieries were extended, and these items occupy a large space in the accounts. When Abraham Darby built Ketley and Horsehay furnaces in 1755 and 1756 they were provided with steam engines which pumped the water which was needed to turn the water wheels for the blast. Soon after Abraham III took over he began the installation of two more engines and after their completion we get the regular monthly charge for looking after them and the 'machine' at the furnaces; the machines would be the box bellows which had now replaced the older hide bellows at the Dale and were introduced at Horsehay with the new engines. The 'Fire Engine' keepers were four in number in 1767 getting 8/-, 10/-, 10/- and 18/- a week, but in September 1770 the number of men at the engines is more than doubled as work began on the erection of the new ones, and in 1772 there are six keepers regularly employed.

In 1756 the outbreak of the Seven Years War had sent up the price of iron and an increased demand had encouraged expansion of the trade throughout the country. The new furnaces at Ketley, Horsehay and Lightmoor were blown in and many new iron works followed in the next few years. Reynolds and Darby refused all orders for guns and armaments and continued with their normal production of pots and domestic castings, steam engine parts and pipe work, and pig iron, now largely for the forges. We have seen already that rising prices of food were used as an excuse for the riots that swept this part of Shropshire in 1757, but soon the increased employment and better wages smoothed over this unrest. The Peace of Paris was signed in February 1763, and by July of that same year a trade crisis of acute depression followed, which brought about the failure of many trading houses. Trade decreased and unemployment spread rapidly in the next few years, but the Coalbrookdale Company with its trade roots deep in the home and domestic market responded less to this depression than did many firms which had based their expansion upon gun founding and other purely war demands. The furnaces were kept in blast and in 1767 and the few years following an outlet for some of the iron was found in the substitution of iron for wood in the Company's railways. By 1772 the iron trade experienced another crisis and Matthew Boulton wrote that 'the trade of Birmingham is so dead at this juncture that the London waggons have to make up their loading with coals for want of merchandise.' In a letter to the Earl of Dartmouth, the Colonial Secretary, on 10 November the same year, he says 'My lord, the trade of this country hath received a very severe shock since June last, even such a one as it will not recover from for many years, particularly in Scotland: there is scarcely any person of considerable Trade in Great Britain but what hath felt the consequences of it in some respect or other either by the immediate effect of some of the great numbers of Bankruptcies or from the general distrust that hath overspread the land.'

Richard Reynolds spoke of this time, in a letter to his wife, 17th of 6 month, 1773—'I hear nothing but bad accounts (as they are generally called) respecting the pig iron trade, and predictions of its being still worse.' However, in 1775 with the outbreak of another period of hostilities, the demand for iron soared rapidly and was accompanied by rising prices. Reynolds and Darby, not wishing to profit by a war condition, proposed to their larger customers that they should name a fair price for pig iron according to the then state of the trade, and also determine a scale by which the price could be proportionately reduced as the price of bar iron fell. This was done and the prices so fixed were accepted for many years and ensured the satisfaction and confidence of the customers.

It was in the spell of rising prices and greater trade that Darby planned and built the Iron Bridge over the Severn which remains as his permanent monument.

In 1768, Richard Reynolds's eldest son William was only ten, but as he grew through his teens, like Abraham Darby, he was introduced into the works, and soon became a close friend and helper to his cousin. William Reynolds had a strong inclination towards scientific studies and for some time studied chemistry with the famous Dr. Black. Throughout his life he remained a careful and accurate experimenter and a student of all branches of science. Richard Reynolds gave him a share of responsibility in the Ketley works, and he soon became almost a liaison officer throughout the Company. William was a great admirer of James Watt, whom he met in connection with the work done for Boulton and Watt by the Coalbrookdale

Company. Boulton and Watt took their cylinders and pump barrels from only four foundries, Coalbrookdale, New Willey, Bersham and Carron, and while Wilkinson with his improved boring mill made most of the cylinders, Coalbrookdale shared with a few cylinders and a good deal of the pump and pipe work. In 1777 the Ketley works were discussing a Boulton and Watt engine and in this discussion William Reynolds took a part. Some letters from him to William Rathbone at Liverpool show both his deep interest in experimental science and his practical interest in the new engine, and they are so informative of his character that two of them might well be quoted.[1]

Ketley 12mo.26.1777

Dear Friend,

I observe the directions in thy last respecting the size of the intended receptacles of Electric Fire & may inform thee that the Cupboard in thy Bookcase will do very well for that purpose. I have again written the Artist in Bristol & desired him to inform thee or myself when the machine is near compleated that we may inform S. G. of its being sent to him desiring him to forward it to Liverpool. The Apparatus I mentioned to thee before is all that is generally sent by this Person with his electrical machines, but he is the most capable of almost any man I ever saw of making all the parts of an apparatus that can be made of Glass—but it will be thy best way to get the other parts made in Liverpool, such as the Bells, Thunderhouse, etc. If thou will inform me in thy next what number of jars thou would have & what other glass vessels I will write for them.

I heartilly join with thee in thy astonishment that no more young people discover a propensity to make disquisitions into these phenomena which present such inexhaustible funds of pleasure and instruction & I look upon it to be a good deal owing to the faults of Education—Children are too often taught to construe a Latin book & write a good hand without ever being made acquainted with the most useful Truths of natural Philosophy which are far better suited to their Capacities & far more agreeable to their inclinations, than droning for years over a Latin Accidence which is often the Case—the knowledge of Things is too much disregarded while that of words is too much attended to & which is the most useful as well as agreeable every one will readily determine. I shall be much obliged to my dear friend if he can give me some information upon the following subject.

We want for an Engine Beam some large strong Timber, but as Oak is very difficult to be got my father was thinking Pine Timber would do, if there is any large enough—Pray is there not some called Load Balk which is very large & full of Turpentine. Shall be obliged to thee to write

[1] These unpublished letters are in the *Rathbone MSS.*

me word as soon as possible how large it is to be had—I mean how thick for the length need not be so great 26 or 30 feet would be long enough & how the price is & whether we could have some soon from Liverpool.

Finding the inconveniency of sending to London for every Instrument that I want I am resolved to turn Carpenter myself & should therefore be obliged to thee to give me thy advice how to get some pieces of good Mahogany to work upon & the price.

Please to give my dear love to all Relations and tell my sister we are all well & should be glad to hear from her oftener and be assured that amongst all those who have the Happiness to call themselves thy friend there is not one more sincerely so than

Wm. Reynolds.

Ketley 12mo. 30.'77.

My Dear Friend,

I am much obliged by thy speedy reply to my Quaeries, but cannot determine what kind of timber will be made use of till Mr Watt the Engineer has given his opinion concerning the propriety of using Fir Timber, when if he approves of it I may perhaps again trouble thee a little further on the same Subject. The above Mr Watts is I believe one of the greatest Philosophers in Europe & has made the greatest improvements in Fire Engines that have ever been since the first discovery of that very useful and most powerful machine, as I have no doubt from what thou says in thy favour, that *Mechanics* will in their turn merit thy attention. I hope thou will give me the pleasure and honour of explaining to thee in propria persona at Ketley this improved Engine which is well worth looking at. I hope Chemistry will not fail to spread her attractive charms for thee & that they will not be spread in vain—it is possible to be a chemist in a study as in a Laboratory, witness Dr Priestley, the greatest man of this Age in the Aerial branch of that Science, all whose experiments may be performed in a Parlour—anything which I can serve thee will always give me the greatest pleasure to undertake. I had a letter a day or two ago from J. B. of Bristol who tells me the machine is almost finished. Thou will therefore write to S. G. to advise him of its coming & I will do so to J. B. to tell him to pay the postage to Birmingham.

My Jar is about 8¼ In high by 6½ In Diameter.

I am obliged to thee for thy kind offer respecting Mahogany & will be obliged to thee to procure me some different thicknesses—for instance part of a plank 1 Inch thick, part of one 2 In thick & another 3 In thick about 4 feet of each will be enough as to price I should like to have neither the worst nor the very best—I have plenty of Beech.

Have you any Box wood imported at Liverpool—it is a good wood for turning.

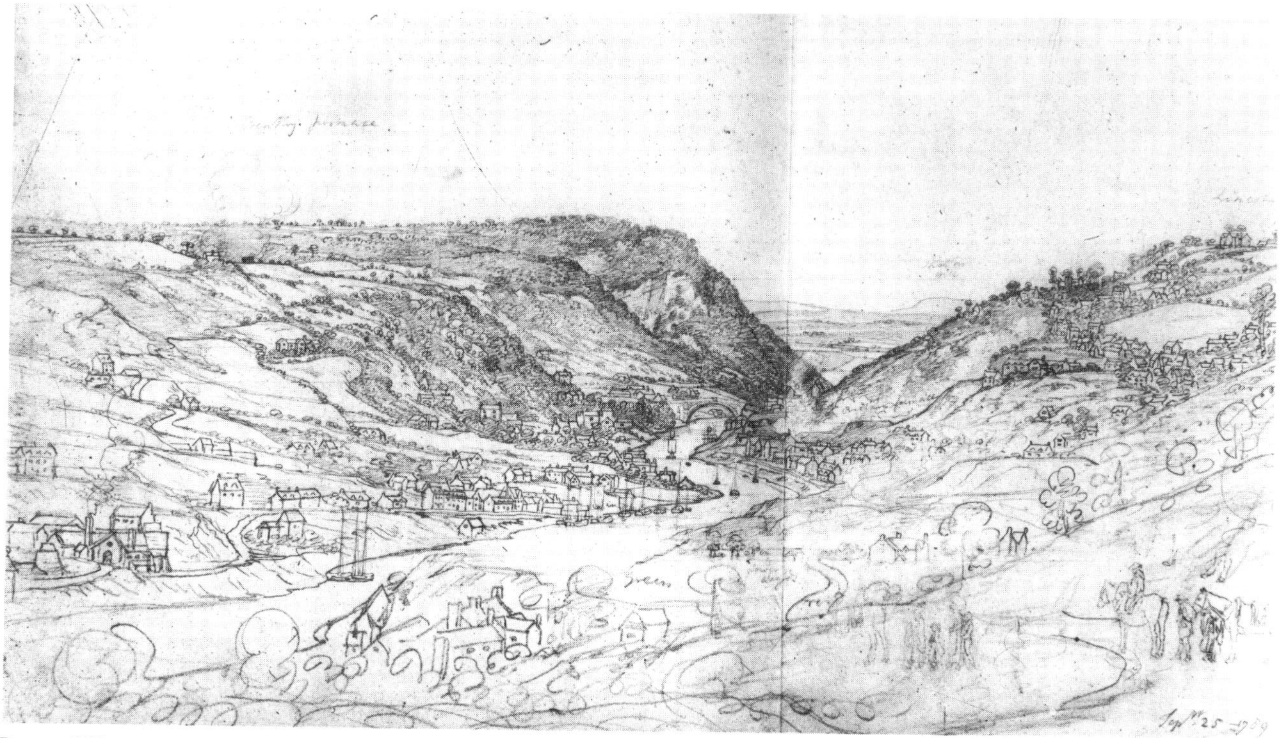

Plate VII *A pencil sketch by Joseph Farrington, RA, drawn on 25th September 1789, looking almost due west along the River Severn towards the Iron Bridge. Benthall Edge rising steeply in the middle background would have been carefully coppiced at this time. On the river bank to the left is one of the other major ironworks in the Gorge, Calcutts, and beyond that the settlement of Jackfield. Just to the right of the Iron Bridge in this view the artist has noted 'Bedlam Furnace', the first purpose built coke smelting furnace in the area.*

PLATE VIII *A team of horses and waggon are seen descending into Coalbrookdale from Horsehay in this 1777 view, on the railway opened in 1756. In the distance a large Newcomen-type steam engine dominates the scene, pumping water from the lower pools back into the Upper Furnace pool. To the right silhouetted by smoke from the Furnace, is Rosehill House.*

We are all well and desire our love to our Relations my sister especially who writes but seldom. A Circumstance has happened since I began this letter which obliges me more speedily than I intended to put an end to this letter by begging of thee that if at any time thou wants any commission executed in these parts thou will freely command thine sincerely

Willm Reynolds

excuse blunders.

There are many interesting references in these letters besides the comment on Watt. The Jars are of course Leyden Jars for his experiments in electricity and it is probable from the mention of Priestley that Reynolds had got possession of Priestley's first scientific book, *The History and Present State of Electricity with Original Experiments*, first published in London in 1767, a third edition of which was printed in 1775. In the second volume Priestley gave an illustrated account of contemporary electrical machines and apparatus along with advice to amateur investigators and it was probably some of this apparatus that Reynolds was having made. It is characteristic of him that he decides to do as much of the work as possible himself, and the mahogany ordered from Liverpool would be for the bases and supports of this apparatus. There are other letters from him to his future brother-in-law William Rathbone, in which they discuss chemical experiments, and occasionally William reports unexpected results—'I have tried it once & that once it succeeded amazingly well—I have undesignedly made use of a very proper word for the explosion I believe amazed all that were with me.'

Watt installed the steam engine that William was discussing with his friend, and it proved to be a great advance on the engines they already had, and in 1781 Watt was discussing plans for large pumping engines at Ketley and Coalbrookdale. In the question of payment, Watt claimed part of the saving of fuel, and the engine installed at Ketley was recorded. The old Newcomen Engine took 12 tons of small coal at 2/6 a ton more than what would be required for every 10,000 strokes of the Watt engine. The engine was a 66 inch diameter cylinder, with 11 foot stroke, going at 9 strokes a minute. It was agreed to pay Boulton and Watt one-third of the estimated saving in fuel reckoned on this basis, or alternatively to pay 10/- per 10,000 strokes as recorded on a mechanical counter, until such time as the patent expired. Within the next few years other Boulton and Watt engines were erected at Horsehay and Coalbrookdale.

Our knowledge of the extent of the works in 1784 and 1785 depends upon letters written by Richard Reynolds during his very active opposition to the proposed tax of 2/– to be raised on each ton of coal at the pit head, the tax to be used for recruiting the war finances. Reynolds, in opposing the tax, gave evidence before the Privy Council and also wrote letters to members of the Cabinet, and one to Earl Gower, President of the Council. In this letter of 1784 he reviews the position of the iron and coal industry. In the following year proposals were made by the government of Ireland, for altering the import duties on iron and iron goods, and these proposals brought forth another letter from Reynolds.

To Earl Gower, President of the Council.

Seventh Month. 1784

Unaquainted as I am with the customary mode of addressing a person so much superior, the experience I have already had of thy condescension on other occasions would embolden me to reply to thee on the present important one in our usual plain manner without a fear of incurring thy displeasure, or of failing to procure that attantion which the magnitude of the object I desire to submit to thy consideration will be found to deserve.

I understand by the papers, as well as by a letter from Isaac Hawkins Browne Esq., that the Chancellor of the Exchequer has proposed a tax upon coals of two shillings per ton, which if enacted, will be of the most fatal consequences, I apprehend, to many branches of manufacture and commerce, and particularly destructive of those which are the support and employment of thousands in this and the adjoining counties; nor do I believe the produce of the land of at least one parish in this neighbourhood would in that case support the poor of it, neither is it to be computed the ill consequences it must have on the landed estates in general; but the difference to those who have mines of coal and ironstone, may be estimated by the consumption of both in the very extensive works on this and the adjoining counties. The advancement of the iron trade within these few years has been prodigious; it was thought and justly, that the making of pig iron with pit coal, was a great acquisition to the nation by the saving the woods, and supplying a material to manufactories, the make of which, by the consumption of all the wood the country produced, was unequal to the demand, and the nail trade, perhaps the most considerable of any one article of manufactured iron, would have been lost to this country, had it not been found practicable to make nails of iron made with pit coal. We have now another process to attempt, and that is to make *bar iron* with pit coal; and it is for that purpose we have made, or rather are making, the alterations at Donnington Wood, Ketley, &c., which we expect to complete in the present year, but not at a less expence

than twenty thousand pounds, which will be lost to us and gained by nobody, if this tax is laid on our coals. The only chance we have of making iron as cheap as it can be imported from Russia, is the low price of our fuel, and unless we can do that, there will not be consumption equal to half the quantity that can be made, and when we consider how many people are employed in making a ton of iron, and the several trades dependent thereupon, we shall be convinced the revenue is much more benefitted even by their consumption of exciseable articles &c., than by the duty on a ton of foreign iron . . . but coal and iron stone have no value in their natural state, produce nothing until they are consumed or manufactured; and a tax upon coal. which as I said is the only article that in any degree compensates for our high price of labour &c., or can be substituted in the stead of water for our wheels and bellows, would entirely ruin this very populous county, and throw its numerous labouring poor upon the parishes, till the emigration of those of them who are able to work shall strengthen our opponents, and leave the desolated wastes, at present occupied by their cottages, to the lords of the soil. . . .
. . . as to the tax on bricks and tiles, if it is not confined to those used in building dwelling houses, it will be very heavy on those concerned in collieries &c., and at any rate be very partial; few bricks if any being used in divers counties in England. . . .

. . . Thy obliged faithful friend

Richard Reynolds.

From another letter of 28th 3mo. 1785, we get more particulars of the works that had been carried out up to that date.

. . . There was a petition sent from Shropshire by the makers of pig and bar iron, the proprietors of mines, and others interested therein, which was to be presented to the House of Commons the 21st Instant, and which I doubt not will obtain thy attention. As a family very materially affected, and who have been emboldened to look up to thee as thy tenants, as well as having experienced thy assistance in their undertakings, permit me in the name as well of my relations in the Dale, as of my children and in my own, to solicit thy effectual interposition against a measure so injurious to us, and to the many hundreds of poor people employed by us in working and carrying on mines &c., for the supply of a large sale of coals by land and water, and of coals and mine for sixteen fire engines, eight blast furnaces and nine forges, besides the air furnaces, mills, &c., at the foundry at Coalbrook Dale, and which with the levels, roads and more than twenty miles of iron railways, &c., still employs a capital of upwards of one hundred thousand pounds, although the declension of our trade has, as stated in a former letter, obliged us to stop two blast furnaces, which are not included in the number before mentioned. Nor have we ever considered ourselves as the first of many others, concerned in iron works or coal works in this kingdom.

In the furtherance of the aims of these letters, Reynolds joined with James Watt, Matthew Boulton, Josiah Wedgwood and many others to form the 'United Chamber of Manufacturers of Great Britain' in 1785, an Association which for many years followed a steady protectionist policy.

So far the account in this chapter has centred almost entirely around Richard and William Reynolds with little more than incidental mentions of Abraham Darby. This is partly due to the nature of the records available for the period. Richard and William Reynolds left an extensive collection of letters, which have been carefully preserved and from which Hannah Mary Rathbone grand-daughter of Richard, was able to compile the 'Letters of Richard Reynolds, with a Memoir of his Life,' in 1852. Many of William's letters are also preserved in the *Rathbone MSS.* and there is a small number of letters from Reynolds to Boulton and Watt, in the Birmingham Library Collections. For the period of Abraham Darby's management, the *Horsehay Waste Book*[1] gives some idea of the kind of work being done, but it is in no sense a personal document, so that we are thrown back on odd scraps of information from which to build up the picture of Abraham III.

In 1776 he married Rebecca Smith (1752–1834), of Doncaster, a zealous Friend who became a great traveller in the ministry of the Society. There was a link again with the Reynolds family, as Rebecca Smith's mother was Ruth Gulson of Coventry, whose sister Rebecca Gulson was Richard Reynolds's second wife. Of their seven children, four survived to adult years and became connected with the Company.

In 1776 Abraham was considering the consolidation of the works, and towards his new planning he made extensive purchases of manorial rights and properties in the Manor of Madeley, and also secured the lease of minerals throughout that area. In order to develop part of these new fields to greater advantage, he built two furnaces at Madeley Wood and equipped them with direct blast steam engines of some design of his own. These were built at Coalbrookdale where many other engines were being made at that time. Abraham Darby can to some extent be judged by the fine series of engines that were built at Coalbrookdale during his time, and by

[1] *Shrewsbury MSS.*, 333.

PLATE IX *The Iron Bridge rapidly became one of the symbols in an age confidently believing in progress through human endeavour. Before the structure was open to traffic, Abraham Darby III commissioned from the London artist Michael Angelo Rooker a painting of this scene, engravings from which were widely disseminated.*

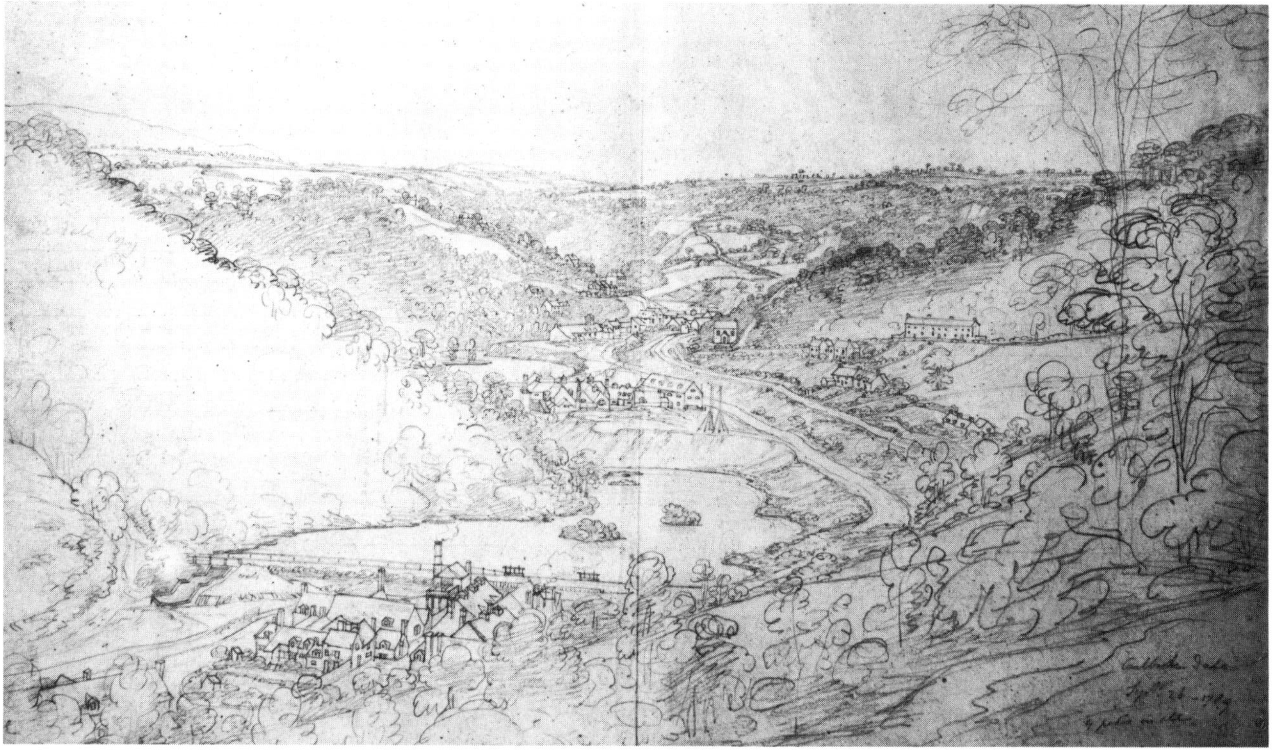

PLATE X *A pencil sketch of Coalbrookdale looking north drawn by Joseph Farrington, RA, on 26th September 1789. In the foreground are the buildings of the Upper Forge with its associated pool behind. Beyond is the Lower Works, and behind this, the Upper Works where the Furnace was situated. Charity Row is prominent on the right having been recently completed by the Coalbrookdale Company.*

the expansion of the Company's interest in canals, housing, the provision of schools, and in the development of the farms so as to provide much of the horse power needed for the haulage of goods.

His boldness of thought is well demonstrated by the building of the Iron Bridge, a task which called for considerable skill in civil engineering for the placing of the abutments, and for the erection of the arches. The proprietors of the bridge were content to leave to him the design and construction of the approaches and roads, and he was able to carry through all this onerous work with the help of a few of his own workpeople. For the twenty years before his death he seems to have acted as the general manager of all the concerns, with Richard Reynolds as his banker and adviser on finance. William Reynolds took much of the management at Ketley and was the correspondent with Boulton and Watt.

On the selling side of the business Darby now attended the Quarterly Meeting of Ironmasters generally held at Stourbridge or at Birmingham, and also the fair at Stourbridge where much of the iron trade was now concentrated.

It was during Abraham Darby III's time that the Cornish trade was expanded and a large warehouse established at Falmouth under care of an agent who could contact the Cornish mines and transmit orders for foundry work to Coalbrookdale.

Like his forebears, Abraham Darby was active in the meetings of the Society of Friends and helped in the establishment of the new meeting at New Dale near Ketley, assisting with the building of the meeting house there. Adam Luccock (1728–1831) whose father had been apprenticed to the first Abraham Darby in 1714, remembering the two, Abraham II and Abraham III, under whom he had worked in the Dale, said of the Darbys, 'they all liked a joke right well; and as for kindness, it seemed as if they thought it a favour to be allowed to assist you.' Abraham Darby died in 1789, and by his will he left provision to maintain the Friends meeting house and burial ground in Coalbrookdale. The meeting house is now a workshop, but the burial ground, behind it, on the steep slope of the hill, is there with its quiet and unostentatious stones, recording the names and dates of the many Darbys, Luccocks, Dickinsons, and others of the Friends, along with one marking the grave of William Reynolds.

Chapter Seven

FURNACE AND FOUNDRY, 1708–1807

IRON founding has had a long history in some parts of England, being documented in Sussex as early as the last decade of the fifteenth century, when cannon-balls were being cast in iron. In the sixteenth century fire backs in cast iron began to be produced; at first probably they were only plain plates, but soon they were being made with ornament. The plates were cast in open sand moulds, and it is clear from many of the examples which remain that the principal ornaments were carved in wood and impressed into the bottom of the sand mould, in separate pieces. Later, wooden patterns of the whole back, of a more elaborate type, were used, often bearing heraldic designs prepared for a particular person. Other articles cast in these early foundries were grave slabs, and forge equipment of hammer heads and anvil blocks. In the seventeenth century pot casting was added, particularly of the small cooking pots known as skillets. The main industry of Sussex however grew up round the gun casting which was started in 1543 at Buxted furnace. A rapid expansion of the industry took place, and in 1568 there were already over forty furnaces at work producing guns, largely for export. It was this rapid growth of founding which led to two serious complaints, first that the furnaces were demanding so much more charcoal that timber supplies for houses and ship building were being threatened, and secondly that potential enemies of the country were being armed with the exported guns. The export of guns was then regulated by the issue of licences for their casting and export, but a certain amount of smuggling went on and the general increase in output made the depletion of the forests by the charcoal burners still more acute. At the beginning of the seventeenth century the annual make of guns was about 800 tons.[1]

During the sixteenth century several enactments were made regulating the erection of furnaces, all with the object of conserving timber from the ravages of the charcoal burner, in particular in

[1] For a detailed account of the Sussex iron industry see Straker, E., *Wealden Iron*, 1931, and Rhys Jenkins, 'Ironfounding in England 1490–1603,' Part I. *Trans. Newcomen Soc.*, vol. XIX, 1938–9, pp. 35–49.

Sussex and the Forest of Dean. The reaction to these restrictions was twofold; iron masters sought out new areas of well-timbered country away from the Crown forests and remote from the demands of the shipbuilders, and set up new furnaces and forges there. At the same time others turned their energies to the task of using some other fuel, coal or peat, which would make them independent of the charcoal burners and owners of woodland, who were rapidly raising the prices of timber and fuel. The migration of the iron industry led to the erection of furnaces along the wooded valleys of the Welsh borders, in Staffordshire, South Yorkshire and a few other areas. In these new centres the furnaces still used charcoal fuel, but for a time they had virgin woodlands for their supplies, and as these began to fail under excessive demands the practice of using replanted coppice wood was steadily developed.[1]

The search for an alternative to charcoal fuel was steadily pursued through the seventeenth century, and many patents were granted. Dud Dudley about 1620 claimed to be smelting iron with coal, and says, 'I also made all sorts of cast-iron Wares, as Brewing-Cysterns, Pots, Morters, and better and cheaper than any yet made in these nations with Charcoales.'[2] His claims are now very severely pruned, and it is certain that his methods were not developed on any commercial scale. In this area of the west Midlands charcoal furnaces were increasing in number and iron-founding, as well as the more general forge work, was being developed on all sides. In Madely in Staffordshire, iron casting was being done before 1686, in which year Dr. Plott published his *Natural History of Staffordshire*, for he says,

> for the *backs* of *Chimneys*, *Garden-rolls*, and such like, they use a sort of cast iron which they take out of the *Receivers* of the *Furnaces*, as soon as it is melted, in great *Ladles*, and pour it into Moulds of fine sand in like manner as they cast other softer *Metalls*. Thus the ingenious *Will Chetwynd* of *Rugely, Esq.*, at Madely furnace cast *Iron Rolls* for gardens, hollow like the mills for *Sugar Canes*, of 5, 6, 7, or 800 weight apieace: the hollows whereof being filled with timber and wedg'd up close, the other *Iron-work* of the *Roll* is fastened to the wood in the same place as in other rolls, which are weightyer and more substantial than any other rolls I have elsewhere seen.

[1] Ashton, T. S., *Iron and Steel in the Industrial Revolution*, 1924, Chap. I. The charcoal iron industry, pp. 1–22, and for a detailed study of the relation of furnace-forge-woodlands, Raistrick, A., 'The South Yorkshire Iron Industry, 1698–1756,' *Trans. Newcomen Soc.*, vol. XIX, 1938–9, pp. 51–86.

[2] Dudley, D., *Mettallum Martis*, 1665.

Burton had a furnace in Coalbrookdale in 1658 and the cast iron bearer of the furnace tapping hole on Coalbrookdale Old Blast furnace, carrying this date, has all the character of an open sand casting, with the various initials and date impressed separately into the sand, exactly as were the ornaments of the early fire backs. It was into this region where iron founding was already being practised that Abraham Darby came in 1708, bringing his two new ideas—the casting of bellied pots in pure sand, and the urge to experiment with coke as a furnace fuel.

The name Darby automatically turns the thoughts of all who have any knowledge of engineering history or of the history of metals, towards the basic discovery of a practicable method of smelting iron ores with coke. The root and origin of the Coalbrookdale industry in every branch is to be found in its furnaces, and whatever picture, verbal or graphic, is to be drawn of Coalbrookdale activities, it must have at its centre the pulsing, throbbing furnace and its glowing fires. The records of the Company which have survived from its two and a half centuries of busy life are discontinuous and we are therefore compelled by their nature to present only a few glimpses and analyses of the furnaces at work at periods separated by gaps of several years. Even then there has to be much selection from the voluminous data which survives. Throughout the life of the works, a return was made for each four weeks of working, and for the first century whose incomplete records are being used for this chapter, the figures are separated under many heads. For each furnace at work, the fuel supplied to it is entered in the separate quantities got and sent in by each collier or small partnership of miners, and it is often further subdivided by the seams or pits from which it came. Ore is similarly entered in many separate parcels by variety and miner. The produce of the furnace is given as Pots and Kettles, Half-Ware, Cast Ware, and Pigs. Consequently, as no totals are given in the books which survive, a figure for each four-week period, giving totals of ore, fuel and iron produced, is only arrived at after many tedious additions in which the units include hundredweights, quarters and pounds, strikes, dozens, loads and waggons. It would be an intolerable task to make complete summations for even those years whose records remain. Sufficient of these hard-won figures have been accumulated to make a general picture possible, and to arrive at average annual figures for important and relevant periods. Nothing will be credited to the furnaces which is not deduced from a perusal of these and comparable figures, running into many thousands of separate entries.

The working of Abraham Darby's first furnace has been described in an earlier chapter, and a comparison was made with the ordinary blast furnace in use at the beginning of the eighteenth century in Yorkshire. The later accounts for bellows, hearths, tunnel repairs and all detail about the furnace, show that there was little to differentiate this first furnace in its working, from those built for charcoal smelting. This type of furnace has been described by Baker and others and the description can be applied without hesitation to the one used by Darby in 1708 and called the Old Furnace, and to the New Furnace built about 1715.[1]

An example of the Yorkshire charcoal furnaces proves to have had a masonry shaft, about 25 feet square, enclosing the furnace body which is about 22 feet high. The hearth or crucible of the furnace is of carefully chosen firestone, 18 to 20 inches diameter inside and about 5 feet high. This is carried upward by rapidly expanding boshes for another 3 or 4 feet in which the section changes from square to round, the inside diameter at the top of the boshes being about 5 feet. The remainder of the tunnel is tapered off to about 20 inches diameter at the top. Thus the furnace shaft is rather tall and slender. This pattern is approximately the same for most of the early furnaces and we have little reason to think the original Darby furnace would vary much from this. The later furnaces at Coalbrookdale, however, have some very significant differences.

We are fortunate in being able to examine one of the old furnaces, in fact the 'Old Furnace' of so many of the accounts, which has been very well preserved. This furnace was blown out early in the nineteenth century and a new moulding shop and stores built around and over it, thus preserving it from the ravages of the weather. The Coalbrookdale Company have now cleared the site and re-excavated the furnace with a view to its preservation.

In its present form it is essentially the furnace of 1777, which may have been a rebuilding or enlargement of the earliest one, built originally by Basil Brooke in 1658. Above the tapping hole the arch is carried by four cast iron beams, the second of which has the initials cast on it, B E w 1658 E w B. The B may actually be a

[1] Baker, H. G., 'Blast Furnace Construction and Costs in 1740.' *Trans. Newcomen Soc.*, XXIV, 1943–4, pp. 112–19, also drawing and description in Raistrick, A., 'South Yorkshire Iron Industry,' *ibid.*, XIX, p. 62.

monogram, BL or LB, and this with the changing position of the three letters make it difficult to suggest what they may represent. In 1777 Abraham Darby was preparing to cast the 378½ tons of bridge members for the Iron Bridge from this furnace and it is highly probable that in its rebuilding he would incorporate all he had learned from his furnaces at Horsehay and Ketley, which had now had a twenty years' run of active production.

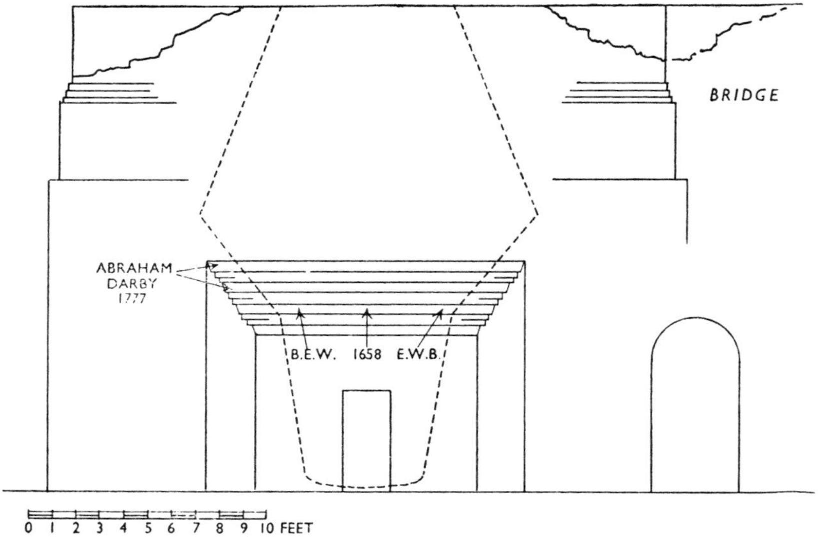

Section of Old Furnace, Coalbrookdale.

The features of the furnace are strikingly different from the older pattern—the shaft is very wide and short and the hearth or crucible very deep. The crucible is 7 feet 6 inches deep, and tapers from 7 feet diameter at the top to 5 feet diameter at the bottom. This in effect would be the blast furnace.

From the top of the crucible the boshes expand rapidly to the unusual width of 13 feet 9 inches at a height of 4 feet 6 inches above the crucible. Above this the shaft tapers into 7 feet 3 inches diameter in a further 9 feet 2 inches of height. The whole of the active zone of the furnace would thus be within the crucible portion, and the rest of the structure would be storage for the charge. The large volume would provide for a slow movement through the furnace, and would give the maximum opportunity for preheating the charge. The steep slope of the upper tunnel would make 'scaffolding' less serious and easier to break down. The large size of the crucible at the tuyer would ensure good dispersion of the blast and would avoid some of the difficulties that might rise from too high pressure or too concentrated blast.

Approximately at the top of the crucible and over the mid line of the tapping hole, there is an opening into the furnace from an annular space of about one square foot section. This passage goes round the furnace at this level, to the back where the bellows were situated. It is the only blast hole, and in many ways anticipates the hot blast. The air in its passage from the bellows round this passage, placed as it is at the hottest zone of the furnace, would raise its temperature considerably before entering the furnace proper. This would be a very high level for blast to enter, in modern practice, but there is no doubt that this worked well in the case of the Old Furnace, which proceeded to make the iron castings for the bridge. A further discussion of the arrangements of the furnace will have to be reserved for a technical study; suffice it to say here, that Abraham Darby seems to have been experimenting with the pre-heated blast, some sixty years before Neilson's patent was taken out.

The outer structure of the furnace is a rectangular, masonry shaft, 26 feet 9 inches by 23 feet 7¼ inches, rising with parallel sides to about 13 feet 6 inches, then stepped in 5 inches to carry a set of cast iron braces. Above this it rises in only two stages separated by three courses which inset a few inches. The bridge, now largely broken and obscured, connected the furnace top with the level area just south of the Furnace Pool, on part of which the coal was coked, and calcined ore and limestone assembled for the charges.

The *Shrewsbury MSS. No. 330*, commencing in July 1718 starts with the inventory already quoted, and then proceeds to give four-weekly summaries of supplies to the furnaces and of the furnace production. Sundry accounts in the cash book, *Shrewsbury MSS. No. 329*, give the details of the remaking of the hearth and boshes of the furnaces, and the general repairs, and with these two sources to check each other it is possible to get an accurate idea of the duration of each blast and of the monthly production. The wages that are paid give some indication of the labour employed about each furnace, but not so clearly as could be desired, as there are many payments made for a few days labour only, out of the four weeks. There were in 1718 two keepers at each furnace, Cranage and Parker at the Old, and Onions and Slicer at the New one, and they are usually paid for keeping the furnace, for moulding pots and hollow ware generally, and for casting. They had many assistants, some of whom stocked the bridge with coke and ore, unloaded the fuel and ore and measured it, while others wheeled away cinders, measured brays, brought sand and did many other odd jobs, some of the men serving both furnaces, part time at each.

At frequent intervals a new hearth is laid and in 1718 and for many later years it was got and laid by John Littlehales, who served both furnaces. A typical set of entries is that in September 1718 when both furnaces were overhauled.

Old Blast Furnace.		
Sep. 3.	Pd Littlehales Lay^{g} a harth gotten from Bats's Quarry viz. 11 days himself att 1/8 & 21 days & $\frac{1}{2}$ his Men att 1/6 & for a harth not yet laid £5.5	7.13. 4
Sep. 4.	Att Blowing out 2/6 Lay^{g} Bottom stone 2/6 fill^{g} etc. 2/–. 22/– pd him this day is in full for fre^{tt}	7. 0
	of 2 Harths to ye Dale one att £4 ye other being from Bats's quarry att £4.5.	
New Blast Furnace.		
	Pd. Thomas Boycot for Blow^{g} out Beef 96 lbs at $2\frac{1}{4}$	18. 0
	pd John Littlehales in pt for Lay^{g} ye Harth	5.10. 0
	in part for fr^{tt} of Harthstones	1. 0. 0
Sep. 3.	pd Jno Littlehales Lay^{g} ye Harth viz 12 Days himself att 1/8, 21 days & $\frac{1}{2}$ his men att 1/6 for the harth £5.5. & for 8 Ton of Bosh stones att 6/– of w^{ch} £5.10.6 was pd hin ye 4th of Aug.	4.14. 9
	in full for fr^{tt} of a harth with 20/– pd before	3. 0. 0
	Gave at Lay^{g} ye Bottom stone 2/6 Unleathering ye Bellows 2/6 Sink^{g} emm 2/6 fill^{g} 2/6 first Blow 2/6	

The beef and a modicum of beer were provided at each blowing out of the furnace, and occasionally there is an item in more general terms for the Blowing-out dinner. Gratuities are always paid on blowing in as well, and sometimes beer or ale is sent into the works on those occasions, which are always marked by a mild celebration. Bat's quarry which provided the more expensive hearthstones was on the Broseley side of the river, as most of the accounts include a small item for the freightage across the Severn. The bellows accounts figure less prominently in the Coalbrookdale books than in some other comparable sets of manuscripts largely because instead of being collected together, they are generally scattered in miscellaneous items through warehouse or sundries accounts.

The performance of the furnaces is best seen in the four-weekly output figures when these are plotted as a graph. This has been done for both the Old and the New Furnace from September 1718 to February 1728, giving almost complete records for nine years.

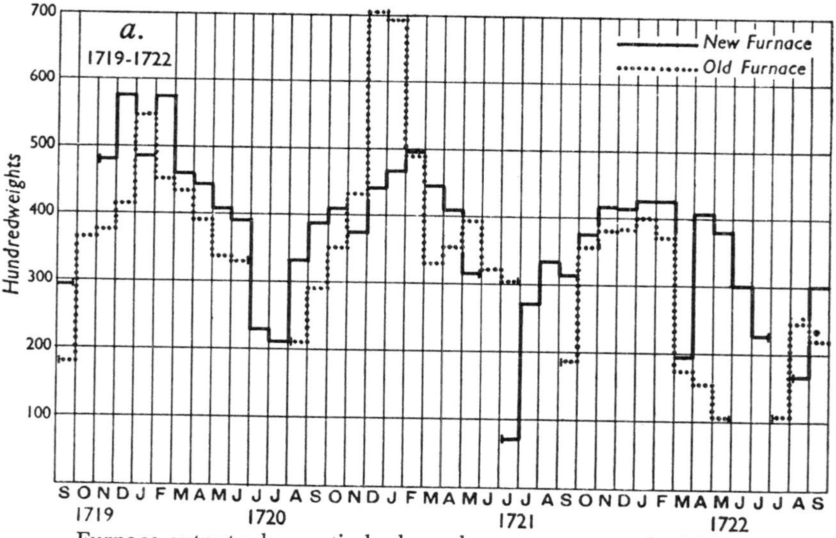

Furnace output when entirely dependent upon water-wheel blast, driven from Furnace Pool.

These graphs are reproduced in part in fig. (a). The total output of metal for these years, is, to the nearest ton,

	Old B. Furn:	*New B. Furn:*	
1719	134	191	
1720	210	273	
1721	223	216	
1722	135	197	
1723	139	177	
1724	169	227	
1725	(155)	(197)	two folios missing.
1726	241	251	
1727	268	234	
	1674	1963	

The higher capacity of the New Furnace compared with the Old, is probably due to the fact that Darby built this furnace after some six or seven years of experience with the old one and it will possibly represent the optimum size for the water power which he had available for the blast. An examination of the graphs of output from the furnaces shows an immediate and absolute relation to the seasons of the year. The main characteristics of the furnace working judged by output, are the very high peaks of production in winter ranging from January to March, and the very deep troughs of low output in summer, with the frequent blowing out of the furnaces for at least eight of the summer weeks.

The supplies of fuel and ore are abundant and regular, and it is only very occasionally in January or February that either of these is cut off, presumably by a heavy snow fall preventing transport along the rough roads and tracks. If we look at the Old Furnace graph, the available figures start in the period 28 June to 5 August 1718, with a production of about 387 cwt., but the continuous records start with 28 September to 26 October, with an output of 314 cwt. The output rises rapidly to a peak in January of 584 cwt., and then there is a break of twelve weeks until 12 April. A short run of sixteen weeks to 30 August is marked by low output reaching at its highest only 273 cwt. In October 1719, after remaking the hearth and doing other repairs, the working of the furnace is started on more regular lines, and for the next six years from that date the graph follows the same pattern. The blasts vary in duration, 36, 44, 32, 40, 48, 28 and 12 weeks, the last one being really a double run of twenty-eight and twelve weeks separated by an eight weeks break in February and March 1725. The blasts are separated by eight or twelve week periods in which the hearth and boshes are overhauled, new ones built in when necessary, and the tunnel repaired.

The curve of production for each blast follows a comparable pattern. After blowing in, which is at the turn of the year towards autumn, generally in September or October, there is a very steep rise of output to a high peak between December and February, but the rise generally experiences a slight check in the second four-week period. After the peak the fall is very steep and from April the production is always low until the furnace is blown out.

The furnace draught was produced by bellows driven by a water wheel which drew its water from the Upper Furnace Pool. Neither of the streams feeding this pool is very large, and during the summer months they were quite inadequate to supply the power demand of the furnaces. The pool would fill up to overflow during the weeks when the furnace was blown out and when the blowing in was made in August or September, the wheels and bellows could run to capacity for a few weeks. If the autumn rains came early and heavy, the pool was replenished and the draught could be stepped up to the maximum capacity of the furnace. It looks as

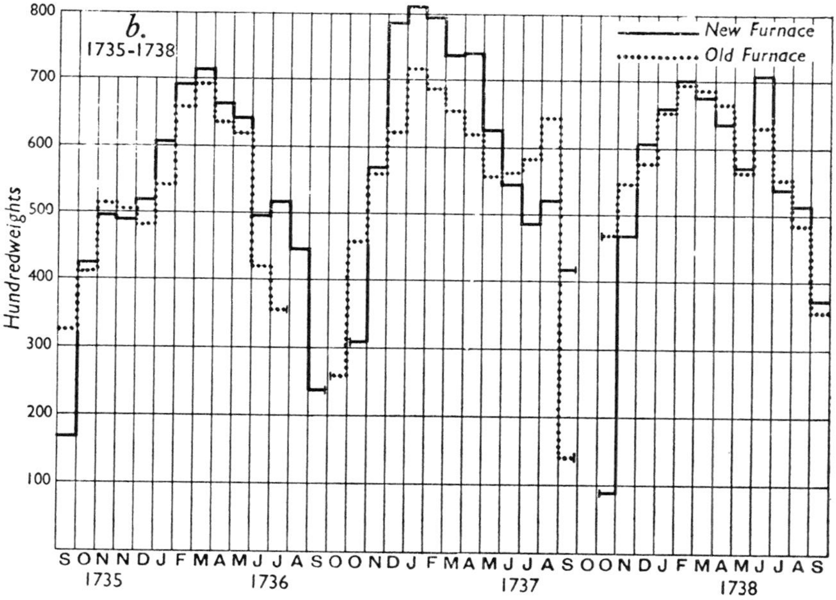

Blast improved by the addition of New Pool and of Ford's horse-driven pumps which returned water to the Furnace Pools.

though the distribution of rainfall in most years was such that, after blowing in, the bellows wheels were stepped up as quickly as possible, but in the course of a month or so over-ran the stream flow and began again to lower the pool level. A stepping down of draught then followed for a week or two until the autumn rain came, when power could be increased to the winter maximum. The fall off comes usually after February or March, and our typical English spring drought brought a rapid falling off in available power.

In fig. *b* the production of both the Old and New Furnaces are plotted, and it is strikingly clear that their performance is absolutely parallel, the only difference seems to be the slightly higher capacity of the New Furnace and a somewhat slower build up from blowing-in to full production.

The combined output graph for the Old and New Furnaces from March 1719 to February 1728, is sufficient to establish this pattern of normal working. It would be tedious to quote all the available figures, so in order to check the working a block of three years has been taken from September 1735 to October 1738. Again the separate graphs for the two furnaces show the strict parallelism of their operation, and the combined graph follows the pattern already set for the earlier period. There are two improvements in the general working, first a production increase from a yearly combined average of just over 400 tons to one of about 600 tons, that is approximately a 50 per cent. step up; this may be accounted for by the effect of Richard Ford's first device for pumping water back from the Lower to the Upper Furnace Pool, together with the second noticeable variation. The graphs for these three later years show a much more rapid build-up to high production, with a shorter period for blowing out and refitting. This period for remaking the hearth is now commonly only four weeks, or possibly five or six, as against from eight to twelve weeks in the earlier runs; also it occurs later in the year, the pumps allowing the furnaces to keep a usable blast through June and July. This probably reflects increased skill, better organization and possibly an improved hearth design, as well as a better blast.

The vital changes in the working of the furnaces were forced upon Ford by two factors operating and reaching a focus in 1733 and 1734. The more general cause was a slight change in the emphasis in their trade. Thomas Goldney had discovered and developed a better demand for pig iron in the Bristol district, at the same time that Ford was building up the trade in engine and pipe castings. This increased demand coincided with a period of unusual drought when for many months in the years 1733 and 1734 there was not sufficient water to provide a blast, or only sufficient for a very light blast which produced an inferior quality of iron. We have seen already that one response to this situation was the leasing of Bersham and Willey furnaces. The second response was a complete overhaul of the blast arrangements. The water wheels were badly worn and needed replacement, but the real weakness was the lack of water in a dry season. We can see the nature of the difficulties from references in

Ford's correspondence with Goldney, reporting the state of the Coalbrookdale furnaces.

12 June 1733. 'ye Water is very Short wch makes ye Furnaces go on but heavily, but am still wishing for a fresh Supply.'

13 July. 'Yesterday was obliged to Blow out ye New Furnace our Water being quite gone, but will put in both ye Hearths with ye utmost Expedition against Water does come.'

In response to renewed requests from Goldney for pig iron he says he will blow

as soone as possible & make Piggs for 2 or 3 Weeks in ye meantime Endeavour to pacifie our Chaps for a month in wch time they shall have Piggs & afterwards constantly Supplied.

In almost every weekly letter the cry is that water is short and that pigs will be made as soon as the rains come. At the end of October and all through November the water is still short and Ford says

Our Water here still continues very Short wch at ye Close of ye year will prove much in our disfavour; there never was Such a Complaint at this time of ye year; I dont think there is a Forge in ye Countrey does half work, but there is no remedy but Patience.

In January 1735 seasonable rain filled the pool but not so as to run over and before February came in the water was low. February again proved a dry month and it was quite impossible to keep the promises of supplies of pig iron. It was when the difficulties of water shortage were mounting steadily higher that Ford saw a possibility of a remedy. He tells Goldney that he

saw in the News Papers that a Patent was past ye Seales for a new Invented Engine for Draining of Water and of Mines wth a greater Force & Larger Qutt. yn any other Engine yet Invented & to be workt either by men, Horses Air or Fire, a modell of wch is now to be seen in London, I think twould be worth while looking at it perhaps there may be Something in it useful for throwing back a part of our Water at a small Expence if it could I am sure twould be worth while. I have for some time & still have a Thought there must be a Machine for Blowing ye Furnace Bellows by Horses without any Water to as much Perfection as Water will do it, I have made a small modell & I am almost sure tis practicable, but more of this hereafter.

ye engine I mentioned a Modell of wch is Erected near ye Faulcon Stairs in Southwark Facing St. Paulls, wch is Workg & shewd (gratis) every Tuesday Thursday & Saturday to all Gentlemen that Desire See ye Same.

On 1 June Ford writes again to Goldney

What hath chiefly occasioned this my long Silence hath been Contriving & Erecting a Machine for Discharging a Part of our Water back into ye Poole wch in great measure I have Perfected, So far as Yesterday I made a Tryall of it & am well assured twill in every Respect answer our Expectation, by ye help of one Horse it Discharges near 2 hhd of Water in a minute, wn I set it to work our Poole was very low & in 6 hours time it raised ye Water 7 Inches Perpendicular so that now with ye help of ye New Wheele I am out of all fear of wanting Water hereafter.

A fortnight later he reports:

We have had very dry Weather wch makes Water short, but wth ye help of ye Engine I hope we shall be able to Blow till we have Wheeles etc ready to put up wch wn done I think we need never fear ye want of Water any moore for I think I may be Sure our Engine discharges above half what a good Wheele will take, these repairs will be Expensive but dont doubt will soon repay it.

12 July. 'As to our Engine tis fixt at ye New Furn: was on account of that wheele being so very bad & ye Bellows harder to Sink, that it took near double ye Water but wn there is a new Wheele I dont fear ever wanting water Ye Charge of returning ye Water is about 28/– p. week, I hope we shall have no occasion to make use of it but in Extraordinary dry Weather & that for some Continuance; that ffurns. have been out a Week & am now putting in ye Hearth & making ye new Wheele & will have it in Blast again as fast as possible, ye Old ffurns. is also Blown out & something sooner than I expected wch was occasioned by ye Shaft wch for many Years we have Suspected giving way Suddenly that I thought it would have dropt through ye middle at onc't & blown us out full Furnace but it held to blow us Clear out Yesterday morning & I have a Shaft ready & will have it in Blast again as fast as possible, ye Furnaces have each of 'em blown about 46 Weeks & for $\frac{3}{4}$ of ye time we have been short of Water.'

At the end of July we learn that the profit on the year is better than was expected although the iron is not so hot in the furnace hearths as it ought to be, through the lack of water; this has affected the quality and produced much iron that will not work well in the Air furnace and which is not so tough and grey in a second melt as is desired. When the furnaces were again brought into blast, with new wheels to the bellows and the returning engine at work, Ford was satisfied with the performance and thought that they could face any contingency of weather. None the less, he was still of the opinion that there was a method of blowing still to be used, which would save a quarter of the water, and he was determined to try it out. In October he reported that both furnaces now made six tons of iron a week 'as good as ever I saw.' In November there was an unfortunate check to this happy state of affairs when the in-wall of the New Furnace collapsed. The hearth and much of the boshes were saved and the in-wall was rebuilt and the furnace in blast in five weeks. The old in-walls had stood ten years of wear and tear and were rebuilt stronger than usual. The Old Furnace at this time was making seven tons a week, and the New Furnace came into blast and blew light and worked very well throughout the winter so that Ford could report that the two Dale furnaces were steadily making more than twelve tons of iron a week. The furnaces both gave great satisfaction and from this time onward, the blasts were of longer duration and a more convenient time was chosen for blowing out one or the other, to replace the hearth, while the other was kept in full blast.

The next great change in furnace practice was the introduction of a steam engine to replace Ford's horse-driven pumps, and the re-building of the Upper Furnace Pool. These changes were made by Abraham Darby in 1742. Unfortunately no books survive which give the production of the furnaces between 1738 and 1755 but there is a run of records for the Horsehay furnaces from October 1755 to December 1761 and when the figures from these are plotted in the same way as the earlier ones have been, a difference is at once apparent. The marked seasonal nature of the graph has disappeared and total output is more than doubled, being now of the order of 1,200 to 1,600 tons a year. The New Blast Furnace was not entered in these books before May 1757 and until the second half of 1761 its output was always a little less than that of the Old Furnace. In July 1761, however, it took its place as the larger producer of the two.

During the forty years just summarized, the routine of the works remained almost unchanged. The coal was carried by pack horses from the pits at Dawley and Coalmere and delivered at the Coal Yard near the Upper Furnace Pool. The larger part of it was coked in open heaps near the bridge of the furnace, and the coke and brays were wheeled to the bridge as required. The form of accounts remains unchanged the whole time, the cost of coking the coal, the limestone used, and sand brought for the casting floor being brought into one account, *e.g.*

1734. Old Blast Furn: Dr. to Sundry Acc^{ts} from April 21st to May 19th	
To And. Cartwright Coak^{g} 120 Stack 4 Ld Coals at 10d.	5. 0. 9
To Jno. Thomas & Co. Mould^{g} 78 Furn: 136c.1.13 at 1/6	10. 4. $5\frac{3}{4}$
To Richd Hanchier Carry^{g} 36 Ton of Limestone at 3/6	6. 6. 0
To Humph: Wheeler for Royalty of 36 Ton ,, at 8d.	1. 4. 0
To Wm. Hazelwood Carry^{g} Leaves 28 L^{d} at $1\frac{1}{2}$d & Maidly Hole Sand 16 L^{d} at 2d	6. 2
To Edwd Martin Royalty of 16 L^{d} of Sand at 2d	2. 8
	23. 4. $0\frac{3}{4}$

New Blast Furn: Dr to Sundry Acc^{ts} in D^{o} Time	
To Henry Cartwright Coak^{g} 113 S 8 L^{d} of Coals at 10d.	4.14.10
To Jno. Slicer Mould^{g} 115 Potts 52c.0.13 at $1/4\frac{1}{2}$	3.11. 8
To Thos. Onions & Co. Mould^{g} 274 48c.1.3 at $1/4\frac{1}{2}$ & 108 6c.2.12 at 2/–	3.19. $6\frac{1}{2}$
To Jno. Brook Carry^{g} 17 Ton of Limestone at 3/6	2.19. 6
To Humph: Wheeler Royalty of 17 Ton Do. at 8d	11. 4
To Wm. North Carry^{g} Straw from Severn 1 L^{d} at 1/4 Bends etc from Forge 1/6	2.10
To Wn. Hazelwood Carry^{g} Maidly Hole Sand 16 Ld^{s} at 2d Brick from T. Stanleys 24 L^{d} at 2d Muck from J. Williams 8 L^{d} at 2d leaves 40 L^{d} at $1\frac{1}{2}$d	13. 0
To Edwd Martin Royalty of 16 L^{d} of Sand at 2d	2. 8
To Jno Brook Carry^{g} 4 L^{d} of Leaves at $1\frac{1}{2}$d	6
	16.15.$10\frac{1}{2}$

The coal for this month is supplied from Coalmere, by William Hayward and William Forrester in the following total quantities—

Old Blast Furnace	120 Strike	9 Loads of Big	&	5 Doz.	9 Loads of Lump	
New Blast Furnace	113 –	8 –	– –	5 –	10 –	–

The whole of the Big coal was coked and the Lump coal used for other purposes about the furnaces. The accounts for iron ore are not entered in the same four-week periods, but are brought into a stock in parcels every few days and drawn from the stock for each furnace as required. The output for the same period as the coal accounts given above is tabulated—

Warehouse & Pigg Yard } Dr to Sundry Acc[ts] for Goods made & way[d] in Do Time

	No.	Potts	Cast Ware	Piggs
		c. q. lb.	c. q. lb.	c. q. lb.
To Old Blast Furn: for	78	136. 1.13	43. 2. 0	208. 3. 0
To New Blast Furn: for	497	107. 0. 0	99. 0.13	174. 0. 0
To Uppr. Air Furn: for	880	113. 1.23	75. 2.17	
To New Air Furn: for	231	42. 2.20		
	1686	399. 2. 0	218. 1. 0	382. 3. 0

Total cast—1000c.2.0.

From time to time there are accounts debited to the furnaces for ladles, shovels and various tools, generally bought from Cornelius Hallam's forge in the Dale. Patterns, boards, boxes and other items for the moulding shops fill in the picture of a normal foundry. Moulds were prepared in flasks and metal was carried from the furnace receivers in large ladles. Some of the moulding is specified as being in loam or 'Loom' and there is a Loom House and work going on there all the time. Blacking and black lead are ground in a mill and sent to the moulding shops, and very occasional items are separated out which show that moulds and cores were baked or stoved. The question of pot casting in sand for very large sizes was investigated by Richard Ford in 1733 and he assured Goldney that 'I think it practicable to Cast Furnaces in Sand up to 150 Galls & Potts up to 35 or 40 Galls ye latter of wch are very much taken to in Ireland Instead of Furnaces for Bucking theire Yarne.' He also says in one letter that he had a flask almost completed for trial of a 150 gallon pan.

Although the form of the accounts rather obscures all the detail of the foundry, there are enough recognizable items to indicate that the normal casting was done in three ways—the pig casting on the floor before the furnace, the cylinder and some other big castings in the sand floor with metal run from the furnace, and the pot and hollow ware mostly cast in boxes or flasks in the moulding shops, the smaller ones with remelted metal from an air furnace. Sand and loam were used for different castings, and occasionally were used together. The only labour about the furnaces which is itemized in the earlier years is that of moulding, much of which was done by the furnace 'keepers.'

The next great advance in furnace work was made with the design and building of the Horsehay and Ketley furnaces. These furnaces were of much larger capacity than any of the old ones, being capable of producing from twenty to twenty-five tons of iron in a week. They were no longer dependent upon a natural stream of water for power, but the method was followed of using a steam engine to pump water onto a water wheel which operated the bellows. At the first Horsehay furnace an engine with a cylinder of 10 foot stroke and 47¾ inches diameter was used for this purpose. At Coalbrookdale, 'wooden bellows' had been introduced in 1742 and twelve years' experience with them would have ensured many improvements in design and performance. The Horsehay furnace was blown in in 1755 and a few years later the accounts include an item for tending the machine at the furnace, as a regular weekly charge, and this is probably the blowing machine, which replaced ordinary bellows.

The accounts for Horsehay which are available run from the beginning of 1755 to 1761, and then for a later period 1767 to 1774. In the first few months of 1755 preparations were being completed for lighting the first furnace. A hearth stone, tymp stones, bricks and fire bricks, with many other materials had been supplied. Coke and ironstone stores were accumulated, and limestone was carried onto the site. For lighting the furnace the Dale Company supplied 92 loads of cord wood and 5 loads of holly roots. The furnace was filled and the blast began in May 1755, and in three months a little over 3,500 cwt. of iron were produced.

In May 1756 a series of accounts for work and materials occurs for the New Furnace, in which limestone, bricks and timber for the furnace and engine house are fully detailed. As in the case of the first furnace, the Company opened a brick yard close at hand and there are accounts for the coals for firing the kilns, and for getting and handling the clay. Bricks are made generally at 5/- a thousand with a few special ones and quantities of tiles at higher prices. In May there is a payment to Abraham Darby for carrying the cylinder of the engine from Sunniside, 15/-, and later, other parts of the engine and the boiler are carried into place and assembled. This engine was larger than the first, having a 60 inches diameter cylinder, with a 10 foot stroke. Later in the year the New Furnace is charged for the cost and freight of 14,000 fire bricks from Broseley, and wood and holly roots are again bought from the Dale Company. In January 1757 the Old Blast Furnace at Horsehay cast 112 cwt. of parts for the furnace structure, and there are final details for the steam engine, and for coke, ironstone and limestone.

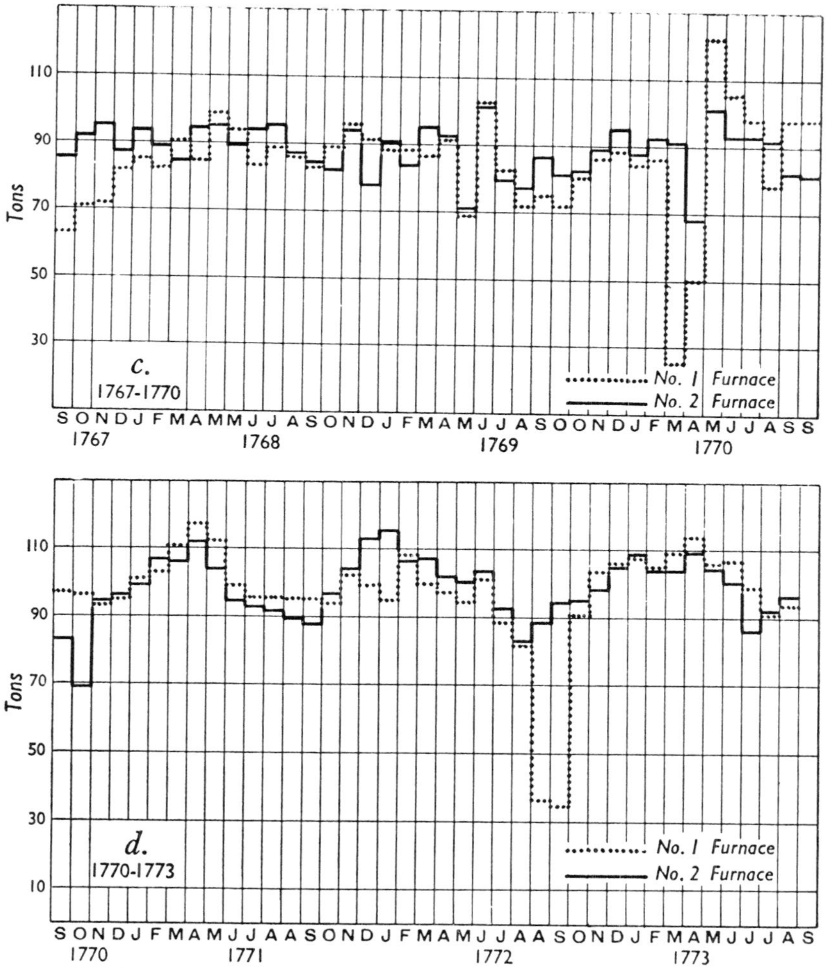

Furnaces blown by steam engine and blowing machine.

This furnace came into its first blast from May to July 1757 and from then until July 1761 the two furnaces worked side by side and are strictly comparable in their working.

The production by four-weekly periods for these furnaces is plotted in figs. (*c*) and (*d*) for the two three-year blocks, September 1767 to September 1770, and September 1770 to September 1773. The 1767 to 1770 graph shows no relation to the seasonal pattern established for the earlier Coalbrookdale furnaces, but production keeps within a reasonable reach of ninety tons a month. In the later group of figures, however, 1770 to 1773, there is a noticeable difference. The production is much higher, its average being above the 100 tons a month figure, but there is the reappearance of something like the seasonal figure with lower points in August and September each year. It is possible that this means that the furnace had been forced up to the limit of the blast, so that a summer low water level in the mines and pools fell below the limits of what the blast machines could make use of. It is only four years later than this that William Reynolds is interviewing Watts for new and improved engines of his design, and a little later that blowing engines, independent of water wheels, are being installed.

The furnace accounts in the *Horsehay Waste Book* for 1767 to 1774 follow a standard form in very great detail, and give us the most complete picture we have of the labour in and about the furnace itself. Although each account is lengthy, it will be worth while to reproduce one as an illustration of the furnace at work.

Paid Workmen &c. on Acco[t] of Blast Furnaces to 4th.7th.mo.1772

The Colliers Loading Coals	484 Waggons	@ 2½d	
John Briscoe unloading do.	444	@ 2d	
Joseph Dakin do	20		
		D S	
Wm Whitehead Nicking on at Measuring Ironstone		375.2 @ ½d	
John Hudson Loading do	152 Waggons	@ 3d	
Richard Growcut do	136		
Joseph Dickin Unloading do.	111 wagns @ 1½d	& 27 @ 2d.	
William Davies do do	82	36	
Thos Skelton Load[g] & Unload[g] Limestone		29	
Edward Griffiths	24 Days	@ 1/6	
Richard Davies	15½	1/2	
Thomas Growcut	16½		
Owen Eaton	8½	@ 1/-	
Sam Miles	3		
Thomas Barnet	21		
Humphrey Daniel	24		
Richard Jones Junr	3	@ 4d	
Samuel & John Parker Dressing Hearth Stones	1044 feet	@ 2d	
William Smith Sawing	2218 feet	@ 2/4	
Jere Hudson Drawing Bricks Limestone & Mine Dust			6. 1
William Hayward Drawing Limestone &c.			12.10

Benjamin Phillips for 6 Deals			1.11. 6
Abiah Darby for Malt 20 Strike @ 5/2			5. 3. 4
Roger Socket Tending the Machine one Month			1. 8. 0
John James Keeping	4 Weeks		2. 8. 0
William Davies Do	4		2. 8. 0
Richard Jones Do	4		2. 8. 0
Richard Williams Do	4		2. 8. 0
Richard Purshall Filling	4	@ 10/6	2. 2. 0
William Ball do	4		2. 2. 0
Thomas Skelton do	4	@ 11/-	2. 4. 0
Thomas Lluellen do	4		2. 4. 0
Joshua Suthons Stocking Bridge	4	@ 12/6	2.10. 0
William Davies do	4	@ 12/-	2. 8. 0
Wm Whitehead Breaking Limestone	4	@ 11/-	2. 4. 0
Thomas Skelton do	4		2. 4. 0
William Price Burn^g Mine	4	@ 10/-	2. 0. 0
Jos: Dakin do & Wheeling Dust	4	@ 13/-	2.12. 0
Richard Wilcox Filling Coaks	4	@ 10/-	2. 0. 0
Owen Eaton do	4		2. 0. 0
William Carter Procuring Cover^g for Fire	4	@ 11/-	2. 4. 0
John Miner Wheeling Cinders & Dust	4	@ 9/-	1.16. 0
Thomas Skelton Raking Brays	4	@ 7/-	1. 8. 0
Robert Brown for Baskets			3. 1. 6
Keepers weighing &c Iron made at Old Furnace 24¾, 24¾, 21¼, & 18¾ Tons			1. 2. 3
Do Do Do at New Furnace 24¾, 23, 24, 21¼ Tons			1. 3. 3
Do Casting Rails 174 @ 9/-			15. 7½
		Total cost of Blast was	£89.16. 2

In the Report of the Children's Employment Commission, published in 1842, there is an account of the work done by boys and men at the furnaces in Staffordshire and Shropshire, and it is sufficiently detailed to show that the routine was still the same, and to illustrate most of the items charged in the above account.

The boys are employed in filling coke into baskets or barrows and ironstone and limestone into what are called boxes, though a stranger would be apt to call them baskets. The young persons and the men convey these to the filling place at the top of the furnace. A certain proportion of each of the three is to be thrown on according to the orders which from time to time they receive, and to ascertain what is the proper quantity an acquaintance with coal, ironstone and limestone is necessary. A skilful and trustworthy person must see that the proper proportions are observed, and there are machines for weighing the ironstone and limestone. As to coal or coke, the eye is sufficient, and the boxes or barrows are not weighed. There are generally two furnaces together, sometimes three, and when the people have put the charge into the one furnace they go on to put a charge into the next. There are never many minutes to rest, but occasionally time may be got to snatch something to eat and drink. Thus they go on all day until after four or five in the afternoon, and at that time the furnace is usually quite full. The boys or young persons then are allowed to go home and the blast is stopped for a time until the melted iron and the cinder be let off.[1]

The furnaces worked a night shift, and there are in some of the accounts amounts paid for stocking the bridge for those filling at night. The furnaces would normally work through Sunday, so as to prevent the iron being cooled, but in all the Coalbrookdale, Ketley and Horsehay furnaces, and all others connected with them, the furnaces were stopped for a time on Sunday, generally from ten to four.

The bridge from which the furnace was filled, with its sheds and rooms and warmth, was a popular place, and the Company found that work was being impeded as the furnace bridges were used more or less as a club or meeting place. They put out notices to counteract this, at various times, one of which has survived.

Looking back over the accounts for a blast it is perhaps surprising to find that the highest paid workman is the one who burns the ironstone and wheels dust. Next to him comes the stocker of the bridge, the trustworthy person mentioned in the Commissioner's report, who would be responsible for the proportions in which the furnace charge was made up. His assistant and the four keepers come next in order with 12/- a week. The keepers were employed at the mouth of the furnace, tapped it, and were responsible for the casting of pigs, rails and other straightforward goods. Loading and unloading the raw materials was paid by piece work, and the burning of coals to coke was accounted for separately, and again was paid for at piece rates. With the coking heaps, and the heaps of burning ironstone not far from the head of the furnace, there is no wonder that the Madeley Wood furnaces got the name of Bedlam, or that early writers like Young and others were tempted to describe the furnaces as scenes of horror approaching the sublime. There must

[1] *Report of the Children's Employment Commission*, I. Appendix on Mines, part I, p. 48, 1842.

always have been clouds of smoke lit up with the glow of fires and hot metal.

Practically the whole output of the Horsehay furnaces, except for rails, was in these years, pig iron, which went to a number of large customers, generally being invoiced to them at first as 'melting iron.' John Wilkinson was one of the fairly regular customers from

WHEREAS ſeveral idle and diſorderly People make a practice of frequenting the Furnaces at Nights in Coalbrook-Dale, who have no Buſineſs there; and alſo ſeveral of the Workmen and Lads in that part known by the Name of the Bridge-houſe, ſo as to interfere with the Fillers, and often behave in a very riotous Manner.

This is therefore to give Notice,

That whoſoever Offends as above in future, (if Workmen or Lads) will be diſcharg'd from the Company's Employ, and any other Perſon or Perſons will be Proſecuted for Treſpaſſing in like Manner, upon Information being given at the Office in Coalbrook-Dale aforeſaid.

MADELEY: Printed by J. EDMUNDS.

1770 but Thomas Foley and Edward Knight were far the largest and most constant from the blowing in of the furnaces at Horsehay to the end of the available records.

From 1774 there is a gap of more than twenty years in the available records, and we know very little about the furnaces during that time, beyond the changes made by the introduction of the Boulton and Watt engines for the blast, and the elimination of the water-wheel driven bellows in favour of the cylinder blowing engines. The next surviving manuscript is the Blast Furnace Weekly Account Book 1798–1807 (*Shrewsbury MSS. 335*). These accounts are for the Horsehay furnaces and forges and for the first time give us a precise view of the charges used and the direct quantitative relation between fuel, ore, and iron produced.

Under the management of Dearman, a broad plan of reconstruction was introduced at Horsehay, the first item of which was the rebuilding of Furnace No. 2. The two furnaces at Horsehay were producing twenty-five to thirty tons of iron a week each, but the rebuilt No. 2, blown in on 4 February 1799, had an output of close on forty tons a week. The demand made on the blast was now too heavy and in April it was noted that the engine was too weak. Six months later the Furnace Book records that the engine 'was standing from October 11th to October 14th to put in a new cylinder being 4 Days and 3 Nights.' Other alterations were made to the valves and the injection and for a short time there was some little difficulty, but this was mastered and the engine proved equal to the new demands made upon the blast.

The furnaces were now run for a number of years at a time, with a stoppage for remaking the hearth only at intervals of three or four years. The replacement usually took a month to make, *e.g.* No. 2 Furnace was blown out on 4 February 1802; putting in a new hearth until 5 March; seasoning until 23 March when blast was put on and the furnace brought into work. The furnace then stayed in work for over four years and the next stoppage is in 1806—'No. 2. blown out about 4.30 am, Thursday Oct. 17th, to have a new hearth. Finished hearth on Tues. Oct. 29th and filled with coke.' All the next week it is noted 'scaffolding every six hours.'[1] It was blown in at 2.0 a.m. 6 November and by 14 November made thirteen tons of pig iron. This time and method of running is now typical of all the furnaces. The stoppage is usually used also as an occasion for renewing some of the casting floor sand, the amount generally brought in being of the order of 150 tons.

In 1803 preparations were started for another furnace for which some changes were made in the buildings at Horsehay.

For team work, men's time, ale given, on Acco[t] for Getting away old Water Engine etc for a foundation for the Intended New Blast Furnace No. 3.	£230.10. 0
Bricks and large Clumpers of bricks as got out of the Engine Walls as will Answer to be made use of in the Foundations, Valued	60. 0. 0
Smith work making, repairing and sharpening Hacks	10. 0. 0

[1] In a blast furnace a 'scaffold' is an obstruction which may arise from many causes, principally from uneven distribution of the charge. The obstruction may hold up the descent of the charge for a time, then allow it to collapse as a 'slip.' The process of scaffolding regularly during the filling is to ensure a regular disposition of the charges by breaking down any temporary scaffold almost at once.

This furnace was provided with a new blast engine, and the pipe work for this and the furnace make occasional items in the accounts until it was ready for blowing in in May 1805. The Furnace Book notes 'May 7th. 1805. at 11 o'clock put the first Mine on the new Furnace No. 3. first time scaffolded was at 6 o'clock at night. May 17th blown with two pipes.[1] Went off very well.' By August it was producing a little over forty-six tons of iron a week.

The furnace routine is best appreciated by taking the weekly accounts for a whole year, and this has been done for Furnaces 1 and 2, for the year 1801. The figures available are those for coal, ore and limestone brought to the furnaces, iron produced, and coal brought to the blast engine. The coal is recorded in Stacks and the ore in Dozens but the iron is in Tons and Hundredweights. A minute of the Company in 1794 says that the Horsehay Furnaces and Forges are to be supplied with coal and ironstone out of any of the Lawley and Dawley pits at Royalties of 2/6 per Dozen of 44 cwt. for ironstone, and 1/- per Stack of 35 cwt. for coal, these to be revised later if not enough. We can therefore use these values to bring the stacks and dozens to tons and find the following weekly average consumption. 553 tons of coal; 164 tons of ore; 63¼ tons limestone; these were used to produce 66 tons of iron. The ratios are, per ton of iron, 8·38 tons of coal, 2·47 tons of ironstone, and 0·96 tons of limestone. From a few pages preserved at the back of the book (a large wad of pages have been cut out at some time), we can get quite comparable figures, the ore ratio varying between 2·25 and 2·75 tons as a rule. It must be remembered of course, that the whole of the ore was calcined before being brought to the furnace, and these are weights of calcined ore. The books contain an annual summary of the varieties of ore mined and the amount of coal used in burning it, and the following years are available.

		Ore in Dozens		
Year ending	*White flat*	*Penny Stone*	*Spar*	*Coal in Tons*
June 1802	3002	2785		1889
June 1803	1605	4124		2032
June 1804	2344	4896		2240
June 1805	2928	3473	774	1804
June 1806	1039	3988	1280	1971
June 1807	974	7435	1479	2371

[1] These are the tuyers which at this date are given as follows: No. 1 furnace, 1½ in. and 1½ in.; No. 2, 2¾ in.; No. 3, 2 in. and 2⅛ in. diameter.

These figures give an inclusive average of 6,892 dozens of ore a year and 2,025 tons of coal needed to burn them, *i.e.* about 7·4 tons of ore was calcined by a ton of coal.

If the quantity of the furnace charges is examined closely it is at once apparent that they form four-week blocks. In each four weeks a particular charge was adopted and filled in for the whole period in exactly equal charges from sixteen to twenty-four charges a day. The charge in the next four weeks is usually different and a graph of the weekly charges goes in these four weekly steps, as its most regular feature. For the daily working, the amount of coke, ore and limestone, which make in each case a charge, is given, and the number of charges put in in the seven day week, *e.g.*

	Weight of each charge			*No. of*	
1805 June	*coke*	*Mine*	*Limestone*	*charges*	*Iron made*
No. 2.	12cwts.	12cwts.	5c.2q.0	148	38 T. 15c.
No. 3.	13cwts.	13cwts.	5cwts.	83	19 T. 3c.
1805 November					
No. 2.	13cwts.	10c.3q.0	4c.0q.20	151½	38 T. 6c.
No. 3.	13cwts.	12c.3q.0	5cwts.	157	43 T. 4c.

The proportions of coke and ironstone vary a little week by week, but cannot be correlated in any way with the quality or kind of iron produced.

The performance of the blast engine can be followed in some detail, as every stoppage is noted with its cause and duration. It is very rare that there is a stoppage of more than one hour in a week; in fact this occurred only twice in the year 1805, when in October the engine was stopped for 6 hours to 'take out the piston and straighten it,' and in June it was stopped for 2½ hours to put in a new piston leather. The remainder of the stoppages mainly follow a recurrent routine. A frequent item of attention, which may indicate a weak part of the engine, is the need to repair the chains and renew links. This occurs seven times in the year and takes about half an hour. 'Changing air-pump bucket' is approximately a monthly job, varying between three-quarters and a full hour. Every five or six weeks the engine stands for half an hour to bleach the cylinder, and at about the same frequency to pack the piston, a job generally taking an hour. These various adjustments with occasional attention to valves and windfalls are spread out so that one job is done each week throughout the year; in the year quoted there are only six weeks without a stoppage, though the total of all the stoppages is only 42½ hours in the year.

The furnace produced a variety of pig iron, often changing from day to day—common pig, grey, strong grey, hard and mottled are some of the terms used in the Furnace Book. Some of the pig iron was sold direct to customers but the greater part went into the forge and rolling mill to produce plate and bar iron. Cast iron goods were now limited at Horsehay to occasional structural and engine castings, blast pipe and machinery replacements, hammers and anvils, with no regular line of production. From 1805 the three furnaces at Horsehay were in blast until 1812 when one was blown out because of the low price of iron. This was blown in again before 1824 in response to rising prices and the increasing demand. Coalbrookdale continued to work its two furnaces for its own casting trade, but took some bar and plate iron from Horsehay in addition to what it made itself. Its demand on Horsehay was often a hundred tons a week.

Coke for the furnaces was made in heaps and not in ovens, and about 1811 a few experiments were made to determine the quantity of coal needed to make one ton of coke. This was calculated on the normal furnace working and gave a ratio of 3 tons 2 cwt. of coal to make 1 ton of coke.[1]

[1] MS. No. 4. *Iron & Steel Institute MSS.*

Chapter Eight

THE STEAM ENGINE, 1722–1772

THE eighteenth century saw the beginning of the Industrial Revolution, the greatest single factor in which was the harnessing of the power of fire and steam by the intermediary of the steam engine. Like all major inventions, the roots of this are traceable in many experiments and numerous improvements which in their cumulative effect gave birth to the integrated machine which has been hailed by popular fancy as being the first. As Stephenson is frequently but inaccurately spoken of as the inventor of the railway locomotive, although he had many predecessors who made successful engines, so Watt has frequently been credited with the invention of the steam engine, although there exists an abundant literature on the pre-Watt engines in use for fifty years before his time. We owe these popular misconceptions of history to the moralizing Victorian and Edwardian writers who delighted to seize upon an incident, often imaginary or ill documented which was capable of being romanticized into a delectable story. The boy Watt, watching his mother's kettle and by intuition grasping its significance for the condensing steam engine, makes a better story figure than the patient country blacksmiths like Newcomen, experimenting, struggling, having many difficulties and failures, and arriving at their imperfect goal only by slow and painful stages. The reader of today is being shown a greater appreciation than formerly of the sustained experiment and co-operative and cumulative efforts that lie behind all great achievements. In the long story of the development of the steam engine before Watt, the Coalbrookdale Company occupies an honourable and vital position, and can count to their name many of the largest engines.

The first successful patent for harnessing the power of fire, through the medium of steam, to the problem of raising water from mines, was taken out by Thomas Savery (1650?–1715), of Devon. His patent, No. 356, was dated 5 July 1698, and is for a 'new Invention for Raiseing of Water and occassioning Motion to all Sorts of Mill Work by the Impellent Force of Fire, which will be of great vse and Advantage for Drayning Mines, Serveing Towns with Water, and for the Working of all Sorts of Mills where they have not the Benefitt of Water nor constant Windes.' The grant was for fourteen years but was soon extended to a period of thirty-five years from the date of the original grant, that is until 1733.[1] Savery's engine, however, had no moving parts, and the parent of the later steam engines, with cylinder and piston, was the one invented and made by Thomas Newcomen. In this engine, Newcomen used a vertical cylinder, closed at the bottom end, with a moveable piston which could travel the length of it. The piston was suspended from the end of a beam which was pivoted near the middle, like a giant see-saw. The cylinder was connected to a boiler so that steam could be admitted to the cylinder below the piston, which by the weight of the pump rods hung from the other end of the beam, and helped slightly by the steam was drawn to the top of its stroke. When the cylinder had filled with steam, the steam valve was closed and a jet of cold water injected, which caused the condensation of the steam and the production of a partial vacuum, so that the weight of the atmosphere on top of the piston forced it down, and so, through the beam, raised the pump rods and pump buckets attached to the other end. By this repeated stroke, the pumps were worked with normal action. The steam did not need to have a pressure greater than that of the atmosphere, so that the boilers need not be very strong, and in fact were at the beginning made of copper, and sometimes with a leaden top.

Newcomen carried on experiments with this engine for more than ten years before his first successful engine was at work. This was 'The Steam Engine near Dudley Castle Invented by Capt. Savery & Mr. Newcomen Erected by ye later, 1712.'[2] Savery's name is retained in this title as his patent was so worded as to cover all possible methods of utilizing the 'impellent force of fire.' Until the expiry of the patent in 1733 no steam engine could be built except under licence of the holder of this patent. Savery died in 1715 and his patent was acquired by a body of men who called themselves 'The Proprietors of the Invention for raising Water by Fire,' and who advertised in 1716 that the engine was already at work in Stafford, Warwick, Cornwall and Flint. The engine in Warwickshire was almost certainly that at Griff Colliery, Coventry, and the one

[1] This was by no means the first patent for the utilization of power from fire or steam, but was the first which worked. For a description of some of the earlier ones, see Dickinson, H. W., *A Short History of the Steam Engine*, 1939, pp. 1–20.

[2] An engraving of this engine with the above title was made in 1719 by Thomas Barney.

in Flint was at Hawarden, under the care of Stanier Parrot and Richard Beech, respectively, both of whom are among the first customers of Coalbrookdale for engine parts.

The steam engines which were being erected by Newcomen and others under this patent, employed in their erection many different craftsmen, and parts were supplied from different sources. The engine was not yet in any sense a unit, built to a basal uniting frame or base plate, and sent out by a particular maker, but consisted of a number of parts which were incorporated with the boiler into a special building. The whole structure—boiler, engine parts, pipework and building—were assembled together by carpenter, mason, plumber, blacksmith and engineer, the various materials being bought piecemeal from the most convenient or best suppliers. An order was thus given, not for an engine, but for a cylinder and cylinder bottom; pipes might be got from the same maker or another; rods and wrought iron work came from the forge or blacksmith, and some parts, like the piston, might need cast and wrought iron in combination.

Among the principal parts of the engine the largest casting is of course the cylinder, and a separate casting is the cylinder bottom to which most of the pipe work connects. The piston head was cast, but had a wrought iron shank which would be forged. The pipe work was very varied—a short, large diameter pipe for the steam connection between the boiler and cylinder; the eduction pipe for exhaust water and air; the injection pipe for the water spray which condenses the steam, and numerous smaller pipes connected with the water supply and cistern. Bars and sleepers of cast iron are for the furnace grate and for some part of the supports. The main weight of the cylinder is carried by cross beams of timber and the main beam of the engine, until a later date, was also built up of timber, these being the main part of the carpenter's work. There was a good deal of blacksmith's and engineer's work in the strapping of the beam, the structure of the arcs at the ends, the bearings and the many rods and levers which worked the various valves of the engine.

The first Newcomen engines had brass cylinders, copper boilers, and pump trees of wood. The brass cylinders were very costly, one of 29 inches diameter costing £250 in 1727, and two brass pump barrels, 13 inches in diameter, costing £90 in 1733.[1] Copper boilers were

[1] These costs are from the engines at Edmonstone, Scotland, and at Jesmond, Newcastle-upon-Tyne. For comparative costs of other engines, see Raistrick, A., 'The Steam Engine on Tyneside,' *Trans. Newcomen Soc.*, XVII, 1937, pp. 131–63.

also expensive and difficult to make of much strength when slightly higher steam pressures were used.

With the success of the early examples the demand for them for pumping duty increased rapidly in the mining districts, but the cost, often as much as £1,000 each, and the difficulties of combining successfully the work of all the artisans we have mentioned, except under skilled supervision, restricted the supply for some years. Abraham Darby's advances in foundry practice were the means of liberating the new invention from some of these restrictions. In 1722, under the management of Richard Ford, the Coalbrookdale Company began casting engine cylinders in iron and rapidly made them a regular part of their production. The Company's interest in engines, however, starts earlier than this. The Inventory of July 1718 includes two significant items, representing stock left by Abraham Darby I.

In the Smith's Shop: 1 Brass Fire Engine	£6.0.0
In the Room over the Bellows: 3 Engines and odd things	£10.0.0

W. G. Norris, commenting on the first of these items, suggests that the brass engine might be a model of the Newcomen engine, but has no comment to make on the other item.[1] There is a third item 'In the Upper Air Furnace: a hand Fire Engine Brass 20/–' and this calls to mind rather a picture of a hand syringe than any part of a steam engine, and the four already mentioned are most probably fire extinguishing engines.

There is no further mention of these items of the inventory but the Stock Book has clear evidence of the Company's contact with the steam engine in 1718 and 1719, and with Stanier Parrot of the Coventry Engine, who became one of their important customers.

1718. Dec. 15. Stanier Parrot of ye Fire Engine.	
1 Cast Box oc.2.5. att 14/– p.c.	7.7½
1719. Mch. 3.	
3 Cast Pipes 6 foot long 6 Inches Bore 5c.0.4.	£20.0.0

The cylinder accounts start in 1722 and in the next few years a trade in cylinders and other engine castings was rapidly developed; with them pump barrels and rising pipe work is also supplied. The change over from brass to cast iron cylinders was not popular with some philosophers and with the brass founders, as was natural, but

[1] Norris, W. G., Appendix I. pp. 673–80, in a paper by Davey, H., 'The Newcomen Engine,' *Proc. Inst. Mech. Eng.*, 1903, pp. 655–704.

the philosophers had a sound case on theoretical grounds. This objection was best expressed by Desaguliers.[1]

Some People make use of cast Iron Cylinders for their Fire-Engines; but I would advise nobody to have them, because tho' there are Workmen that can bore them very smooth, yet none of them can be cast less than an Inch thick, and thereby they can neither be heated nor cool'd so soon as others, which will make a Stroke or two in a Minute Difference, whereby an eighth or a tenth less Water will be raised. A Brass Cylinder of the largest size has been cast under 1/3 of an Inch in Thickness; and at long run the Advantage of heating and cooling quick will recompense the Difference in first Expence; especially when we consider the intrinsick Value of the Brass.

Although this objection is perfectly sound, the great difference in cost, and the possibility of having a larger cylinder which would more than cover the loss of power at a far less cost than a brass one, made the cast iron cylinder so popular that it completely ousted brass. Coal was very cheap near the coalfields, as most of the colliery engines were able to use the large quantities of slack coal for which there was little sale.

The principal records of the engines are to be found in the Stock Books and Cash Books of the Company, the items in the Cash Books being wages and gratuities paid for moulding, casting, dressing and transporting cylinders and engine parts, and these are the fullest record.[2] In the Stock Books the entries are the actual receipts of payment for goods delivered to customers, and these are not always specified so as to differentiate engine parts from other goods. The first entries in the Stock Book which refer to engine work are for 1722, and are typical of most of them.

1722. Dec. 20. Pd Crannage & Parker Cast^{g} 813 gall^{ns} in Loom at 3d & for 5 Days work at ye Cilendar 8/4d.

1722. Dec. 30. Pd Crannage & Parker for casting & other work done to Xbre 15th: 344 gall^{ns} in Loom att 3d. 116 holes 9/8. 144 Purgatorys att 6d. A Malt Kiln Stove with Pipes to it & 4 Pitt Barrells £6. 5 Ton of Bannisters at 20/–. 146c.1.14 of Bushes etc att 10d. p.c. & for keep^{g} ye Furnace 12 Weeks 1 Day at 10/– p. week, in all £29.3.1

[1] Desaguliers, *Experimental Philosophy*, II, 1744, p. 536.

[2] The Stock Books are for 1718–27, *Shrewsbury MSS.* 330, and 1727–38, *Coalbrookdale MSS.* 1. Cash Books are for 1718–32 and 1732–49, *Shrewsbury MSS.* 329 and 331. In these of course the old style dating is used, the year changing in March, but in the quotations the year has been changed to present style, throughout.

In the wages accounts made up in four-week periods, the payment for casting is usually set out in this form. Crannage and Parker were the moulders and casters at the Old Blast Furnace and for a few years they seem to have done nearly all the engine and pipe work.

In 1723 there are only three relevant items, but they are of importance as introducing some good customers.

1723. Feb. 16. recd. of Moses Smith for 4 Pitt Barrells
7c. att 30/– del^{d} xbr 6.1722. £10. 10. 0

These four pump barrels are most probably those cast by Crannage and Parker in the period up to 15 December and noted in the previous account. The next item deserves more notice—

May 11. To Mr. Beech recd. Earnest on a Bargain made for Casting Pipes £1. 1. 0

Richard Beech of Walton near Stow became an important customer for pipe and engine work and this item marks the opening of his long connection with the Coalbrookdale foundry. Between this date and July 1727 he ordered three engines for his property at Walton, Staffordshire, and one for his colliery at Hawarden, Flintshire. His brothers or relations, Robert and Thomas, had taken a lease of collieries in Flintshire in 1714, and in 1723 he had inherited these along with the property in Staffordshire which included a colliery at Walton. His accounts taken from the Coalbrookdale books illustrate the general form as well as any, and the first few items relating to the Walton engine might well be taken together at this point.[1]

1723		
Stock Book. Sales.		
July 23. 3 Iron Pipes	27c.1.16 at 25/6	34.18. 6
Sep. 14 7 Pipes	36c.1.13 at 25/6	46. 7. 6
Sep. 30. 4 Pipes	35c.3.0. at 25/6	45.11. 7½
Oct. 10. 4 Pitt Barrells	27c.3.6 at 25/6	35. 9. 0
Oct. 21. 4 Pipes for Pump	26c.0.26 at 25/6	33. 4. 4
Nov. 28 8 Pitt Barrells	53c.3.24 at 25/6	68.15.10½
Cash Book. Cash Received.		
Dec. 10. To Richard Beech		150. 0. 0

[1] These as far as 1727 have been extracted by A. Stanley Davies in his paper 'The First Steam Engine in Wales and its Staffordshire Owners,' 1714, *Trans. Newcomen Soc.*, XVIII, 1937–8, pp. 67–71. Recently the Stock Book 1727–38 has been recovered and this carries Beech's connection with the Coalbrookdale Company much further.

Stock Book. Sales.

1724		
Aprill. 24. 1 Cillinder	31c.0.0. at 40/–	62. 0. 0
May 8. 1 Pistern Bottom	10c.1.6 at 18/8	
5 Buckitts	1c.0.23 at 3d	
1 Pipe	2c.3.12 at 25/6	
2 Brass Do	88 lb. at 14d	
1 Wrought Barr	1c.2.15 at 3½	
Patterns for Buckitts	17c.3.4. at 7/6	24. 7.11¾

Cash Book. Cash Received.

Apl. 4. To Richd. Beech	80. 0. 0

Stock Book. Sales.

Oct. 16. 1 Pistern 1c.1.24 att 3d	1.17. 7½
2 Brass pipes and Brasses to ye Pistern 1.c.1.14 att 14d.	8. 8. 0

Cash Book, Cash Received.

1725	
March 10. To Richd Beech	20. 0. 0
May 29 To Richd Beech	55. 4. 0

A. Stanley Davies places all these items to the engine at Walton, Staffordshire, but it seems most likely that this piston was supplied for the Hawarden engine. Many of the accounts give the address town of the person to whom the bill is sent, rather than the town to which the goods were sent, and whenever Beech is favoured with an address it is Walton.

The remaining item in 1723 is 7 August 'Gave men boring barrells 1/6.' This is the first mention of boring, but after this barrels and pipes are both supplied, sometimes bored and sometimes unbored, there being a difference in price. It is some years later that the larger cylinders were bored.

If we take the items relating to the steam engine, during the next two years, some more features of the accounts will become apparent.

1724 Feb. 5. By gave Casting a Cilinder	5. 0
Feb. 10–Mch. 8. To Teame Hawl^ng^ Carry^g^ ye Cilinder	2. 6
Apl. 5.–May. 3. To Joseph Jones Carry^g^ a Cilinder to Winster 31c. Short wt £1.7.6 to Winster	5.14. 0
July 9. Forge pd Wm Crannage Drawing a Stake for a cylinder	2. 6
Aug. 29. by gave Casting 2 Cilinders	10. 0

Sep. 20.–Oct. 19. Carry^{g} a Cilinder to ye Mill	1. 6
Carry^{g} a Cilinder to Harding near Chester 20c. att 3/–	
Nov. 21. By Humphrey Wheeler for 5 Thrave of Straw for ye Cilinders	7. 6
Rich Ford for Hay for Pipes etc 2 Years 16c.	1. 4. 0
1725	
Feb. 26. By gave Casting a Cilinder	5. 0
Apl. 4.–May. 1. Carry^{g} a Cilinder to ye Mill	2. 6
July 26 gave Casting 2 Cilinders	10. 0
Jul. 25–Aug. 22. Carry^{g} a Cilinder & Pipes to ye Mill 2 Ld 2/6 do to ye Severn 3/6	
Aug 27 By Hustice Beard Carry^{g} Cillinder Pipes etc to Worster	1.13. 8
Aug. 14. Stonnier Parrot of Coventry 4 Pipes 1 Cilinder & Bottom 1 Pistern 74c.1.11 att 32/6	120.16. 4
Aug. 22.–Sep. 19. Pitt Barrells to Shiffnall 1 Ld.	10. 0
Oct. 1. By Tho Crannage for a Cillinder Bottom & Pipes 5/– 3 Pitt Barrells at 10/– 2 Elbow Pipes	5. 0
By allow^{d} him for overwork in making 5 Cillinders & Sundry Pipes in ye preceeding year	5. 5. 0
Nov. 8. Tho. Crannage By Do making a Cilinder Bottom with Pipes 5/–	
Dec. 31. Stannier Parrot, Coventry Small pipes 2c.1.17	3.18. 1

The first three items refer to the same cylinder, cast on 5 February; it was carried a little later to the mill, and this is the first record of the boring mill. The account for the carriage to the mill is not given an individual date but is in the four-week period from 10 February. Between 5 April and 3 May the cylinder was carried to Winster. This may well be a cylinder supplied to the London (Quaker) Lead Company, who took leases of the lead mines in Winster parish, Derbyshire, in 1721, and whose reports soon show them to be involved in considerable water troubles. Their agent, Anthony Barker of Gadlis, bought at least five steam engines from various places including Coalbrookdale, before 1733.

In September the payment for carriage to Harding (Hawarden) near Chester is for the cylinder supplied to Richard Beech for an engine there, and some other items from the Cash Book belong to this same engine:

1724 Oct. 17. Richard Beech.	
a Cillinder & Bottom 25c.0.10 att 32/6	40.15. 5
a pcll of Wrought Iron Screw Pins 40lb att 9d.	1.10. 0
Carridge of Do to Harding beyond Chester	3.16. 0
Nov. 16. 1 Pistern 1c.1.2 att 3d	1.17. 7½
2 Brass Pipes & Brass to ye Pistern 1c.1.4 att 14d	8. 8. 0

The last two items are the ones already claimed by A. S. Davies for the Walton engine, but these fall more naturally into place in this Hawarden account. In August 1725 a third complete engine was sent to Worcester, and in the same month Stanier Parrot had an engine sent to Coventry. Rhys Jenkyns says that Sir Richard Newdigate had a set of castings from Coalbrookdale in October of 1725[1] which were probably to replace an earlier brass cylinder.

Among the smaller items the payment for straw, bought at 1/6 a Thrave, is one that is repeated from time to time, and no doubt this, with the hay which is also a regular commodity, was for use in the loam moulding. In the pot and kettle accounts, in the same way, great quantities of straw were used, but the amounts bought for the cylinders were always paid for separately. Stanley Davies has suggested[2] that a further item,

July 9. 1724. Drawing a stake for a Cillinder 2/6d

refers to 'the wooden bar around which the core of the casting was built up.' The facts that the cost of the stake is credited to the Forge account, and that it was made by William Crannage, forge master, indicate that it was of wrought iron, and not of wood. This is the only such entry, so that the article must have been something more permanent than a wooden stake, and was probably in use for many years.

In October 1725 Crannage is given five guineas for his overwork or overtime at the five cylinders cast in the preceding year, and this must refer to the Company's financial year, which ran from August, and not to the calendar year from March; the account would then

[1] Jenkyns, R., *Savery, Newcomen and the Early History of the Steam Engine*, in Collected Papers, 1936, p. 82.

[2] Davies, A. S., 'The First Steam Engine in Wales,' *Trans. Newcomen Soc.*, XVIII, 1937–8, p. 70, footnote.

agree with the numbers of cylinders we have noted, and with the later regular payment of 21/– for moulding a cylinder.

During the next five years the casting of engine parts proceeded, slowly at first, but increasing in number in 1731 and 1732. The royalties which were due upon every engine, payable to the Proprietors of the Patent, were very heavy, *i.e.* £150 a year, but as 1733, the year when the patent expired was drawing nearer, there was some encouragement to put in a steam engine, knowing that the royalty in all probability would soon cease. The Coalbrookdale figures for casting cylinders show this trend quite clearly.

1722	1	cylinder	1728	2	cylinders
1723	–	„	1729	–	„
1724	3	„	1730	–	„
1725	3	„	1731	7	„
1726	1	„	1732	10	„
1727	–	„			

Ford anticipated a great increase in business when the patent finally expired, as is evidenced in a letter to his partner Thomas Goldney, 26 March 1733 'and as ye patent for ye Fire Engine is about expiring, that business will consequently more increase.' His anticipations were only realized in part, and in the next fifteen years just over fifty cylinders were cast, but there was a large increase in pipe work, and more cylinders were sold with a more or less complete set of castings for the engine.

The pricing of the engine parts was done by a fixed charge per cwt. of the casting, and up to 1733 the prices were constant. Cylinders were charged at 32/6 per cwt., and in their making 21/– was paid for moulding one. When the casting was complete, a gratuity of 5/– was invariably paid to the caster. There is occasionally a small extra gratuity 'for getting it out' and in 1732 a gift of 5/– 'for getting it out in one Day.' Up to 1732 all the cylinders were moulded by Thomas Crannage and were nearly all cast at the Old Blast Furnace by Crannage and his partner Gilbert Parker, but in 1728 a cylinder was cast by them at the New Blast Furnace and in 1731 a second one was made there, in each case the payment for them being credited to Parker & Co. This second cylinder made at the New Blast Furnace was charged 31/6 for 'making' and this probably included both the moulding and casting fee and some other small gratuity or charge, as there is no separate entry for either casting or moulding. It looks as though Parker were being given some experience, for after this second casting the accounts cease to specify payment to Thomas Crannage and take the form 'paid Crannage & Parker,' or 'paid Parker & Crannage' for both moulding and casting, as though they now took equal responsibility. While most of the cylinders continued to be cast at the Old Blast Furnace, a few, along with more pipe work, were now made at the New Furnace. Other incidental charges on the cylinders are ranged under carriage to the mill, dressing, then carriage to the Severn. Usually the further carriage to their eventual destination is entered in a separate series of accounts for the carriage of goods in general.

Cylinder Bottoms were charged at 32/6 per cwt., and for casting them the gratuity was 5/–, though this frequently is paid for a cylinder bottom and pipes, and not often for a cylinder bottom alone. For moulding the cylinder bottom only 5/– was paid.

The charges for pipe work are related to the size and in the early accounts it is not clear how the price is reckoned. There are several items for pipes about 4 to 4½ cwt. sold to the engine customers, which are always charged at 32/6 a cwt., like the cylinders and bottoms. Other pipes vary greatly in price, as witness these examples:

1 pipe 4c.2.10 att 32/6d p.c.
12 pipes 72c.1.15 att 20/– p.c.
4 pipes 6c.1.15 att 28/– p.c.
3 pipes 8c.1.24 att 32/6 p.c.
6 Elbow Pipes 10c.1.2. att 28/– p.c.

The payments for moulding pipes vary even more widely; pump pipes are moulded for about 1/– or 2/– each, other pipes vary from 1/– to 10/– for moulding, but the weights and sizes are not given so in most cases it is not possible to determine the kind of pipe made:

1732 Crannage & Parker for moulding—
3 Pipes, 22/6d; 4 Pump Pipes att 1/–;
2 Pipes att 7/6d each; 3 Pipes att 10/– etc.

The change in the engine trade which Ford expected after the expiry of the Savery patent came slowly, and in the years 1733 to 1735 inclusive there are notes of nine cylinders being cast, but only six of them are detailed in the sales accounts. These were as follows—

1733. Richard Beech & Co for Harding.
Feb. 26. 1 Cillender 1 Bottom 2 Pipes 2 Clacks 57c.3.23 at 32/6d.
Other expences leading it at Salop 18/– £95. 1. 6¼

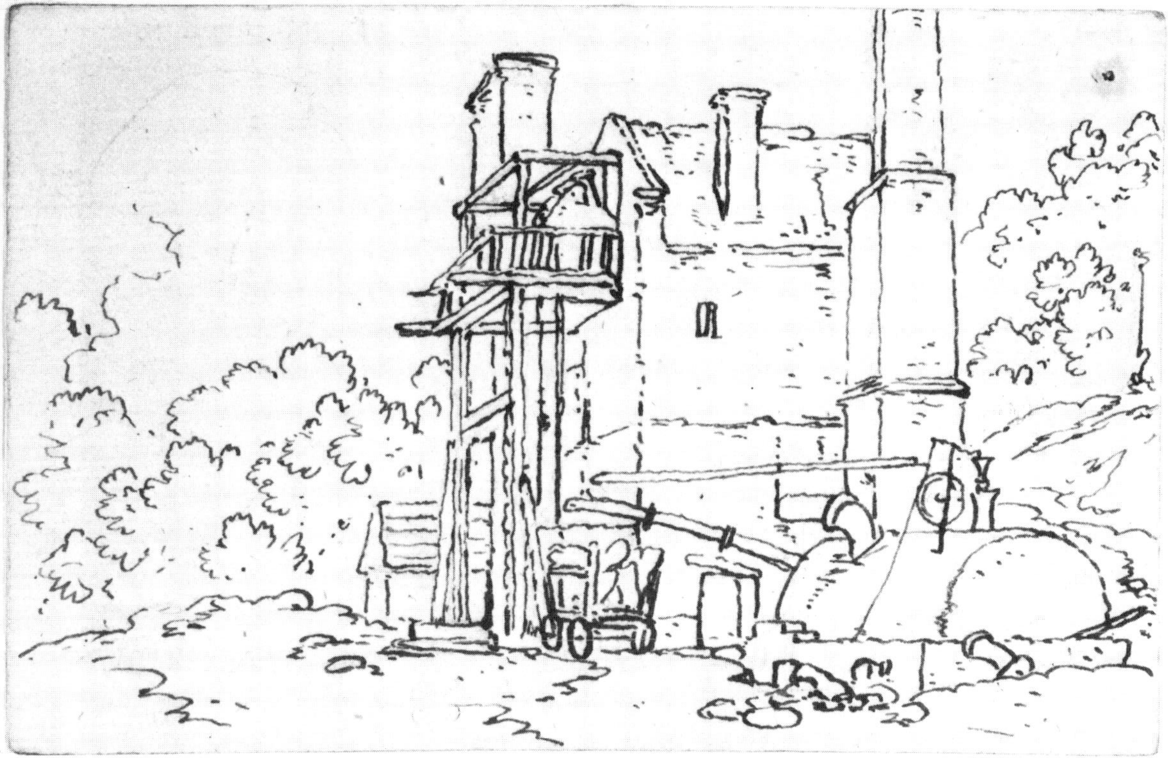

Plate XI *The Watt steam engine 'Resolution', installed in 1781-2 to replace the Newcomen engine seen in the painting by William Williams* (Plate VIII) *was the largest in the area at the time. The Coalbrookdale Company paid Boulton & Watt an annual £200 premium. The engine survived 40 years before being dismantled in 1821.*

PLATE XII *A large cast-iron cylinder for a Newcomen steam engine makes its way past the Coalbrookdale Works in 1758. Sights like this were already familiar by this date for nearly 100 cylinders had been made by the company for such engines since 1718.*

Apl. 13.	Earl of Scarborough 1 Cillendr 2 Bottoms 1 Barrell 6 Buckets etc. 73c.2.23 at 32/6d.	119.15. 5
Aug. 1.	Ld. Middleton 1 Cillendr 1 Bottom 5 Pipes 71c.3.20 at 32/6	116.17. 8
	14 Pipes 40 yards at 52/6d.	105. 0. 0
1734 Sept. 24.	Sr George Beaumont For Wykin 1 Cillendr 1 Bottom 8 Barrells 14 Pieces 138c.1.8. at 32/6d. 33 Barrells unbored and 4 Waggon Wheels 271c.3.15 at 20/– 4 Weights 1c.2.4. at 14/–	497.14. 7¼
1735 Mch 13.	Richard Beech & Co. Pistern 5c.1.10 at 32/6d. to Charges in boring a Cillinder £7.2.9	15.16. 3¼
May 6.	Jno. Crow 1 Cillendr 1 Bottom 59c.2.20 at 32/6d	96.19. 6½
Oct. 14.	Henry Lambton of Lambton near Durham 1 Cylinder 2 Bottoms 3 Pipes bored 97c.3.8. att 32/6d. 14 Pipes unbored 118c.2.0. att 20/–	277. 9. 1¼
Nov. 24.	Wm Richardson Esq of Smalley nr Derby 3 Barrells Bored 2 Sinking Pipes 18c.3.1. att 32/6d 22 Barrells unbored ye Length 63 yards 2 foot att 47/6d	181.13. 9¾

In the same period there was an increase in the casting of pipes and pit barrels, and these latter are now generally specified whether bored or not. By the lengths, in which some of them are now being reckoned, it is seen that the bored pipes were used as the barrels in which the pump bucket worked, and the unbored ones as the rising main through the shaft.

1735 Nov. 24.	Jos Hornblower of Birmingham 3 Pitt Barrells bored 18c.0.26 at 32/6d 12 Do unbored 72c.3.25 at 20/– Jno Unett Smitheman & Jno Giffard 1 Pipe bored 5c. at 30/– 6 Pipes unbored 32c.2.15 at 20/– 6 Wheels 14 lbs at 1½d	40. 4. 5

These go with the account quoted above to William Richardson, though from this date onward the unbored pipes are more frequently sold by length at 47/6 to 57/6 a yard.

In 1734 a new boring mill was set up, for which Ford ordered a 'wrought-iron spindle 12 feet long and full 3 inches in diameter; one end to be left square for 6 inches, and the remaining 10 feet to be left round, but to be as true as may be, and to be made of right tuff iron and right sound.' This boring bar was made by an anchor smith at Bristol and cost £26.10.0. It was obtained by September of that year and the first notice of its use on a cylinder is seen in the account already quoted, to charges in boring a cylinder for Richard Beech, in March 1735. Norris[1] says that Ford had experienced considerable difficulty in boring the larger cylinders, through the frequent breakage of boring bars; the new bar seemed to be successful and in 1745 another one was got, weighing 5c. 3q. 15 lb. at a cost of £21.19.4, or 8d. per lb.

The Sales accounts for the engines only go as far as 1738 but the gratuities etc. for casting or dressing cylinders are available until 1748, and details of a few engines are preserved after that date. In the three years 1736 to 1738 there are ten complete engines whose sale is entered in the books, the purchasers including many old customers, Lord Middleton, Burslame Sparrow, and Alderman Richard Ridley. In the same three years there are gratuities for thirteen cylinders and several separate payments for cylinder bottoms. No indication of the actual sizes of the cylinders can be got from the charges, as the book-keeper invariably puts together all the castings which are charged at 32/6 a cwt. so that every entry varies. One will give a cylinder, cylinder bottom, and three pipes, weighing about 40 cwt. and the next item may be a cylinder, 2 bottoms, and a piston at 45 cwt. but within a year there is a similar charge for a cylinder, 2 bottoms and a piston, weighing 74 cwt. In nearly all cases one or more pipes, buckets or clacks are included in the total weight, but there are sufficient examples to show that cylinders were being made in varied sizes. In 1736 Lord Dudley bought a cylinder and cylinder bottom of just over 25 cwt. Lord Middleton bought only two months earlier, a cylinder and cylinder bottom, weighing nearly 44 cwt., and two months later a cylinder and cylinder bottom for Joseph Hornblower weighed 34 cwt. In 1738 a cylinder and cylinder bottom for Richard Ridley weighed 58 cwt.

In 1742 there is the first notice of a steam engine being built for the works, although the account is very incomplete, being mainly

[1] Norris, W. G., Appendix I to 'The Newcomen Engine' by H. Davey, *Proc. Inst. Mech. Eng.*, 1903, pp. 673–80.

itemized for the work done in building the engine house with few details of the engine itself.[1]

By the accidents of preservation we have only an incomplete record of the work of the Company, so that for the steam engine, after 1748, such records as remain are of varied type. Until 1738 there had been a careful note of both the gratuities paid for moulding and casting cylinders, and the sales accounts for some of the engines. About 1737 the payments for casting are no longer itemized, but the furnace accounts merely carry a lump sum paid for an aggregate weight of cast goods, which includes engine cylinders and parts without specification. However, as this source of information failed, a substitute is found, in that from 1738 to 1748 separate payments are entered for 'dressing' or fettling pipes and cylinders; these accounts usually include the weight of pipes and the number of cylinders dressed. The last entry of this series is the one exception, where £2.18.0 was paid for 'dressing pipes & cylinders' and we have no means of checking the proportions or numbers of pipes and cylinders so dressed. As pipes are usually charged only 1/– each for dressing, and cylinders are 5/–, it seems likely, in comparison with

[1] Hall, J. W., in his paper 'Notes on Coalbrookdale and the Darbys,' *Trans. Newcomen Soc.*, V, 1925–6, pp. 1–8, says that Abraham Darby II put in an atmospheric engine in 1732, and that the scheme to return the water to the furnace pool, for which this was installed, was completed in 1742 to 1744. There is no indication in the available books of the Company, however, of any steam engine being made for use in the works before 1742, and it may be that Hall has taken the letter of Richard Ford, already quoted, in which he describes a horse engine in 1732, to refer to a steam engine. Hall says that a letter exists which shows that this engine worked two 18 in. diameter pumps, 7 ft. 9 in. stroke with a lift of 84 feet.

Norris, W. G., in his appendix to the paper on the 'Newcomen Engine,' *Trans. Inst. Mech. Eng.*, 1903, pp. 673–80, says that in 1743 Abraham Darby decided to erect a pumping engine for the furnace pools which had a difference in level of about 120 feet. He quotes the cost of the engine under the date 1745—

Cylinder, working barrels and cast iron articles	£307.	18.	7
Brass work and Lead	108.	14.	1
Plate iron and Bricks	70.	15.	8
The Oak Regulating Beam	10.	15.	0
Various labour in and with the Erection and Pit	356.	0.	3
	854.	3.	7

The cost of the Oak Regulator Beam identifies this account with the engine of the 1742 accounting, so we may assume that the building of the engine occupied much of the years 1743 and 1744 and that when the final summation of cost was made in 1745, it was at work and satisfactory.

earlier entries, that there would be four, or less likely five, cylinders in this account. To the autumn of 1748, however, the record is no mean one, as it contains evidence of more than 94 cylinders made and accounted for. After 1748 the nature of the records changes and we now have only occasional sales accounts of engines made for the Company's own use at Coalbrookdale, Horsehay, Ketley and Dawley.

The earliest fairly complete account for a Coalbrookdale engine that still remains is the holograph letter and bill, sent to the London Lead Company in 1748, for an engine supplied to the Mill Close Mine, Derbyshire, and signed by Abraham Darby. This engine is of particular interest because there are still two plans in existence which show the arrangement of the engine and the mine workings and pumps, and though the drawing of the engine is obviously copied from one of the prints or engravings then available, it was accepted as a satisfactory picture of the actual engine. The account is addressed with a letter, to

Joseph Whitfield, Bower's Mill near Chesterfield, Derbyshire.
A Single Sheet.
For the Governour & Co. for Smelting down Lead with Pit and Sea Coal.
For Mill Close Mine.

1 Cylinder 42 Diam.	54.3.18		
1 Bottom	16.0.0		
1 Sinking Pipe 6 In Diam, 8 foot Long	6.2.7		
1 Workg barrell 12 Diam 9 foot	10.1.11		
1 Jackhead Tree bored 9 In Diam 6 foot Long	5.2.7.		
4 Buckets 4 Clacks	1.2.27		
1 Workg Barrell 9f long 9 In Diam Spigot ends	7.1.14		
1 Do	7.2.24		
	110.0.24	at 30/-	£165. 6. 5
1 Clack Seat	5.1.9		
Pipe 9ft 12¾ Diam Spigot	10.2.11		
1 Clack Seat	10.2.2		
1 Blast Hole	7.2.14		
1 Bucket Tree 12¾ Diam 9 f. Long	15.0.6		
	49.0.24	at 18/-	44. 5.10¼

1 Door Frame	2.1.10		
25 Bars	16.1.14		
6 Sleepers	15.0.13		
2 Braces	1.3.7		
Cast Iron in the Piston	8.1.14		
	44.0.2	at 12/–	26. 8. 2½
2 Wrot Iron Stems in ye Piston	2.3.14	5.0.11	
1 Wrot Gudgeon turn'd	2.0.25	at 6d	14. 5. 6
5 Dales	at 1/6		0. 7. 6
			250.13. 5¾
Allow'd on the Bars & Sleepers 31c.1.27 1/6 p. cwt. towards carriage			2. 7. 3
	Remains due		£248. 6. 2¾
Allow'd as p. Bargain			2. 2. 0
			246. 4. 2¾

4th: 11mo: called Jany. 1748. Recd of Joseph Whitfield Two Hundred Forty Six Pounds Four Shillings In Full Payments for the Within Mentioned Goods Delivered him For the Governour & Compa. for Smelting down Lead With pit & Sea Coal; For Mill Close Mine: For Self & Compa:

Abraham Darby.

p. Bill	170.–.–
Cash	76.4.0
	246.4.0

On the fold of the letter there is a further account and message.

2 Furnaces 25 Gall-50 Gall.			140 Gall. at 8d	£4.13.4
1	do	30		
1	do	60		

4th 11mo: Calld Jany. 1748. Recd of Joseph Whitfield Four pounds Thirteen Shillings & 4d In Full for Self & Compa.

Abraham Darby

Coalbrookdale 30th. 9thmo.1748.

Loving Friend
Joseph Whitfield

I had not time this morning to draw out the bill of Parcells before the Waggons were Gone, but I hope thou hast recd the whole ere this reaches thee safe and in good Order, & that they please: Upon Notice from thee I purpose Meeting thee in Derby; and if Joseph Jones the Engineer Continues in the Mind to have the Crank he was talking of, if he has time I Should be pleased to see him along with thee to have his directions about it, please to Mention the Inn thou puts up at, and If thou Canst, allow me a Day or two to set out in. I am for Self & Compa.

With due Esteem

Thy Loving Friend

Abraham Darby.

In the letter there is the interesting reference to a crank wanted by the engineer Joseph Jones, but there is no further trace of this, unless the reference is to a bell-crank lever. In 1756 there is a rough sketch section which shows the arrangement of the Mill Close engine shaft, with two Jacks, or bell-crank levers, and a sixteen yard slide of connecting rods, by which the engine was linked to pumps in a nearby shaft. The pumps in the engine shaft are stated to be 12 inches in diameter and 48 yards below the level, while the second set connected by levers and rods are 10 inches in diameter, and 50 yards below the level.

The engine worked successfully at the mine for a number of years, but in 1752 an Act of Parliament was obtained to drive a sough or drainage level through part of the ground immediately north of the Mill Close mine and cutting the Mill Close vein, and as this level was driven, many prospects in the area were changed. In 1759, on 1 May, a trial of the engine was made on a 24-hours run, in which 4 tons 11 cwt. of coal was used, the equivalent of 32 tons 4 cwt. a week, at a cost of 12/- per ton. From the test it was reckoned that the engine was of approximately 47 horse power. Following this test, on 15 May, an agreement was made for the sale of the engine to Thomas Stephens of the Dalefield Mine, but as the prospects of the mine improved slightly, the sale was deferred for a while. The parts to be sold were specified as the cylinder, cylinder bottom, piston and sinking pipe, a total of 85c.3.11 at 23/- per cwt. comes to £98.14.6. A note a little later says 'N.B. the two wrot Iron Stems in ye Piston weighed 2c.3.14 & not included in ye above weight but were set against that part of the sinking pipe left.' In 1764 there is a minute of the general Court meeting which reads

Mill Close Mine, Derbyshire, has effectively been tried under level and there is no prospect of success.

Resolved to stop the Fire Engine and sell the coal and store such material as will not spoil.[1]

In 1754 the Coalbrookdale accounts include items for the steam engine in the works, being entered at first under the caption 'Fire Engine Dr to Sundry Accounts.' In the first account payments are made to William Hallen for rod iron and other forge goods and on one occasion payments are entered to Richard Ford for similar materials. Richard Ford senior had died in 1745 and his son Richard had become a partner in some small ironworks at Caynton, Sawbrook and Tibberton, with William Hallen as his manager, but he still kept a close connection with the Coalbrookdale Company. The account of materials debited to the Fire Engine is very mixed, but in the course of a year, the complete engine is detailed and the total cost is about £760 for an engine of 10 foot stroke and with a cylinder of 47¾ inches diameter. Without giving the whole account which includes a great variety of small parcels of bricks, iron work, etc, the following may be noted as giving information of the engine parts.

Cylinder 10ft lo. 47¾ in. Diam.	72c.0.0
Cylinder Bottom	14c.2.7
2 Working Barrels 10ft. lo 24 in. diam.	52c.2.6
2 Plain Pipes 8ft. lo. 25in. diam.	
2 Blast Holes 7ft. 22in. diam.	132c.3.1
2 Clack Seats Do	
1 Working barrel 6½ft lo. 9 ins. diam	7c.0.19
8 Buckets and Clacks	9c.3.0
1 Brass Clack 1 Regulator & Sinking Clack	1c.2.12½
1 Piston Ring in four parts	
Gudgeons, brasses, pipes, etc.	
1 Air Vessel & 1 Engine Pan ring	50c.0.0
1 Air Vessel Top	10c.0.14

From William Hallen's forge they got, in addition to rod and bar iron, plates for the boiler—

228 Engine Plates	65c.2.5
34 Round Plates	2c.0.27
14 Valve Plates	2c.2.18

The boiler plates were small, hammered plates, of an average weight a little over 32 lb. each.

[1] For more detail of this mine and engine, see Raistrick, A., 'Mill Close Mine, Derbyshire, 1720–1780.' *Proc. Univ. Durham Phil. Soc.*, X, 1938, pp. 38–47.

This engine was followed by another in 1756 with a cylinder of 60 inches diameter and 10 foot stroke, weighing 72c.1.7. The piston 9c.3.8 was turned and the engine completed during 1757 for the Horsehay furnaces. The fact that these engines were immediately followed by others for various parts of the works, is a proof of their success and the accounts for three others occur in the next few years for both Horsehay and Ketley. The most complete, except for the cylinder, is the one entered as the New Fire Engine, erected in 1758. In 1760–1 an engine was supplied for the Dawley Collieries with a cylinder of 60 inches diameter and 10 foot stroke, and one to Ketley furnace.[1]

The erection of these large engines marks the period of the expansion of the works, and they are a consequence of the direct leases taken of the Ketley and Dawley coalworks, and the blowing-in of the new furnaces at Horsehay and Ketley, in 1755 and 1756. The engines were needed to provide the heavy blast demanded by the new furnaces, which could no longer be provided by natural water power. A lease of Ketley, Dinnington Wood and Wrockwardine in 1759 included power to erect fire engines and furnaces, and Madeley Wood furnaces in 1766 were also provided with a steam engine for blast.

In the North of England the Company had as an agent on Tyneside, Isaac Thompson, a relation by marriage of Abraham Darby, to whose wife Rachel Thompson so many of Hannah Darby's letters are addressed. Thompson was a close friend of the well-known William Brown who about 1750 was building engines in the Tyneside coal field and gradually assuming a dominating position as engineer. Brown's letter books[2] contain references to some of the dealings with the Coalbrookdale Company. On 28 November 1752, Brown was writing to his friend Carlisle Spedding, colliery owner of Whitehaven, Cumberland, and tells him that Throckley Colliery, near Newcastle, wanted a pumping engine, and were designing to have one with a 47 inch diameter cylinder.

And this moment has had a letter from your old friend Isaac Thompson who is Concern[d] for the Coalbrook Dale Company to Inform me he has just now Imported a Cylinder of our size with Bottom Peston and all

[1] The detailed accounts for these engines are of great interest, and are transcribed for reference in the Appendix, No. 4.

[2] These are preserved among the manuscript collections of the North of England Institution of Mining Engineers, Neville Hall, Newcastle-upon-Tyne.

other utensills fit for it all which he offers Cheaper than can have Them at N. Castle and which I think [I] will buy Sence its been rumerd about our Place that we Design for a fire engine I have had Several Brass Foundiers at me and as they are so plentiful has some thoughts they will reduce the prices. . . .

In December Spedding replied to this letter with a request for information:

. . . and please to Enquire when you see Mr Isaac Thompson w^{t} price we could have an Iron Cylinder 42 Inches Coalebrough Dale. I would have it a pretty strong one to w^{t} 54 Hundred weight without the Bottom tho I w^{d} have Bottom and peston. One of our cylinders we have at work has been ill Casten and the Boring is true on the inside made a thin place between the Beams which is worn through.

Please enquire where the Co. w^{d} liver the Cylinder or I suppose at Bristol w^{d} be the likeliest Place to ship it at I sh^{d} be glad to know how to Direct to the Companys Agent at Coale brook dale. . . .

He also wants to know how much coal would be consumed by an engine with a 42 inch diameter cylinder, and Brown answers both queries in his next letter.

The Coale brook dale Company sells their Cylinders at £1.12.0 per Hund Wt and he thinks they will deliver one of your Dementions & Wt at Whitehaven for that money as he is Agent to the Company here And I find has comission money to himself Therefore wd be glad to give him the order if wd Choose to have one.

The Cos Agent at Coale brook dale is Abra. Darby we usually calculate that an Engine that is much Burthened and works as you mention Burns & Consumes about 20 Bolls of Coales every 24 Hours Each Boll 36 Winchester Gallons ale measure.

There is a complete estimate available date July 1753 for the fitting of an engine and boilers, buildings, pumps etc., the cylinder to be 42 inches diameter and the weight 55 cwt. which estimate is almost certainly a copy of one made by Brown for Spedding's guidance.[1] The total cost was to be £1,324.5.0.

Brown was also associated with the erection of what is probably the best known of all the early engines on Tyneside, that at Walker Colliery, of 1763. The first shaft sunk at Walker Colliery reached the coal at a depth of 99 fathoms, in January 1762. This and two other

[1] Among the author's manuscript collections—part of a group of mining papers mainly relating to the Quaker Lead Company, and including several estimates for engines etc. by Darby, Brindley, Brown, Watson and others.

shafts were in the charge of William Brown who erected two engines for the pumping. As the colliery was situated within the deep Tyne coal basin, where water troubles were rapidly increasing, Brown decided to add to the two engines already at work, an exceptional one with a 74 inch diameter cylinder. This cylinder was obtained from the Coalbrookdale Company, and the engine was built and put to work. The engine had a stroke of 10 feet 6 inches, and was described as 'the most complete and noble piece of ironwork' that had been to that date produced in Coalbrookdale.

In 1767, Coalbrookdale supplied an engine to the Killingworth Colliery, Northumberland, for the Killingworth High Pit, which much later took an honoured place in engineering biography. It was this engine which George Stephenson tended as a young man, and the working of which he improved in such a way as to draw the attention of his employer, securing thereby the promotion which set him firmly on his career as an engineer. This engine remained in work until after 1850.

There is one other engine belonging to this period which is worth individual mention, that is the one built for Mr. Thomas Broade of Fenton Vivian, Staffordshire, which was superintended by James Brindley. Brindley devised a new type of boiler to serve this engine, and secured a patent for the boiler, carrying out some of the experimental work upon it at Coalbrookdale. W. G. Norris, however, says the boiler was unsatisfactory; this was in 1756, and some few years later the Coalbrookdale accounts carry items to close the affair of what is called in them Brindley's machine.

To Brindley's Machine for sundry pipes etc. 228c.1.15 at 15/–	57. 1.11
To Brindley's Machine for the balance of that account	170. 2. 4½

The cylinder was of iron, supplied by the Coalbrookdale Company, as noted in their books—

1756. Mr Broade of Fenton, Stoke-on-Trent, (60 in. cylinder 10 ft. stroke, superintended by James Brindley).[1]

In 1759 Brindley was again experimenting with a boiler and for this an account at Coalbrookdale gives some detail.

[1] Davies, A. S., 'The Coalbrookdale Company and the Newcomen Engine,' *Trans. Newcomen Soc.*, XX, 1939–40, p. 47, is responsible for the statement that this is a 60 inch cylinder. All the evidence is that it was 36 inches diameter.

8.9mo. 1759	Brindley's Boiler 2 Fire Pans in Loam & 15 Pipes	175c.3q.8lbs.	@ 18/-
	4 Plates & 6 Sleepers	28 3 2	@ 12/-
	1 do & Barrs	10. 1. 5	@ 12/-
	2 Grates & do	4. 3. 17	@ 12/-
	1 Communication Pipe	5. 1. 12	@ 18/-
			£189.10. 5½

We have a description of Brindley's engine and boiler in 1759, sent by Mr. Spedding of Whitehaven to William Brown, the Tyneside engineer.[1]

. . . the Cylinder 36 Ins. and lifts or forces the Water 26½ Fa^ms. to the Level & Dry Rods (or Spears) 17 Ins. more to the Top of the Pitts, and agreed to support the Engine with all Repairs & men to work her (exclusive of Coals) for 80£ p Annum for 15 Years, the Engine has now Wrought near three Years & Ans^rs very well. . . .

. . . Expense on the Engine House was saved by building the cylinder into one wall and making the opposite wall act as the pivot bearing at the centre of the beam—the boilers were outside and made of Brick laid only in fine Lime is about 18ft long 12ft wide & 6ft deep in form of an Archd Vault, under it he has 4 small fireplaces like those of a Common Sett Pott, with Iron Doors & Brick instead of Iron for the Grate Bars which he does not clean from Clinkers above once in 10 or 12 Weeks his fires are so moderate as not to run the Coals. Above the Fire are laid Cast Iron Plates wch make the Boiler Bottom in that Part, the rest being paved with Brick the fire plays against the Iron Plates & goes into a Flue on the Backside the Boiler & is there recd in 4 Iron Pipes one for each Fire Place wch come thro' the Water & Steam in the inside of the Boiler & then are conveyed into the Chimney.

The links of the Regulator Beam chains were made of wood plates hinged together with long iron bolts. 'The Pumps are 8 Ins Bore are all made by the Coopers of Staves of Wood and hoopd wth Iron'; the bottom pump cylinder was 20 inches diameter. The Engine worked ten or eleven strokes a minute and was said to be very quiet indeed. The boilers of this design were not a permanent success and could of course stand very little above atmospheric pressure of steam.

[1] William Brown's Letter Book, p. 61. Manuscript collections. Institution of Mining Engineers, Newcastle-on-Tyne.

Chapter Nine

THE STEAM ENGINE, 1772–1805

FROM the time of the introduction of Newcomen's engine about 1715 and up to the last engines described in the previous chapter, there was no change made in the essential parts of the machine. The Coalbrookdale foundry had made possible the almost universal use of the cast iron cylinder, and had developed methods of boring which were reasonably good. The effect of the use of cast iron was to cheapen cylinders considerably, so that it was now an economic proposition to apply a large cylindered engine to mine pumping. This in turn made much deeper and more extensive mining possible and a cycle of development by interaction—foundry—engine parts—deeper and better pumping—easier and cheaper ore and fuel—larger furnaces and foundries—larger engines—was soon established. There was a rapid increase in size of the engine cylinders in use, up to the giants of the 1760's such as the Walker Colliery engine on Tyneside, for which Coalbrookdale cast a cylinder of 74 inches diameter already referred to. In 1732 in anticipation of a greatly increased demand for engine parts when the Savery patent expired, Ford had joined with Goldney in leasing the Willey furnace, but such cylinders as were cast by them were made not there, but at the Coalbrookdale foundry. In 1759 John Wilkinson and others took over the New Willey furnace, with very little record of what it had accomplished during these twenty-seven years of joint ownership except the production of pig iron for the Bristol market. In 1762 Darby made a price agreement with Wilkinson acting for the New Willey Company, Isaac Wilkinson at the same time acting for the Bersham Company. The substance of the agreement was that identical prices were to be charged for engine parts, cylinders and bored parts at one price and articles not bored at another, on equal deliveries, but London to be excluded from the operation of the new prices. In 1763 the New Willey Company of Broseley passed into the sole possession of John Wilkinson and during the next few years a few engine cylinders were cast there.

With the increased size of the engines the consumption of fuel went up by leaps and bounds, and the difficulty of boring the cylinders to a close limit of truth made these largest engines somewhat less efficient and very costly in coals, leathers for the pistons, and other incidentals. As the demand for power was steadily increasing it was clear that the time was ripe for some great change in engine design or working, if more power were to be available at a reasonable price. It was in this approaching crisis that James Watt made his revolutionary improvement in engine design. From the earliest days of the Newcomen steam engine an outstanding source of heat loss and inefficiency had been due to the cooling down of the cylinder at each stroke when the steam was condensed within it by injecting a cold water spray. Both fuel and time were consumed in reheating the mass of metal in the cylinder, in some cases over five tons in weight. Watt conceived the idea of the separate condenser, *i.e.* passing the steam into a separate chamber where it could be condensed without cooling the cylinder, and this idea of 1764 was developed to the stage of a patent in 1769. It took much time however to translate the ideas in the patent into a completed engine which would be acceptable to industry, and another six years of experiment passed by before this end was attained. In 1769 his first engine was erected at Kinneil House, Stirlingshire, but it was not strikingly successful due to faults in workmanship. Dr. John Roebuck of the Carron Ironworks and Matthew Boulton of Birmingham encouraged and financed Watt and, along with Dr. William Small also of Birmingham, tried to form a four part partnership in the new engine; no successful working agreement was reached, however. Dr. Small tried in 1770 to secure materials and castings for the new engine, and some of the castings were got from the Coalbrookdale foundries, but were not acceptable to him.

Perhaps the most important step in the engine's progress was due to the invention by John Wilkinson of an improved boring mill.[1] In this new mill it was possible to attain a bored cylinder which was true in three dimensions. In the earlier mills, with a rotating bar and cutter, the shape of the cylinder was truly circular at any one position, but the longitudinal section was not necessarily a true rectangle, hence the path of the piston was not an absolutely straight line. With the production of this new standard of true bored cylinders, the Boulton and Watt engine became a practical and commercial proposition and Wilkinson became for some time

[1] Patent No. 1063, for a Mill in which the casting, cylinder or cannon, rotates around a fixed boring bar along which the cutting tool can be traversed.

the sole producer of them though Coalbrookdale continued to provide much of the pump and pipe work for the engines.

Through the middle and later years of the century, alongside the problem of increased engine efficiency, the needs of industry were demanding a second desideratum, that of rotative motion derived from the steam engine. The linear motion of the Newcomen engine was ideal for pump work and as early as 1742 the Coalbrookdale Company harnessed it to pump water into a pool from which it could flow over a water wheel and so give the motion needed for other purposes than pumping.[1] Smeaton applied the engine to pump water directly onto a water wheel without the intermediary of a reservoir, and this became a general method of securing rotative motion. The crank which could convert linear to rotative motion had been known from time immemorial but its application to the steam engine was patented in 1780 by James Pickard of Birmingham. It was assumed that this patent blocked the way for Watt to make use of the crank and so he turned his attention to some other means of achieving rotary motion. In 1781 he patented the 'sun and planet' motion and was then able to supply engines to work forge machinery, blowing machines, etc., direct. For the twenty years 1760–80, however, Coalbrookdale were making steam engines of the old type, to pump water for a wheel, and some of these engines are worth noticing.

In 1770 the Horsehay works paid for two engines, each with a cylinder 54 inches diameter by 7 foot stroke; but the cylinders were not identical, weighing 49c.2q.24.lb. and 43c.1q.16.lb. respectively and all other parts in the second engine being similarly a little lighter. These engines cost about £200 each. The following year two more were built, but the sizes are not given; however as the two cylinders weighed just over 40 cwt. and 39 cwt. they were a little smaller than the first pair. It was at this time that Abraham Darby III was building up Horsehay as an integrated furnace-forge group, and two of these engines were for the forge machinery.

In 1776 the Coalbrookdale Company built a Newcomen engine at Handley Wood, which remained in existence for over a hundred years. The cylinder has the name and date cast on it—

COALBROOK DALE
COMPANY 1776
W 68.1.8 48 dia 11 long

[1] It is perhaps significant that the earliest patent for obtaining rotary motion in this way was taken out by Nehemiah Champion of Bristol, the close associate of Coalbrookdale. *Abridgement of Specifications*. Steam Engine. I. 50.

In 1827 the engine was bought by a Mr. Barrow of the Staveley Colliery Company and in 1849 it was moved to a new site and re-erected. Nothing seems to be known of its history prior to the purchase in 1827, and it is not clear whether it was bought at that date from the Coalbrookdale Company, having been in use in their own works, or whether they had erected it at Handley Wood originally and maintained it, charging the colliery owners a premium for its running. It was probably at the second re-erection that some considerable alterations were made. The cylinder was originally made for the usual direct connection to a boiler beneath it, but this connection had been altered and replaced by a vessel forming a 'pickle-pot' condenser, so making the working follow partly upon Watt's principle. The steam connection was changed to the inlet formerly used by the injection condenser water. The engine ceased work on 1 December 1879, and when it stopped it was fully described with an engraving of it, which is here reproduced (facing page 150).[1]

In all descriptions of the engine, the stroke is given as approximately 5 feet 6 inches, with a variation of about 2 inches, but the inscription on the cylinder gives the cylinder dimension as 11 feet long. A comparison of the engraving will show that this is correct, and it is interesting to note that probably nearly half the cylinder length was taken by piston and clearances, leathers and water seal, etc.

The Company continued to build engines on the Newcomen plan, both for their own use and for sale, for a few years after Boulton and Watt started to supply their new engine with cylinders cast by Wilkinson. Coalbrookdale at that time had agents for the sale of engines in Truro and Newcastle, but were in danger of being displaced by Boulton and Watt whose engines were more economical to run for the equivalent coal. The account books of Richard Trevithick senior have items for pumps and other engine work supplied by the Coalbrookdale Company to the Dolcoath Deep Adit, Cornwall, in 1775; through their agents and also by the interest of the engineer, Hornblower, they had developed quite an important trade in pump work and engines in the Cornish mining areas. William Reynolds was a sincere admirer of Watt, as is seen in the letter to William Rathbone in 1777, quoted in an earlier chapter. It seemed inevitable that, with their long tradition of good engine work, the Coalbrookdale

[1] The engine is described, with the engraving and with the indicator diagrams in *The Engineer*, 1880, p. 80–4, and also, with the same engraving, in *Trans. Chesterfield and Derby Inst. Engineers*, IX, 1881–2, p. 37.

Company must sooner or later come into working relations with Boulton and Watt, and in fact in 1777 Reynolds was taking the opinion of Watt on the advisability of a timber beam for a new engine. An engine was designed for the Ketley works and was placed in work in 1778, the design being supplied by Watt and the engine parts made at Coalbrookdale, the Company paying the usual royalty on the running of the engine. In that year also, pump barrels were being cast at Coalbrookdale for Boulton and Watt, and this trade increased. In May 1780 William Reynolds wrote to Watt, 'We are now putting up a mill at the Dale to bore cylinders in the manner J Wilkinson bores his, and as we are in hopes we shall be able to do it as correctly as he does, we shall wish to give the order for the cylinder, Hotwell and Air pumps to the Dale Co. and as some order might perhaps soon have been given to J. W. for these, I thought it proper to aprise thee of our Intentions.' This was a procedure followed in all subsequent engines, the designs being ordered from Watt, with permission to make the engine work at the Coalbrookdale foundry.

The erection of the new boring mill, probably under licence from Wilkinson, marked the end of Wilkinson's virtual monopoly of cylinder castings for the new engines, and Coalbrookdale in the next few years became his serious rival. Ketley, Horsehay and Coalbrookdale now ordered Boulton and Watt engines for all their works. With increase in height of the furnaces the provision of an adequate blast was one of the urgent problems which the Company were now facing, and although they had made improvements on their wooden bellows and were using a 'blast machine,' they had not found it possible to dispense as yet with the intermediary of a water wheel. Reynolds in writing to Watt about the first engine says, 'As the present state of our works does not admit of the immediate application of it to blow Furnaces we determined to erect an engine at Ketley to work two pumps.' By the time the 1780 engine was being made a method of direct blowing had been worked out, and other larger engines were made for Ketley and Coalbrookdale and the old engines at Madeley Wood furnaces were rebuilt on the Boulton and Watt plan.

Watt had supplied his first rotative engine, with sun and planet gears, to Wilkinson's forge at Bradley in 1782, and within a few months a similar engine was applied to the forge hammers at Ketley, and in May 1783 Reynolds wrote to Watt expressing his satisfaction with the performance of this engine. An order for two more forge hammer engines followed in 1784 and the Company considered the possibility of applying the engine directly to drive the train of rolls in a rolling and slitting mill. Reynolds told Watt that 'the Coalbrookdale Company will wish to have a fire Engine rolling and slitting mill and therefore hope your ideas on that head are brot so near perfection as to induce you to have one erected.' The reply to this was delayed for some time, but in June 1786 Boulton and Watt wrote to Thompson[1] 'We have never erected any Engine for Slitting and Rolling Iron, but our friend Mr Wilkinson has by licence from us annexed a Slitting and Rolling Mill to one of our Engines.'

The Ketley Forge was also anxious to apply the engine to working heavy shears and stamps and their very friendly relations with Boulton and Watt are illustrated by the procedure over this matter. Reynolds wrote to Watt outlining his proposals for shears and stamps and asking for a suitable design of engine for this work. The reply is in a letter of 22 February 1787.

> As the engine you mention seems to be intended for experiment and as we are well inclined to forward you in everything in our power, we consent to your erecting a single Engine with a Cylinder not more than 20 inches dia^{r} not more than 6 feet long in the Strokes, without paying any premium for the same, provided the same is applied only to cold stamping or cutting off the new ends of the barrs drawn at the forges, and also providing the Dale Company make you a present of the Cylinder etc. as you intimate.

In 1789 another Boulton and Watt engine was built at Coalbrookdale for their own use, again from drawings supplied by Watt. In addition to these many engines for their own various works, Coalbrookdale made pumps and engine parts for other Boulton and Watt customers. The patent at first enjoyed by Wilkinson was fast diminishing and expired in 1788. In 1795 Wilkinson quarrelled with his brother, closed the Bersham furnace, and cancelled Boulton and Watt's outstanding orders for cylinders. These orders were transferred to Coalbrookdale, but the boring mill there was not of sufficient capacity to keep pace with the demand, and delays in finishing the cylinders occurred. Boulton and Watt in view of this difficulty decided to erect their own foundry and in 1796 opened the Soho Foundry at Smethwick for engine work. This was not the end of the connection between the two Companies, as Coalbrookdale were

[1] An Agent of the Coalbrookdale Company.

making a Boulton and Watt engine for the North Downs Mine in 1795 and made a second one for the same person in 1798. In connection with these engines, the Agent for the Company wrote in October 1795, 'The cylinder for North Downs upon boring proves a faulty one which will cause a delay of near two weeks in getting another ready.' In 1798 there is a similar occurrence with a 40 inch diameter cylinder 'in going through the last cut with boreing your cylinder, it proves faulty and we have condemned it as unfit for your purpose.' The fault was most probably a blow hole in the casting.

In the 1790's the Coalbrookdale Company were making engines for colliery winding, and at the same time working at a new type of engine which they thought might supersede that of Boulton and Watt. This was the Heslop engine of which more will be said later. A letter from William Reynolds to William Rathbone gives a picture of this trade, and part of it is worth quoting.

To William Rathbone Ketley
Merchant, Liverpool. 1st April. 1790

My Dear Brother,

I should have written to thee long ere this time in consequence of a letter thou wrote to my Father & wch or part of wch was put into my hands respecting some of thy friends have taken a part in a coal mine & who wished to learn something respecting the fire engine for winding coals—I shd I say have replied long since but have waited the success of an experiment depending at the time my Father received thine & of wch I expected we shd have had the result much earlier. It is an entire new engine wch I think peculiarly adapted to the purpose alluded to, as being, I believe less expensive in the erection, better calculated for removal from one place to another and one wch will take less fuel to produce the same effect than any hitherto invented—we are still in process of working a Patent for it & Mr Parry now assures us that a fortnight will compleat the business & as it is yet quite secret & if as good a thing as I believe it, will supersede Boulton & Watts I would not wish till we are quite secure that it shd meet the public ear—at the same time I do not feel easy that thou shd be so long without an answer to thine wch I dont doubt Father has informed thee he has transferred to me—if thy friends can wait a while I think they had better if not I may say in respect to the engines we now use they will cost about £240 compleat & erected anywhere within 20 miles of Liverpool & will wind 60 Tons of coal p day 100 yards deep or 100 Tons 60 yards—& Boulton & Watt expect to be paid £5 per ann for every horse the engines save—we give about 10/- per week for working them—the expence of the small slack on the pit bank necessary to work them is scarcely an object—and we can give no better proof of our good opinion of them than our already having eight at work & proceeding with others. . . .

William Reynolds

It is evident from this letter[1] that in addition to the many engines connected with furnaces and forges, the Coalbrookdale and Ketley Companies had found a beneficial application of the smaller Boulton and Watt engine to the problems of winding at their numerous collieries, and were also making them, under licence, for sale.

During the twenty years of co-operation with Boulton and Watt, the Coalbrookdale works acted in many ways as a stimulant to the development of the steam engine for new uses. Reynolds wrote frequently to Watt, asking for an engine suitable to some new use—for blast engines, for driving rolls or shears—for a portable engine capable of being moved from one place to another, and so on, and when Watt supplied drawings, the construction and testing, modification and proving, were carried out in the Dale works. As in all the previous history of the Company, this new line of work was never allowed to become an obsession to the exclusion of other work. The normal work of the foundry, pot and hollow ware castings, continued, bridge and structural members were being made in cast iron, and other types of pump and engine work were done.

In 1780 Matthew Boulton had visited the Dale to consult about engines for Cornwall, and there were discussions with both partners, Boulton and Watt, on the rating of the various engines. They were offering a pumping engine for the Ketley Furnace Pool, of 66 inches diameter cylinder and a 9 foot stroke, to work two pumps of 26 inches diameter. These were to raise 516,000 cubic feet of water against 93 feet of head, with a consumption of coal guaranteed not to exceed 148 cwt., the mean effective pressure on the piston to be 9·7 lb. per square inch. This is equal to a duty of 180,782 foot-lb. per lb. of local coal burned, and Watt felt that an improvement could be obtained above that guaranteed figure. The Newcomen type of engine actually at work took 388·8 cwt. of coal to raise the same quantity of water, and the first proposal for payment for the use of the Boulton and Watt engine was a premium of one-third of the cost of the coal saved. Reckoned on the strokes of the engine this was approximately

[1] In the *Rathbone MSS.*, miscellaneous letters.

12 tons of small coal for each 10,000 strokes which, at 2/6 per ton, would be 30/–; therefore the suggested premium was 10/– per 10,000 strokes as recorded on a mechanical counter to be attached to the engine.

The Coalbrookdale foundry had gradually made their own modifications and improvements on the Newcomen engine, and in particular the enlargement of the cylinder bottom and the addition of a 'hot well' had improved the working. W. G. Norris[1] says that experiments were being made on the expansive use of steam, and that it was partly these experiments which led Jonathan Hornblower to take his patent of 1781. The father, Jonathan Hornblower, had been a good customer of Coalbrookdale and he and his son were regular visitors there to discuss problems of engines for Cornwall, and some of these experiments may have been made on their behalf. Jonathan Hornblower junior introduced a second cylinder to the Newcomen beam engine, using steam at a higher pressure in this, then passing it on to the ordinary low pressure cylinder, thus 'compounding' the engine, or using a 'two-stage expansion' of the steam. Because of the low steam pressures then available, the engine was not a great success but it was the pioneer of the later normal development of the expansive steam engine.

About the time that Hornblower's engine was being discussed and contested by Watt as an infringement in part on his patent, a local man, Adam Heslop, was being trained at Ketley. Heslop followed rather similar lines to Hornblower, in placing two cylinders on a beam engine of Newcomen type, but in his case the cylinders were differentiated as hot and cold. In 1790 he took out a patent for 'An Engine for lessening the consumption of steam and fuel in fire or steam engines, and gaining considerable effect in time and force,'[2] and several of his engines were made and applied at the Company's works and mines. This engine had two cylinders, one the operating, or hot cylinder and the other the cold or condensing one, usually on the opposite end of the beam to the hot cylinder. Steam was admitted to the hot cylinder at a few pounds above atmospheric pressure for the outward stroke, and on the return the steam passed by a cooled eduction pipe to the cold cylinder where a water jet condensed it. In this compound engine the hot cylinder was working as a single acting steam powered cylinder while the cold end was in effect an

[1] *Proc. Inst. Mech. Eng.*, 1903, pp. 673–80.
[2] *Patent Specifications*, No. 1760, July 1790.

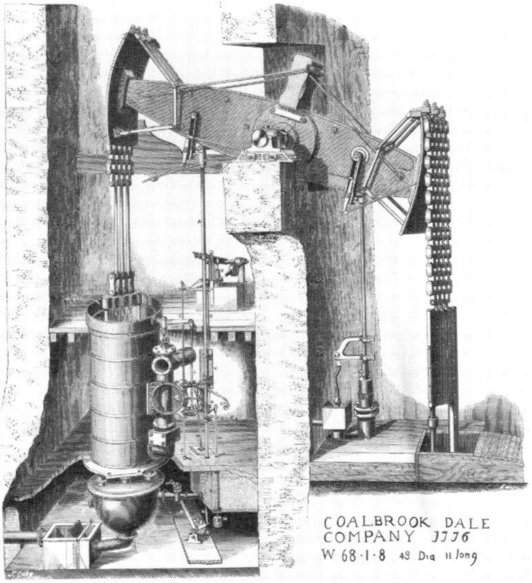

PLATE XIII *This engraving was done in a deliberately eighteenth century style to reflect the age of the original Coalbrookdale Newcomen-type steam engine it depicts. However, by the time it was engraved in 1879, the engine had acquired many later features such as cast-iron beam and separate condenser.*

PLATE XIV *A Heslop steam engine at a pit in Madeley Wood, photographed in 1879. Three others were still working in the area at this time, the last surviving until 1890. Fortunately an engine of this type is preserved at the Science Museum, London.*

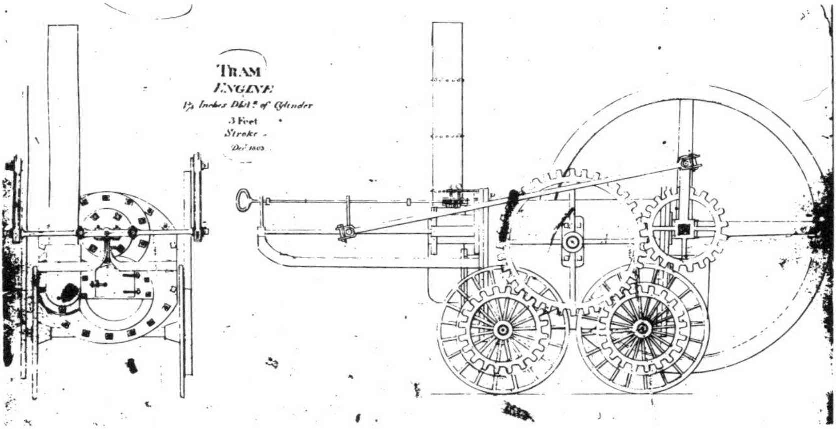

PLATE XV *The World's first steam locomotive designed by Richard Trevithick and built at Coalbrookdale in 1802 with support from William Reynolds. For many years this drawing was believed to depict the Penydarren locomotive, but closer examination showed that the gauge matched some of the larger plateway used in the Gorge at this time, which was nevertheless much smaller than those used in Wales.*

PLATE XVI *This Watt engine drained the Madeley Wood Company pit at the Lloyds, between Ironbridge and Coalport, until 1912. The building originally housed a Newcomen-type steam engine for the pit that was sunk in the late eighteenth century. A similar building housed the 'Resolution' engine in Coalbrookdale* (see PLATE XI).

additional 'atmospheric' engine. Numbers of these engines were employed around the Coalbrookdale works and in 1791 one was made and sent to Lord Lonsdale's colliery near Workington for winding and pumping.

Heslop left Coalbrookdale soon after obtaining his patent and set up a foundry on his own near Whitehaven, Cumberland, from which he supplied at least fourteen of his engines to that coalfield. The Coalbrookdale Company found the engine to be cheaper and more compact than the Boulton and Watt type. Some of them were in use for a long period, and Randall tells us that

> When Mr. Reynolds removed from Ketley to Madeley Wood, he also removed from the former place to the latter, some very primitive steam engines, from the fact that they were constructed by a man named Adam Hyslop, and differed from the ordinary condensing engines of Boulton and Watt in having a cylinder at each end of the beam: one a steam cylinder and condensing box; the other a condensing cylinder only, into which the steam having done duty in the steam cylinder is conveyed. They were invented prior to Boulton and Watt's final improvements. Three of these singular looking engines are still used in the field, and work most economically with five pounds of steam to the square inch.[1]

In 1878 an engine of this type was presented to the Patent Museum, and is now to be seen in its successor the Science Museum, London. Mr. W. R. Anstice of Madeley Wood said that at that date they still had three Heslop engines at work and formerly they had eight. One worked on a coal pit until 1890. The engine which was presented to the Patent Museum had worked at Kell's Pit, Whitehaven, and had been erected about 1795.[2]

About the time that the Company were making the Heslop engine, they had close contact with another remarkable engineer, James Sadler of Oxford. Sadler is better known as 'the first English Aeronaut.'[3] In February 1784 Sadler had made and launched, before great crowds at Oxford, a balloon about ten feet diameter inflated with hydrogen. In October 1784 he made an ascent in a much larger balloon, this time lifted by hot air. In 1785 his main

[1] Randall, J., *History of Madeley*, 1880, p. 99.

[2] This engine has been figured and described by Fletcher, H. A., *Proc. Inst. Mech. Eng.*, 1879, p. 85, and in the Catalogue of the Collections in the Science Museum. *Stationary Engines*, 1925, p. 41.

[3] Hodgson, J. E., *History of Aeronautics in Great Britain*, 1924, Chap. vi and also 'James Sadler of Oxford' *Trans. Newcomen Soc.*, VIII, 1927–28, pp. 66–82.

interests were deflected to chemistry and invention and in 1796 he was appointed as chemist to the Board of Naval Works. It was during this appointment between 1797 to 1799 that he superintended the erection of the first steam engine in Portsmouth Dockyard, which was actually the first in any Naval establishment.

There is a reference in a letter from Watt to Boulton in September 1786 which mentions Symington and Sadler throwing away their time and money hunting shadows, but we know nothing of the actual work which Sadler was doing to call for this comment from Watt. The first detailed information we have of Sadler as an engineer comes from Coalbrookdale where drawings of some of Sadler's engines are preserved in William Reynolds' sketch book.[1] This is one of the many volumes referred to by Randall, and it was compiled by William Reynolds, by pasting into a brown paper folio book, drawings in pencil, pen-and-ink, or in colour, by himself and by his friend S. Venables, of engines and arrangements at the various Coalbrookdale works, or of inventions of interest to him, such as methods of dealing with excavated material in making canals, and so on. The sketches numbered 5 to 9, as well as some later ones, are of Sadler's engines; No. 5 is titled 'Small engine as it worked on the hill at the Dale made by Jas. Sadler 1792.' The next sketch is 'S. Venable's drawing of Sadler's engine as it stood when T. Griffiths was puttg. it up at the bank, September 1793.' (Facing p. 176.) The engine was rotative and was arranged and used for winding from a pit.

It can best be described as a tandem single-acting compound engine. Steam above atmospheric pressure is admitted to a small high pressure cylinder, whose open end is seated in a tub of water, and presses down the piston till the piston of the low-pressure cylinder on the same rod, strikes a valve in the diaphragm between them. The steam enters the l.p. cylinder and by its greater area forces up the pistons till a valve in the l.p. piston strikes the cover and the steam exhausts to the condenser. The valve gear is sketchily indicated. The diameters of the cylinders are in the ratio 1 : 2. It will be noted that work is done on both strokes so that the turning moment is uniform.[2]

The next sketch, No. 7, shows an improvement in the valves and is said to be 'sent by Dr. Beddoes, May 1793.' There is another sketch,

[1] Now in the Science Museum Library, a folio book of drawings which have been listed by Dickinson, H. W., in *Trans. Newcomen Soc.*, II, 1922, pp. 133–40. All the other volumes are lost.

[2] Hodgson, J. E., *Trans. Newcomen Soc.*, VIII. 1927–8, p. 74.

No. 8, 'Drawings of an engine by Jas. Sadler before he went to London with Dr. Beddoes to which he wants to make additions not being complete.' Another sketch of 1794 labels it as 'never completed.' Dr. Thomas Beddoes was a famous physician in Bristol and had been reader in chemistry in the University of Oxford between 1788 and 1792 where Sadler probably knew him. One note describes the engine as 'Sadler's Idea of Engine when he came from Bristol 1792,' and there seems little doubt that his engine was first built and put to work in the Coalbrookdale works, from designs which he had worked upon in Bristol. His patent of 1791 was for an engine which would be more correctly described as a reaction turbine, which is not mentioned again and does not seem ever to have been built.

In 1796 the Dale were still using Sadler's engines and no doubt they found their steady turning effort an advantage for winding, over the less steady effort of the Boulton and Watt type. There is a drawing 'Wm. Reynold's idea of the application of Sadler's engine to a rotative motion, lower cylinder communicating with the boiler; this method is applicable to rowing boats with circular oars. S. Venables, Feb. 1796.' It is possible that the 'pair of partially rotatory brass cylinders which Mr. Reynolds intended as models for a boat on the Severn,' which Randall mentioned as being in the works in 1860 among material made and left by Reynolds, were a pair made according to the idea of this drawing.

After proving his engine at Coalbrookdale, Sadler, like many others before and since his time, left the works and, after setting up some of his engines in London, proceeded to his appointment at Portsmouth Dockyard and the building of his engine there. At the date of Sadler's engines, Watt's patent for a separate condenser was still in force, but a direct infringement was avoided by Sadler by retaining a jet at the bottom of his cylinder and by treating the air pump as a separate cylinder also with a jet. Hodgson says 'it may perhaps be said of Sadler that he took a big step in the direction of making the steam engine direct-acting and self-contained.'

The interest taken by Coalbrookdale in the making of this and other engines which were in some respects rivals to the Boulton and Watt type engine, seemed to make no difference to the terms of friendship which existed between the members of the Coalbrookdale Company and Boulton and Watt. In fact William Reynolds seems to have had a genius for making friendly relations with many men of science and invention and for making Coalbrookdale a contact between such eminent men as James Watt, Dr. Priestley, James Sadler, Adam Heslop, Richard Trevithick, David Giddy, Dr. Black and others.

The high quality of the Coalbrookdale engine work, and the willingness of the Company to carry out experiments attracted the attention of Richard Trevithick junior, at the time when he was making his experiments with high pressure steam and with the steam locomotive. Trevithick senior had had contact with the Company through many engines and pumps which they had supplied to Cornwall. Hornblower in 1791 had erected one of his engines at Tincroft Mine and young Trevithick was employed to report on the performance of this engine. The Hornblower family as long established friends of Coalbrookdale had no doubt spoken about them to young Trevithick, who would thus find it natural when he came to the making of an experimental engine, to turn to the foundry whose work he already knew, both by repute and by actual experience. In 1798 Trevithick erected a water pressure engine at Roskear, on the Prince William Henry Mine and followed this with other similar engines. At the same time he was thinking in terms of a high pressure engine and was experimenting with a model at Redruth.

The Coalbrookdale Company had given a good deal of attention to the improvement of boilers, and as early as 1750 they were forging boiler plates of wrought iron under a 'plating, *i.e.* a helve hammer,' though only of small sizes up to about 30 lb. weight. Narrow plates were built up into spherical boilers and it was not until about 1790 that the Horsehay forge began to roll plates and to make them of larger sizes. These rolled plates were normally about 4 feet long, 8 inches wide, and ½ an inch thick. From them a boiler could be built with less joints and fewer rivets, and these would stand a higher pressure than was previously in use. At the beginning of the new century the Coalbrookdale Company were building high pressure boilers for Trevithick and in 1802 they carried out some of his decisive tests on both boiler and engine.

Davies Giddy (1767–1839) later President of the Royal Society, was Trevithick's friend and gave him the assurance that if he sacrificed the condenser from his engine and allowed the exhaust steam to escape to the atmosphere, he would lose the effective power of one atmosphere only, and would have, to counterbalance part of this loss, the saving of an air-pump with its friction and its cost, and also the saving of condenser water. Trevithick was now thinking in terms of pressures around 50 lb. per square inch or more, and it was therefore necessary for him to find a new design of boiler.

Trevithick's high pressure engine marked a great revolution in engine design. Instead of the ponderous ten or eleven foot long cylinder five or six tons in weight of the older engines, with the massive beam and all other moving parts in proportion and the many months taken to build such a huge engine into its housings, Trevithick obtained the same power with a small cylinder acting directly on to a crank shaft. This dispensed with the ponderous beam and air pump and the tremendous inertia which was to be overcome in restarting from rest at the end of each stroke. With its moving masses so much smaller, the high pressure engine could run at high speeds and could utilize a fly-wheel to carry the piston over the dead centres.

At the same time that he was developing the high pressure engine Trevithick saw the possibility of its application to the propulsion of a road carriage and on Christmas Eve, 1801, the famous road trial was carried out at Camborne. This established steam locomotion on highways as a practical proposition and led to the joint patent with Andrew Vivian for the 'improvement in the construction of the steam engine and application thereof for driving carriages.'[1]

Trevithick had been at Coalbrookdale in 1796 and was there again in January 1802, presumably arranging for the making of one of his high pressure engines for use as a locomotive. His biographer says[2] 'In August 1802 the Coalbrookdale Company were building for him a railway carriage or locomotive, though they feared to attempt its construction.' He would have found a very sympathetic helper in William Reynolds whatever the rest of the engineers may have thought as Reynolds was already interested in the idea of possible steam locomotion and according to Randall[3] he had already made some experiments in this idea.

We have a number of large foolscap MS. volumes of experiments and extracts neatly copied, with pen and ink drawing of machines, parts of machines, etc., showing that while Smeaton and Watt were engaged in perfecting the construction of the steam engine, Mr. Reynolds was endeavouring to apply it to purposes similar to those to which it is

[1] Patent No. 2599, March 1802.

[2] Trevithick, F., *Life of Richard Trevithick, with an account of his inventions*, 1872, vol. 1, p. 152.

[3] Randall, J., *History of Madeley*, 1880, pp. 90–1.

now applied as a locomotive. Thus he constructed a locomotive with waggon attached, the cylinder and boiler of which are still preserved. An accident, we believe a fatal one, which happened to one of the men on starting the engine led Mr. Reynolds to abandon the machine; but he by no means lost faith in the invention.

It was prior to 1787, when Symmington exhibited his model steam carriage in Edinburgh, and to the time when Darwin (1793) wrote—

> Soon shall thy arm unconquered steam afar
> Drag the slow barge or drive the rapid car.

Mr. Reynolds indeed contemplated, it is believed, a subterranean tram road from the banks of the Severn right up into the heart of the iron districts of Ketley and Donnington Wood, upon which his engine was to travel, but the prejudice against the scheme was too great. . . .

A little later Randall, while relating some reminiscences of W. A. Reynolds, nephew of William Reynolds of Coalbrookdale, says,[1]

In 1802 the Coalbrookdale Company were building for him [Trevithick] a railway locomotive the engine of which was tried first in pumping water and its performance astonished everyone. In a letter of his to Mr. D. Giddy dated from Coalbrookdale 22nd August, 1802, he says: 'The Dale Company have begun a carriage at their own cost for the railroads and are forcing it with all expedition.' There was a beautifully executed wooden model of this locomotive in my Uncle William Reynolds's possession, which was given me by his widow, the late Mrs. Reynolds of Severn House after his death. I was then a boy fond of making model engines of my own, and I broke up this priceless relic to convert it to my own base purpose, an act which I now repent as if it had been a sin.

The Coalbrookdale engine is, I believe, the first locomotive engine on record intended to be used on a railroad. The boiler of it is now to be seen in use as a water tank at the Lloyd's Crawstone Pit and the fire tubes and a few other portions of it are now in the yard at the Madeley Wood Works. I never knew how it came to be disused and broken up.

There are also a pair of partially rotatory brass cylinders in existence which Mr. Reynolds intended as models for a boat on the Severn.

There is no reason to doubt these references as Randall had access to all of William Reynolds's papers, since lost, and it would therefore be easy for Trevithick to explain to Reynolds what he wanted in the way of his experiment. A boiler and engine were built to his design and were ready for trial in August. We have his

[1] Randall, J., *History of Madeley*, 1880, p. 179.

own account of the performance of the engine, in the letter written to Giddy, and dated from Coalbrookdale, 22 August 1802.

Shod have writ you some time sence, but not haveing made sufficient tryal of the engine, have referd it untill its in my power to give you an agreeable informeation of its progress. The boiler is 4 ft. Diam; the Cylinder 7 in. Diam, 3 feet Stroake. The water piston 10 In, drawing and forceing 35½ feet perpendr, equal beam. I first set it off with abt 50 lb. on the Inch pressure against the steam-valve, without its Load, before the pumps was ready, and have sence workd it several times with pumps, for the inspection of the engineers abt this nibeourhood. The steam will get up to 80 lb. or 90 lb. to the inch in abt one hour after the fire is lighted; the engine will sett off when the steam is abt 60 lb. to the inch, abt 30 Stroakes pr mt, with its load. Their being a great deal of friction on such small engine and the steam continues to rise the whole of the time its worked; it go at from 60 lb. to 145 lb. to the inch in fair working, 40 Stroakes pr mt: It became so unmanageable as the steam encreased, that I was obliged to stop and put a cock in the mouth of the Dischardging pipe, and leve only a hole open of ¼ by 3/8 of an inch for the steam to make its escape into the water. The engine will work 40 Stroakes pr mt with a pressure of 145 lb. to the inch against the steam valve, and keep it constaintly sweming with 300 wt. of Coals every four hours. I have now a valve making to put on the top of the pumps, to load with a Steelyard, to try how many pounds to the inch it will do real duty when the steam on the clack is 145 lbs. to the Inch. I cannot put on any moore pumps as they are very lofty already. The packing stands the heat and pressure without the least ingurey whatever; enclosd you have some for inspection that have stood the whole of its working. As there is a cock in the dischardgeing pipe which stops the steam after it have don its office on the piston, I judge that it is almost as fair a tryal as if the pump load was equal to the power of the engine. Had the steam been wire drawn between the boyler and Cylinder it wd not have been a fair tryal but, being stoped after it is past the engine, it tells much in its favour for haveing a greater load than it has now on. The boyler will hold its steam a considerable time after the fire is taken out. We worked the engine three quarters of an hour after all the fire was taken out from under the boyler, and it is also slow in getting up, for aftr the steam is atmosphere strong it will take half an hour to get it to 80 or 90 lb. to the inch. Its very accomadatay to the fire man for, fire or not, its not soon felt. The engineers abt this place all said that it was impossible for such a small Cylinder to lift water to the top of the pumps, and degraded the principals, tho at the same time they spoake highly in favour of the simple and well contrived engine. The say it is a supernatureal engine for it will work without either fire or water, and swears that all the engineers hitherto are the biggest fools in creation. They are constantily calling on mee, for the all say the wod never believe it uless the see it, and no persone here will take his nebiours word even if he swears to it, for the all say its an imposiabelity, and never will believe it unless the seeit. After the say the water at the pump head, the said that was posiable, but the boyler wold not mantain it with steam at that pressure five minutes; but after a short time the setts off with a solid countenance and a silent tongue. The boyler is 1½ In thick and I think their will be no danger in putting it still higher. Shall not stop lodding the engine untill the paking burn or blow under its pressure—will write you again as soon as I have made farther tryal. If I had 50 engines I cud sell them in a Day at any price I wod ask for them, for the are so highly plesd with it that no other engine will pass with them.

a postscript adds

The Dale Co have begun a carriage at their own cost for the realroads and is forceing it with all expedition.

This postscript tallies well with the account which Randall gives of the interest taken by William Reynolds in the possibility of a practicable steam locomotive.

In the Coalbrookdale *Settling Journal, 1798–1808,* folio 331, there is an account headed 'Richd. Trevithick & Co. Dr to Warehouse,' which is for materials and time expended in the experiments made in the year 1802. As this account is of considerable interest and importance it is transcribed in full as Appendix 5 to which reference can be made. A sub-title of the account is

For Castings for Trying Experiments—now at the Dale.

The heaviest single item is for a boiler and its casing, £65.10.11¾. The engine used in the trial so vividly described by Trevithick in his letter to Giddy may be represented by an item '1 Cylinder top & pipe 11c.1q.13lb.,' but there is no mention here of the size of the cylinder. Later the account includes a charge for

1 Cylinder 5in. with Skews cut at ends for the floating Engine } 10c.3.20 @ 40/–

and 'Expence in Pumping the Engine 18.10mo.1802.' From Trevithick's letter written on the 22nd of 10th month (August) we know that the engine which was tested had a seven inches diameter cylinder so could not have been the one first quoted. The account thus relates to two separate engines.

In 1884 a visitor to the Coalbrookdale Works, describing much of the machinery and the technical processes,[1] says after speaking of some of the older plant, 'An old cylinder is also cherished as a valuable relic. It originally belonged to Trevithick's first locomotive. It is 4 inches in diameter, with a stroke of about 3 feet, and was taken out by the Company, who replaced it with one of 8 inches diameter.'

Trevithick was again at Coalbrookdale in September 1804 and was busy with the application of his engine to propel a boat, and he had made satisfactory trials already of his engine as applied to ordinary uses, as he writes to Giddy, 23 September, that there are now six of his engines nearly finished at Coalbrookdale and seven begun at a foundry at Bridgnorth.

In 1804 Napoleon collected at Boulogne harbour a flotilla of transport boats with troops standing by, ready to invade the south coast of England, and desperate attempts were made to destroy this fleet in the harbour where it waited. The general idea was to send fire ships into its midst and it was suggested in some quarters that such fire ships might be towed into the harbour by a steam driven boat. Trevithick writing to Giddy on 5 October 1804, says about all this

> Several Gentlemen of late have calld on mee to know if these engins wod not be good things to go into Bolong to destroy the flotels &c., in the harbour by fire ships. The told mee that a Gentleman from Bath was then in London trying experiments under Government for that purpose, but wither by engines or by what plan I do not know.
>
> There was a Gentleman sent to speak to mee yesterday on the business, from a marquiss; the name I amnot at liberty to give you. I put him off without any encoragement, because I wod much rather trust to your opponion and bringing this business forward than to any other man. I have two 10 in. Cylinders here compleatly ready; they are exceeding well executed, and I will not part with them untill I hear farther from you in the business. If you think you could get Government to get it putt in to execution, I wod readily go with the engines and risque the enterprize. I shold think its posiable to make these engines to drive ships into the middle of the fleet, and then for them to blow up. . . .

He was sent later to the Admiralty Office to discuss the proposition but on 10 January 1805, again wrote to Giddy saying that he was tired of waiting and was much wanted at Coalbrookdale; 'when

[1] *The Coalbrookdale Iron-works and what they produce*, 1884. Reprinted by the Coalbrookdale Company as a pamphlet, from the *Machinery Market*, November, 1884.

they send for mee again, the shall say what the want before I will again obey the call.' At Coalbrookdale he carried out another experiment, either on the Severn or on the Shropshire Canal, to convince himself that his ideas about steam propelled barges were practicable.

There was an engíne, a 10 In Cylinder put in a Barge to be carried to Macclesfield for a cotton factorey, and I tryd it to work on board. We had a fly wheel on each side [of the] barge and a crank shaft that was thrown across the deck. The wheels had flat boards of 2 ft 2 In long and 14 In deep, six on each wheel, like an under-shot water-wheel. The extremmity of the wheels went abt 15 Miles pr hour. The barge was between 60 & 70 Tons burthon. It wod go in still water abt 7 miles p. Hour. This was don onely to try what effect it wod have. As we had all the apperatus of old matls at the Dale, it cost little or nothing to put it together. I think it wod have drove much faster with sweeps.

We know little more about this experimental steam barge except that the account includes a 'Crank used in working the Barge afterward broken up.' Dickinson[1] suggests that a drawing by John Urpeth Rastrick, 'Design for a Steamboat,' embodies Trevithick's ideas, as Rastrick said later in evidence about his work, that he had never had anything to do with steam boats. Rastrick was apprenticed with his father, John Rastrick of Morpeth, then went to Ketley to improve his knowledge of engineering and of the use of cast iron in structural and engineering work. He was at Ketley about 1802 and remained there for some years, so would be familiar with Trevithick and his experiments. From Ketley he joined Trevithick, probably as the resident engineer under him, on the Thames Driftway in 1808,[2] then later he became a partner with John Hazeldine in the foundry at Bridgnorth, in the firm of Hazeldine, Rastrick & Co. where Trevithick's famous London locomotive was built. It seems certain that the close friendship and co-operation that continued for many years between Trevithick and Rastrick, began in the workshops at Coalbrookdale and Ketley. It is probable that Rastrick's experience there encouraged him at a later date to design and build the cast iron bridge still in existence over the Wye at Chepstow.

From the various accounts quoted above we get references to a rather mixed group of Trevithick engines, which it would be very

[1] Dickinson, H. W., *Richard Trevithick. The engineer and the man*, 1934, pp. 79–80.

[2] Dickinson, H. W. and Lee, A., 'The Rastricks—Civil Engineers,' *Trans. Newcomen Soc.*, IV, 1923–4, pp. 50–1.

interesting to identify completely if this were possible. They are as follows—

1. The locomotive being built by Coalbrookdale Company for their own railways. (Trevithick's letter, 1802.)
2. The 7 inch cylinder, 3 foot stroke engine which was tested in August 1802.
3. The 5 inch diameter cylinder with 'skews.' (*Settling Journal* account.)
4. The 4 inch diameter cylinder, 3 foot stroke, seen in 1884, and said to be from the first locomotive.
5. The engine for the barge trials, made for Macclesfield cotton mill, 10 inch diameter cylinder. 1804.

Of these engines we can perhaps dispense first with the 10 inch cylinder used on the barge trials. Trevithick tells us that he had this ready for carriage to Macclesfield, to be used in a cotton factory there, and that having all the apparatus at the Dale, he tried it in a barge; it was to this that the crank belonged.

The locomotive which the Company were building for themselves, No. 4 in the above list, might be identified with the cylinder seen in 1884, or it might be represented in the drawing which has formerly been accepted as being of the Penydarran locomotive. This drawing has been the subject of many discussions and an opinion was expressed by Mr. E. A. Forward in 1932,[1] that 'he was more doubtful than ever as to whether or not it represented the original Penydarran engine.' Since the discovery of the *Settling Journal* accounts, Mr. Forward and Dr. Dickinson have been strengthened in their conviction that the drawing is actually that of the first Coalbrookdale locomotive. The drawing is to a scale of one inch to one foot and this agrees with the note that the cylinder was 4¾ inches diameter and of 3 foot stroke, but would make the gauge of the rails about three feet. The few lengths of old railway still remaining in the Dale have a gauge about 28 inches, but Randall, speaking of the early railways in the works says,[2]

> The waggons, wheels and axletrees continued to be used long after cast iron rails had been substituted for the wooden rails, and until a narrower gauge of road and a different pattern of rail were introduced.

[1] In the discussion of a paper by Mason, W. W., 'Trevithick's first rail locomotive.' *Trans. Newcomen Soc.*, XII, 1931–2, p. 94.

[2] Randall, J., in *Victoria County History*, Shropshire.

The accounts for the railways and their extensions are extant until the year 1808, and up to that date no change had been made in any dimensions of waggons, rails or sleepers, so the reduction of gauge must date after that, and at the earliest to many years after the construction of the locomotive. It was most probably part of the large scale reorganizations which were started by Alfred and Abraham Darby about 1830. Dr. Dickinson says[1] for himself and E. A. Forward,

> We feel satisfied that this drawing represents the Coalbrookdale Railway locomotive, and not the Penydarran one. We are satisfied that the crank shaft in question was for the Macclesfield barge; also that the engine that was tested for pumping was a distinct one not yet identifiable.

This last engine of course is No. 2 on our list, the one with a 7 inch cylinder.

If this argument is accepted then the Science Museum drawing becomes of direct interest to us as being a representation of the first Coalbrookdale locomotive made by the Company, and also Trevithick's first railway locomotive. This confirms the local tradition that the Company actually built the first steam locomotive in the world, to run on rails.

The remaining engine with a 5 inch cylinder and described as for a 'floating' engine, may have been for an earlier experiment with a steam propelled barge, as Trevithick says about his experiment with the Macclesfield engine, in 1804, that he had all the apparatus of old materials at the Dale, with which to fit out the barge. For the present however, this can remain only as a speculation, until further evidence becomes available to decide the question one way or the other.

The Trevithick engine was being made at Horsehay and Coalbrookdale, as well as the Sadler and Heslop engines. John Burlingham of Worcester was charged in 1805 for 'a steam engine on Trevithick's plan (18 ins. cylind^{r}) complete £688.6.8.' 'Wm. Heath for a horizontal Engine on Trevithick's plan £260.0.0.' is one of other similar entries. These contrast with another type of entry, 'T. Rowlands & Co. 1805.5mo. a Steam Engine with 27 ins. Cylinder on the Common plan; a cast Beam and wrot Boiler 9ft. 3ins. Diam. £300. Outside work over the Pit £35.10.2½.'

[1] In a letter to the author, May 1951. E. A. Forward, since this was written, has set out his views in a paper 'Links in the History of the Locomotive: Trevithick's first railway Locomotive, Coalbrookdale 1802–3.' *Engineer*, Feb. 22, 1952, pp. 266–268.

From the same *Settling Journal* we get a glimpse of their own organization of engines on their own collieries. The engines used for winding were mostly around 20 inches diameter cylinder and of Heslop's or Sadler's improved types. They were made at Coalbrookdale and were built onto a framework which rendered them more or less portable. As one pit became exhausted or was abandoned

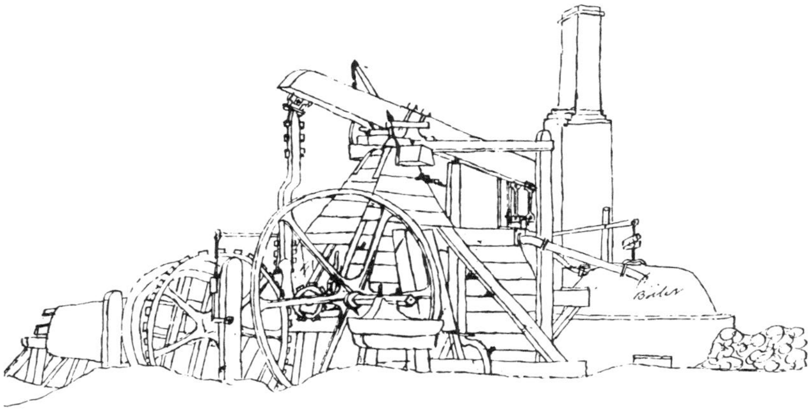

Arrangement of colliery winding engine and boiler, Lawley and Dawley Pits. Drawing No. 62, Reynolds' Sketchbook.

for some reason, the engine was dismantled and moved to a new site. This is particularly noticeable when the Lawley Collieries were being reorganized and when several engines were exchanged between them and the group known as the New Work Collieries. Each engine was valued into the general Warehouse, then reissued, sometimes after overhaul and repair, to the new colliery.

Lawley Co. for Sundries removed from New Work.			
For Winding Engine No. 2. Cylinder 20 Ins. with one			
Barrell in midling repair, boiler good			£210. 0. 0
To do. do. No. 11. 22 ins Cylinder in good repair			260. 0. 0
No. 4. Pit Frame with taking			9. 9. 0
6 Plain Pipes 6ft long 4 ins. diam	9c.3q.0	@ 10/-	
5 Feed pipes $2\frac{1}{2}$ft x 2 ins.	2. 2.26		6. 4.10

This is typical of several accounts and we hear of the movement of Engines 2, 7, 11, and 12. The engines Nos. 2 and 7 were removed from the New Work to Lawley in 1801 and returned to the New Work in 1807, when both are noted as having the boiler in bad repair. Some winding engines were made for sale, *e.g.* '1803. Rowley & Emery, Dr. to Warehouse for a Winding Engine complete 26 ins. Cylinder £440.0.0. Extras £36.5.11.'

This period just described is typical of the position long held by the Coalbrookdale Company, including Horsehay and Ketley, as a concern of the highest repute in the engineering world, not only as suppliers of castings and foundry work, but as a place where experimental work was welcomed and where experiments could be carried out. The Company was visited regularly by such engineers as Brindley, Watt, Hornblower, and Trevithick, and had among its trainees Heslop and Rastrick. Never content to settle down to repeat one standard engine, each engine it produced for its own use or for a customer was an experimental advance either in design or application, so that from the early atmospheric engines of Newcomen to the establishment of the high pressure engine, railway locomotives and steam ships, every stage of development has called upon the skill and co-operation of Coalbrookdale.

In addition to the material products of the foundries and forges, Coalbrookdale contributed quite a number of well trained workmen and engineers to the industry at large. When Dr. Roebuck was contemplating the founding of the Carron Company in 1759, he enquired as to the working arrangements of the Coalbrookdale furnaces and foundries, and his new works in Scotland were modelled on those of the Dale. Further he obtained many of his workmen from the Dale area. He took with him Robert Hawkins, the son of Richard Hawkins of Bersham Furnace and nephew of Abraham Darby, who had been trained at Bersham and the Dale, and was their outside superintendent at the time. He also took several moulders and others to take charge of the moulding and casting floors. Among these was a young man, Peter Price, who became a foreman in the boring shops there. Later when Watt was thinking of setting up works in Cornwall, he wrote to Boulton: 'There is one Peter Price a Quaker in this Country that was once foreman in the Boreing Mill at Carron and afterwards agent for the Dale or Ketley Company at London, a man of character and a great deal of knowledge in the foundry way.' Price was associated with Robert Were Fox and other Falmouth Friends in starting the Perran Foundry in 1792 and later he was one of the partners of the Neath Abbey Company, Glamorgan, who became great engineers, making engines and large castings, chiefly for the Cornish mines.

Chapter Ten

RAILWAYS AND CANALS, 1745–1800

In an organization such as that of the Darby works, transport is an ever-present problem of major significance. In a modern works branch lines from some main line railway penetrate the site and a complex of lines and sidings links up all the buildings, yards and stores, and where necessary runs through them. Locomotives, overhead cranes, conveyer belts and a multiplicity of special machines ensure the mechanical handling of all material from the raw ore and fuel to the finished product. In the early part of the eighteenth century, however, few of these mechanical aids were available, and the muscular power of men and animals had to be organized to deal with the problem. By 1750 the firm was producing about a hundred tons of iron each week, and this meant handling six or seven times that weight of coal and ore, lifting it from the mines, conveying it a few miles to the furnaces and, after many handlings, getting the finished castings from the works to the wharves and onto barges on the river. The problem was really a double one. The everyday supply of ore and fuel and its movement to the works called for a simple and cheap method capable of indefinite extension and expansion. The movement of finished goods, especially such big castings as engine cylinders of several tons weight,[1] was likely to present problems calling for an *ad hoc* treatment, and not capable of an easy 'once for all' solution.

During the first forty years of the works effort, the movement of ore and fuel had been accomplished almost exclusively by large trains of pack horses, each horse carrying his regular load of not more than 2½ to 3½ cwt. This method of transport was almost universal at the time both for short distance and for long stage traffic, but for any large scale trade it involved very large numbers of ponies or horses, and was slow and costly. In 1766 about 150 packhorses each week carried Manchester cloth to Bridgnorth; the journey took some days and the carriage cost £3.10.0 a ton.

[1] *cf.* Acct. Book. 1.9mo. 1756.

To Abraham Darby Carr. of a Cylinder 107 cwts. 2 qu. olbs.		12. 0.
,,	an Engine Boiler 70 cwts.	10. 0.

As we have seen some of the earlier leases of collieries and ironstone mines included clauses laying down, as a condition of the lease, the regular delivery of coal and ore to the furnaces. Abraham Darby I had introduced his own horses to carry the ironstone, but there were many difficulties, the chief of which was the badness of the roads and tracks. In wet weather the tracks became quagmires and the horses were led along firmer ground to one side or the other, so that in a comparatively short time the way became a broad belt of boggy trenches which concentrated the drainage and made matters rapidly much worse. No wonder the land owners objected to this increasing spoliation of their land, and that way-leaves became more difficult and expensive to obtain. In Hannah Rose's narrative of the Darby family, there is a hint of trouble with 'a remarkable Circumstance of awful memory.'[1] She is speaking of John Darby, father of Abraham I.

John after the death of his wife went to live with his daughter Esther, who was married to Anthony Parker, a sober honest Man, a Farmer. They lived in Dawley and there was a dispute about a road which a neighbour of theirs claimed a right to. He was a Farmer and A Darby had a gang of Horses to carry Ironstone that went that way; and one day the man fell into a passion and said he wished he might never speak again if the Quakers Horses should go thro' his ground: and immediately his speach was taken from him and he never did speak more although he lived several years after.

In the Northumberland and Durham coalfield, the problem of the transport of coal from the pits to the river Tyne had become acute during the sixteenth and seventeenth centuries, and waggon-ways had been introduced between 1632 and 1649,[2] but had not come into very general use until some forty years later. These waggon-ways were at first simple tracks of wooden planks on which small waggons could run, either pushed by boys or drawn by horses. The historian of the coal trade, Galloway, speaks of the Shropshire coalfield with considerable respect and credits it with the use of waggon-ways at an earlier date than their use on Tyneside.

It contests with the north of England the honour of being the first to employ railways at its mines. At what date these were introduced we have no record. Professor Pepper (*Playbook of Metals*, 1861, p. 23) speaks of

[1] *Norris MSS.*, vol. X, pp. 122–31.

[2] Taylor, J., 'Archaeology of the Coal Trade.' *Proc. Archeol. Inst. of Great Britain and Ireland,* vol. I, 1858.

Coalbrookdale, in this county, being celebrated as the place where railways of wood were first used in the years 1620 and 1650, though without adducing any authority in support of the statement. There seems however, to be no reason to doubt the fact, inasmuch as we have independent evidence that this method of conveying coal was in common use in various parts of the coalfield about the end of the seventeenth century. The railways appear also to have been thus early carried into the underground workings; and the same small waggons conveyed the coals direct from the working places of the collieries to the point of shipment on the Severn.[1]

Evidence from Coalbrookdale itself points to the railways there having been imitated from the North country. But there is definite evidence of the existence of railways in Shropshire in 1705, and probably before 1695.

There are references to 'tylting railes' at Broseley in 1606 (*Star Chamber Proc. James I.* 109/8, 310/16); which appear to indicate a waggon-way down to the river.[2]

There is other evidence of the early use of waggon-ways in Shropshire, to be found in the evidence given during the consideration of a complaint by Sir Humphrey Mackworth, when workmen were taken forcibly from his mines at Neath, Glamorgan, and part of his waggon-ways were destroyed.[3]

Witnesses gave evidence that Mackworth had made waggon-ways and had used

a Level and Wind-way commonly called a Foot-rid or Waggon-way after the manner used in Shropshire and New-castle and at great expenses continued the said Waggon-way on Wooden Railes from the face of each Wall of Coal twelve hundred Yards under Ground quite down to the Water-side, about three quarters of a mile from the Mouth of the Coal-pit; the said Coal-works without the conveniency of this Foot-rid and Waggon-way could not be carried on at any profit . . . it requires great Skill as well as Labour to keep the Waggons upon the Rails underground.

The evidence further says that the waggon-way had been in use for upwards of eight years, so that we may assume that similar waggon-ways had been in use in Shropshire before 1697.

In 1711 coal was being mined in Madeley parish from many small adits 'which [coal] by small carriages with four wheels of about

[1] Galloway, R. L., *Annals of Coal Mining*, 1898.

[2] Marshall, C. D. F., *A History of British Railways down to the year 1800*, O.U.P., 1938, p. 6.

[3] Report of the Case of Sir Humphrey Mackworth and the Mine Adventurers with respect to the irregular proceedings of several Justices of the Peace for Glamorgan and their Agents, 1705.

a foot diameter, thrust by men, they convey, not only out of the underground passage, but even to the boats which lye on the Severn ready to receive them.' This description agrees in all details with that of the Foot-rid at Mackworth's works and this may be the source from which the Welsh tram ways were copied. The introduction of waggon-ways at the Coalbrookdale iron works seems however to have been long delayed. Abiah Darby writing about the year 1775, and giving an account of the work of her late husband, Abraham II, says:

> They used to carry their coal upon horse's backs, but he got roads made and laid with Sleepers and rails, as they have them in the North of England. And one waggon with three horses will bring as much as 20 horses used to bring on horse's backs. But this laying the road with wood begot a scarcity and raised the price of it, so that of late years, the laying of the rails of Cast Iron was substituted; which altho expensive, answers well for ware and duration. We have in the different works, near 20 miles of this road, which costs upward of £800 a mile. That of Iron Wheels and axle-trees for these waggons was, I believe, my Husband's invention.[1]

As Abraham Darby only came into the works in 1732 on reaching the age of twenty-one, and assumed part management in 1738, this makes the date of the introduction of railways to the Coalbrookdale works, somewhat later than elsewhere in the area, and not earlier than about 1740.

The earliest account for the construction of a railway occurs in 1748,

28.3mo.1748 Paid John Beddow & Co. Laying the Rails & making

Waggons for the Lake Head foot-rid.	2.15. 8½
pd. Cadman for 35 Days driving Waggon Way	2. 3. 6
pd. Browne for 32 Days 40/– Holmes for 24 Do 26/	3. 6. 0
pd. John Jones for 33½ Days Levelling the Rail Way	1.13. 6
pd. Thos. Rowley for Levelling 18½ Days	18. 6
pd. for Coggs & Rounds	1. 0. 3

This is clearly a small waggon-way and marks the beginning of the Company's use of rail transport, and it was followed by the application for way leaves for a longer railway, in the following year.

It may seem strange that the Company did not embark on the construction of waggon-ways until nearly the middle of the century, when by all the evidences such waggon-ways were in use in the district around them from the very beginning of their venture. The reason for this long delay probably lies in the fact that for some years the leases of some of the coal and ironstone mines serving the

[1] *Darby MSS.* Letter of Abiah Darby, not dated, but about 1775.

Company included clauses by which the operators of the mines were bound to deliver a certain amount of their output to the furnaces, and also that the produce of the furnaces was such that it could be handled easily by pack horses, or was in some cases quite unsuited for such handling and far too heavy to be moved on a waggon-way. The transport of pots and kettles and such small and medium castings from the works to the river presented no problem. The cylinders and engine parts were a special problem and the largest bulk products, coal and ironstone, were mainly carried by other people.

The accounts for the first forty years have regular items for carriage, paid either in large sums to Richard Hartshorne's Company, the lessors of the collieries and to other mining groups, or to several individual carriers. The magnitude of the problem was not made obvious to the Coalbrookdale Company until Darby and Ford took out their own leases of coal and ironstone mines, to be worked for themselves. It is a testimony to the alertness of these people, that within a year or two of entering seriously upon the problem of bulk carriage, they began the construction of railways in a part of the country which, by the steepness of its hills, presented the maximum difficulties of construction and operation.

The Company's Accounts for the period 1754 to 1761 include a great many items entered under the headings 'Railways Dr. to the Dale Company' and 'The New Railway Dr. to Sundry Accounts,' the latter first appearing in 1755 and being the cost of the extensions first to Ketley and then to Horsehay. The accounts are at first mainly for materials, rails charged at a sum per hundred yards, or round timber charged by the ton. The Railway materials were supplied mainly by two companies and typical early accounts will make clear their nature.

21st. 6mo. 1754. Sundry Acc[ts] to Ford, Dukesell & Thorpe.

Railway	for	329	Yards of Rails	at 33/4	5.19. 0
Do	for	37	Sleepers	at 6d each	18. 6
Do	for	102	Sleepers	at 6d each	2.11. 0
Do	for	1162	Yards of Rails	at 33/4	19. 7. 4
Do	for	201	Sleepers	at 6d each	5. 0. 6
Do	for	396	Sleepers	at 6d each	9.18. 0

Railway Dr to Richard Davies & Co

for 32 Tons 38 Feet Round Timber at 35/-	57. 6. 7

1st. 1mo. 1756

Ketley Co. for 39 Tons round Timber at 35/-	68. 5. 0
New Railways for 26Tons 37 Feet Do at 35/-	46.15.11

Randall says, 'The rails were of wood $3\frac{1}{2} \times 4\frac{1}{2}$ inches fixed on sleepers of wood laid transversely. Abraham Darby retained the accustomed size of the waggons and adopted for them a cast iron wheel having an inside flange, and a cast iron axle-tree, onto which the wheel was wedged. The waggons, wheels and axle-trees continued to be used long after cast iron rails had been substituted for the wooden rails, and until a narrower gauge of road and a different pattern of rail were introduced.'[1]

There is an abundance of scattered items which refer to the making and upkeep of the railways or waggon-ways, and regular charges for 'waggoning' are paid to a large number of individual drivers. Some of the waggons cost £12 each complete, when bought from an independent craftsman, but in the same year nine waggons and one carriage were made in the works and were charged at 11/- each for the making, exclusive of materials. The wheels used at this early period seem to have been very big and massive, judged by charges made to the New Railway in 1755.

8 Wheels and 2 Axle-trees 24cw.3q.8lb. @ 10/- p.cw.
4 Waggon Wheels 12cw.2q.21lb. @ 10/- p.cw.
16 Bank Wheels 44cw.2q.20lb. @ 10/- p cw.

This approximate weight of 3 cwt. per wheel is common throughout the accounts.

The introduction of iron rails to replace the wooden ones was due to Richard Reynolds in or about the year 1767, and his grand-daughter says:

> For the conveyance of coal and iron to different parts of the works, and to the river Severn, wooden rails had been in use, which from the great weights carried upon them, were not only soon worn out, but were liable to give way and break occasioning loss of time and interruption to business, and great expense in repairing them. It occurred to him that the inconveniencies would be obviated by the use of cast-iron. He tried it at first with great caution, but found it to answer so well, that very soon all their railways were made with iron. He did not attempt to secure by patent the advantage of this invention, and the use of cast-iron in the construction of railways was afterwards generally adopted.[2]

Smiles is very definite in his statement that 'in 1767, as appears from the books of the Coalbrookdale Works, in Shropshire, five or six tons of

[1] *Victoria County History. Shropshire*, vol. I. p. 461.

[2] Rathbone, H. M., *Letters of Richard Reynolds with a Memoir of his Life*, 1852, p. 27.

rails were cast, as an experiment, on the suggestion of Mr. Reynolds, one of the partners; and they were shortly laid down to form a road.'[1]

The entries in the Coalbrookdale Company's records to which Smiles refers can no longer be checked from the original book as this cannot now be traced, but fortunately a few letters of later date preserved among the *Rathbone MSS.* include the essential details. In 1823 Robert Stevenson wrote to Joseph Reynolds, who was then living at Bristol, the following letter.

Edinburgh 8 August 1823

Sir,

The Highland Society having put a number of Prize Essays on the subject of Railways into my hands for the purpose of examination before sending them to press, I beg that you will permit me to request the favor of you to give me such information as you can conveniently regarding the first application of Cast Iron as an improvement upon the Tram or Wooden Railway.

I think I was some years since told by a person who obligingly conducted me through your works at Coalbrookdale that the cast iron rail was first introduced there.

Now I see in more than one of these Essays in my hands that this is ascribed to the Butterley Iron works through Mr. Outram.

As it may be of importance to establish this at present in the Transactions of the Highland Society being an authority likely to be referred to on a subject which is comparatively new and likely to rise more and more—I shall thank you to say how this matter stands in your estimation as I know some of your connections were at least very early concerned in the formation of cast iron Railways. I am to be away from home for three or four weeks by which time I beg the favour of an answer.

Trusting you will excuse so much trouble
I have the honour to be
Your servant.

Robert Stevenson

On 5 September he writes a further letter—

Edinburgh 5 Sept. 1823

Sir,

On my return from the north coast I had the pleasure of receiving your letter of the 27th ult. regarding the early use of Cast Iron at Coalbrookdale. In so far as my inquiries have gone I have not met with any establishment at which Cast Iron rails were introduced prior to 1767 the date you mention in reference to this subject. . . .

[1] Smiles, S., *Lives of the Engineers*, 1862, Vol. III, p. 7.

The letter of Joseph Reynolds to Robert Stevenson has not yet been traced, but it contained only the information which was supplied to him by his cousin Barnard Dickinson, manager of the Ketley works, and Dickinson's letter has survived among the Rathbone MSS.

Coalbrookdale 8mo 23rd. 1823

Dear Cousin,

On my return from the Half Year's Meeting, I found thy favour of the 19th instant, and have since had many dusty old Books examined & much enquiry made relative to the introduction of Cast Iron Rails, most of the Old Men here that know anything on the subject agree that it is upwards of 50 years since Iron was substituted for Wood rails, but in our Ledger we find but one *old* entry of Iron Rails which is on 13th of 11 mo 1767—100 Iron rails 111c.2q.11 lb. @ 7/- but no other Ledger entry do we find respecting them until 1781—Stephen Hughes an old workman who is very particular in his acct of past events says it is 56 years since he first worked for the Compy & that Iron rails were used about 2 years after, and we have found a Moulders acct. in which the first entry of Iron rails is in 8 mo.1768, made by what are called French Men, 232 rails at 1½ each & from that date there is a regular entry every Month, so there is no doubt but they were used here in 1768, & continued from that period, but we have nothing to prove their invention here, or that they were imported from any other place, yet I should think the Butterley Co were not in existence 55 years ago.—In the Moulders Accts for about a year from 8mo.1768, we find near 3000 rails moulded at 1½ each.

The next paragraph relates to Reynolds's health, then a short note on the state of the iron trade, with the following concluding statements—

We know little about Perkin's new Steam Engine, but from that little we are not very sanguine, that it will ever do the great things that he sets forth, & some expect.

Should it be in my power to give thee any further information respecting the rails, I shall have pleasure in answering thy inquiries in the interim I remain

thy affectionate relative

B. Dickinson

Several other references support the same date. Gillespie in a history of Falkirk says, when speaking of the Carron Ironworks,[1]

The first line, stretching from Kinaird Colliery into the interior of the works was constructed in 1766. The rails in that instance were of wood,

[1] Gillespie, Robert, *Round about Falkirk*, 1868.

covered with a sort of hoop-iron. In the course of the following year, however, rails wholly of iron were cast at Coalbrookdale Iron-works.

Of the many other references to the railroads at the Coalbrookdale works, it will suffice to include one more, the statement made by Jabez Hornblower before a committee of the House of Commons.[1]

Observations by Mr. Hornblower on the subject of Roads and Carriages, addressed to Sir John Sinclair, Bart. M.P.

Railways have been in use in this Kingdom time out of mind, and were usually formed of scantlings of good sound oak, laid on sills or sleepers of the same timber, and pinned together with the same stuff. But it was not until the proprietors of Colebrook-Dale Ironworks, a very respectable and opulent company, determined to cover these oak rails with cast-iron, not altogether as a necessary expedient of improvement, but in part as a well-digested measure of economy in support of their trade.

From some adventitious circumstances (which I need not take time to relate) the price of pigs became very low, and their works being of great extent, in order to keep the furnaces on, they thought it would be the best means of stocking their pigs, to lay it on the wooden railways, as it would help to pay the interest by reducing the repairs of the rails, and if iron should take any sudden rise, there was nothing to do but to take them up, and send them away as pigs.

But these scantlings of iron (as I may call them) were not as those which are now laid in some places, they were about five feet long, four inches broad, and one inch and a quarter thick, with three holes by which they were fastened to the rails, and very complete it was both in design and execution. Hence it is not difficult if two persons on horseback should meet on this road, for either to turn his horse out of the road, which on the railways now introduced would be attended with some serious doubt as to consequences.

This last sentence about the ease of turning horses out of the road is probably Hornblower's way of commenting on the difference between the first flat rails, easy to cross over, and the later flanged or edge rails which could make a horse stumble. Some years later the rails were described by a visiting engineer.[2]

In Coalbrookdale there is a cast-iron tramroad extending from the Severn as far as the lower Ironworks of the Dale Company, which, like

[1] Committee on the Acts now in force, regarding the use of Broad Wheels and on the Preservation of the Turnpike Roads and Highways of the Kingdom. 3rd Report, 19 June 1809, p. 154.

[2] Oeynhausen, von C. and Dechen, von H., *Ueber Scheinenwege in England, 1826 und 1827*. Berlin, 1829.

all the tramroads laid down in this district, is of this kind: the tram plates are 5 and even $5\frac{1}{2}$ feet long and lie in cast-iron chairs. The tramroad at Coalbrookdale comprises really two: a small one of 20 inches gauge, which is worked with small receptacles, lies in the middle of a large one of 36 inches gauge. It is worked by horse traction and it deserves to be mentioned that here in this neighbourhood the narrowest gauge which is anywhere to be found is employed for horses; on some roads it only attains 18 inches.

During the years 1768 to 1771 800 tons of iron rails were cast, the rails being 6 feet long, $3\frac{1}{4}$ inches wide and $1\frac{1}{4}$ inches thick and in a letter to Earl Gower, in 1785, Reynolds says that the works then had more than twenty miles of iron railways. The main lines of these railways were between Horsehay and Ketley furnaces and the Coalbrookdale works, between the works and the Severn wharves, and (according to Priestley) between Horsehay furnace and the Shropshire Canal which entered the Severn at Coalport.[1]

The rails cast at the Coalbrookdale furnaces would be for the short line from the works to Severn wharf, which was the first part of the railway system to be built. In the same year that these rails were being cast, the Horsehay furnace had already started casting large quantities of axle-trees for the waggons, and in the following year, 1768, rail casting on a large scale was started. The first entry in the books[2] is for 10th month, October 1768, when the furnace keepers at Horsehay were paid for 'dressing 809 rails' and casting and dressing 41 axle-trees. From that time onward there is a four-weekly account for casting rails, and the totals available in this surviving book, are some indication of the scale of the work.

1768, 3,718; 1769, 8,762; 1770, 1,234; 1771, 1,181; 1772, 809; 1773, 1,454; first three months of 1774, 307; total 17,465 rails. One entry says that 150 of these rails were 7 feet long and so were equal to 175 standard rails, or in other words, the standard rail was 6 feet long, and therefore each single rail was equivalent to one yard of track. Thus in the years 1767 to 1774 Horsehay furnace cast nearly ten miles of track. The laying of the rails went on steadily at the same time, starting in the autumn of 1769 with the Park Railway, on which about thirty men were employed for eight months

[1] Priestley, J., *Historical Account of the Navigable Rivers, Canals and Railways throughout Great Britain*, 1831.

[2] Horsehay Waste Book. 1767–74. *Shrewsbury MSS.* 333.

in laying rails. On this line there was a bridge, and for Park Bridge there was a considerable amount of timber supplied from Lawley Coppice, as well as bricks and stone. About the same time there was a smaller but steady amount of rail laying for which the accounts are made to General Railways, and in 1770 there was a short spell of work on the Bank Railway.

While all this work was being done the Dawley Railway was being reconditioned but with wooden rails and sleepers of which 2,022 yards of new rails were used in the year 1769 and similar amounts the following year.

The axle-trees for the waggons seem all to have been cast at Horsehay, up to the year 1770, by which time about 1,500 had been made. The wheels were made at Coalbrookdale, as the accounts for all the railways mentioned in the Horsehay book include frequent charges, in the carriage section, for a waggon load of wheels from the Dale.

The railways were all operated with horse-drawn waggons until the very end of the century, but on some of the steeper sections, inclines were formed where a gravity balance was used. One such place was the steep bank descending into the Dale on the site of the present road to Wellington; on this bank the waggons loaded with coal and ironstone were lowered down the incline, and pulled up empty or lightly loaded trucks. The speed was controlled by a brake drum or 'jigger,' a name which is still preserved in the name of the place as Jigger Bank. It was possibly the successful experience of this and other inclines that gave William Reynolds the idea and confidence to introduce canal inclines into his canal schemes.

It is often stated that the originator of the iron tramway was John Curr of Sheffield[1] but as the earliest date claimed for his first tramroad is 1774, he must relinquish the claim of originator to Darby and Reynolds who were casting iron rails at least six years earlier than that date, and had already put a long length of rails, not less than 800 tons weight, into use. Curr's rails had inside flanges to keep the trucks on the line, and in that respect were less in line with later developments than were those at Coalbrookdale, which were designed for flanged wheels. The rails were laid on wooden sleepers but these were replaced by stone blocks, a type of sleeper which remained in use for many years.

[1] Bland, F., 'John Curr, Originator of Iron Tram Roads.' *Trans. Newcomen Soc.*, vol. XI, 1930, pp. 121–30.

Canals.

The problem of the easier and more rapid movement of bulk materials, which was forced upon the attention of Reynolds and Darby between 1750 and 1770, was by no means unique to their organization. In the Tyne coalfields the waggon-ways were being extended at a great rate to cope with increasing outputs of coal, and in other centres in which industry and population were being concentrated, the transport of food and fuel was an equally acute problem. One such area was that around Manchester, which was making heavy demands for coal and food on all the surrounding districts. The great traffics in wool and salt which had steadily increased through the sixteenth and seventeenth centuries had used the rough roads over the hills, and the goods had been carried by pack horses. The numbers needed to carry a large bulk of material and the terrible deterioration of the roads and tracks were, by the middle of the eighteenth century, forcing a crisis both in trade and in the markets, and was causing a grievous rise in the price of food. It was against the background of this increasingly difficult situation that Brindley, employed by the Duke of Bridgewater, built his first canal. River transport had been of prime importance in the development of the Severn basin, in the lower Tyne and Thames valleys, and in many other areas, and rivers in many cases had been deepened and controlled to make them navigable for some extra miles, but the benefits were still limited to those places which were within comparatively easy reach of the river banks. Brindley's work, in effect, extended the reach of water borne traffic, by making artificial waterways through areas which were not possessed of a good river. In making a canal, the introduction of locks allowed the waterway actually to mount over moderately hilly country, provided sources of water for its filling and replenishment could be found.

The first canal to be built, the 'Bridgewater Canal,' was made from the Duke of Bridgewater's collieries at Worsley to Manchester. An Act of Parliament was obtained in March 1759, to make a navigable canal from Worsley Mill to Salford, and this canal, with its extraordinary underground connections through the Worsley collieries, was completed and opened in 1761.[1]

The successful completion of the Bridgewater canal at once stimulated other canal schemes which had been little more than

[1] These works were well described and illustrated by figures, in Young, A., *A Six Months Tour through the North of England,* 1770. vol. III. pp. 251–91, and plates 4 to 9.

PLATE XVII *This 1788 view of a small coal pit, shows the use of waggons with flanged wheels on a railway. It is impossible to tell whether the rails and wheels are wooden or of cast-iron although it is likely that metal was by this time the more common material.* (Inset) *In September, 1986, eighteenth century wooden rails were uncovered at Bedlam Furnaces, Ironbridge, of the same type as those depicted in the 1788 engraving.*

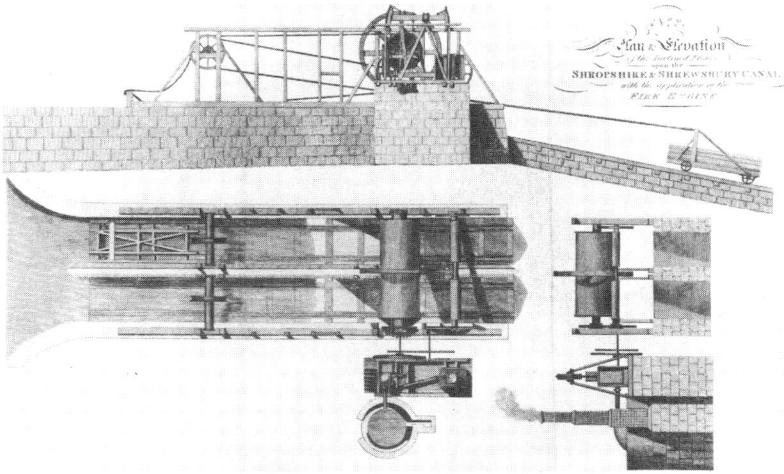

PLATE XVIII *The use of railways and plateways was well established when canals were built through the East Shropshire coalfield at the end of the eighteenth century. The inclined planes that were developed for these new canals showed the advantages and ingenuity of combining both forms of transport.*

Plate XIX *An engraving of the Coalbrookdale Works in the 1840's with the impressive Great Warehouse with its 1843 clock tower in the centre of the site. In the foreground three horses are pulling a loaded plateway waggon down the Dale to the Severn Warehouse.*

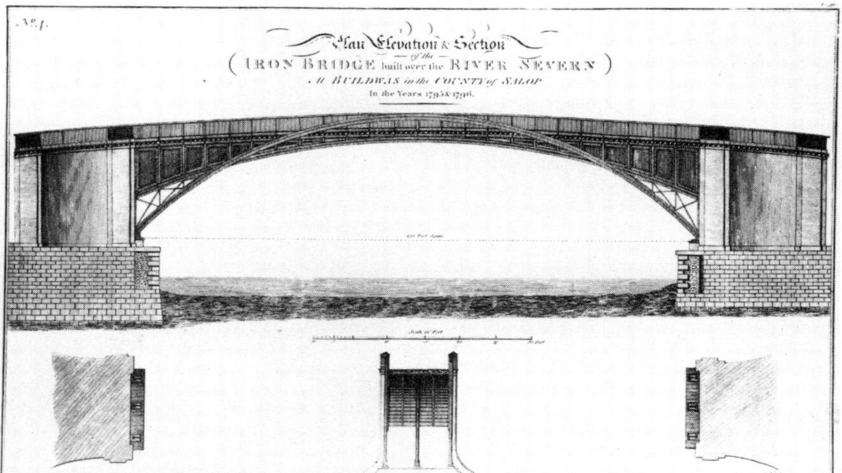

Plate XX *Built to replace the stone bridge damaged by floods on the River Severn in 1795 this new structure at Buildwas was confidently designed by Thomas Telford in cast-iron and made by the Coalbrookdale Company. Of all the bridges on the River Severn, the Iron Bridge had remained undamaged after the floods, and this undoubtedly gave much impetus to the use of cast-iron for bridge construction.*

tentative ideas. While still employed on the Bridgewater canal Brindley had made some preliminary surveys to test the possibility of a canal through the Potteries to connect the rivers Mersey and Trent. Josiah Wedgwood entered into this scheme with great enthusiasm and by 1766 an Act of Parliament was obtained for making such a canal, under the title, suggested by Brindley, of the Grand Trunk Canal. The Wolverhampton Canal Act was obtained in the same year to make a branch canal from the Trent to the Severn near Bewdley, and to make connection with Birmingham. This canal system affected the trade of Coalbrookdale by making the distribution of its products both easier and cheaper towards the north and north-east. The rising pottery industry used flint from the south-east of England and china clay from the south-west. The flint was carried by coastal shipping from the Thames to Hull, and then up the river Trent to Willington, and finally by an overland journey of forty miles to Burslem. The china clay of Cornwall and Devon went either by sea to Liverpool or by the Severn to Bridgnorth; from the Mersey there was an overland carriage of eighteen miles and one of forty miles from Bridgnorth, to the Potteries. The cheapest carriage was about 8/- a ton for ten miles, and much of the normal carriage rate was in excess of 10/- a ton mile. Carriage was by pack horses and occasionally by waggons, and breakages and pilfering were very serious. A pamphlet published in 1766 says of this trade,

> There are three or four waggons go from Newcastle and Burslem weekly through Eccleshall and Newport to Bridgnorth, and carry about eight tons of pot-ware every week at £3 per ton. The same waggons load back with ten tons of close goods, consisting of white clay, grocery and iron, at the same price, delivered on their road to Newcastle. Large quantities of pot-ware are conveyed on horses' backs from Burslem and Newcastle to Bridgnorth and Bewdley for exportation—about one hundred tons yearly at £2.10s. per ton. Two broad wheeled waggons (exclusive of 150 pack-horses) go from Newcastle through Stafford weekly, and may be computed to carry 312 tons of cloth and Manchester wares in the year at £3.10s. per ton.[1]

The opening of the canal system at once increased this traffic and provided a cheaper outlet for Coalbrookdale goods to the north. At the same time, in 1766, Brindley was commissioned by Joseph Whitfield for the London (Quaker) Lead Company to draw up plans for a canal from Chesterfield to Stockwith on the Trent, to

[1] Whitworth, R., *The Advantages of Inland Navigation*, 1766.

facilitate and cheapen the transport of their lead by the Trent navigation to Hull.[1]

In Yorkshire, John Hustler of Bradford, a Friend, was promoting the Leeds and Liverpool Canal to link Liverpool and Hull, the canal making a junction with the Aire and Calder navigation near Leeds. Brindley again was the surveyor. In these various schemes that were being promoted or built about 1766, Brindley was brought into close contact with Quakers like Hustler, Whitfield, the Lloyds of Birmingham, all of them close friends of Darby and Reynolds. Brindley himself was well known at the Coalbrookdale works; in 1756 when he was erecting a steam engine for Mr. Broade at Fenton Vivian in Staffordshire, he had the boiler, pipework, and some of the iron work made at Coalbrookdale, and according to his diary he occasionally spent several days at the works superintending the making of the boiler plates. In 1763 the steam engine for Walker Colliery, Newcastle-on-Tyne, was made by the Coalbrookdale Company, and he made visits to the works during its manufacture. There can be no doubt that through their knowledge of Brindley and in their close contacts with Lloyd, Hustler and Whitfield, Darby and Reynolds would have no lack of stimulus for many discussions of Brindley's canal works, and it is not surprising that they soon turned their thoughts to the possibility of using canal transport in their own immediate neighbourhood. With interests now spread over collieries, ironstone mines, furnaces and forges at Ketley and Horsehay, there was a good case for a short canal linking all these with Coalbrookdale and the Severn. The nature of the country, however, discouraged all attempts—the ground was very hilly, there seemed to be insufficient sources of water for lockage, and most serious of all, the Severn near Coalbrookdale was in a deep gorge into which any descent by canal seemed impossible.

Whatever discussions there were on canals, the difficulties seemed almost insuperable for many years. Richard Reynolds had taken a great interest in the navigation of the river Severn and in particular had worked to secure a towing path which would make possible the use of horses. The barges were at that time hauled by men, who in many places literally scrambled along the precipitous and rocky banks of the river. The work was described by Telford as 'barbarous and expensive . . . slave-like.' Richard Reynolds in 1769, writing

[1] For details see Raistrick, A., *Two Centuries of Industrial Welfare*, 1938, pp. 84–7.

to his friend George Harrison, speaks of his recent experiences at Manchester: [1]

> We went to the Duke of Bridgewater's coalworks, and came along the side of the navigation as far as it extends towards Warrington, which is, I think, within two or three miles. There have been frequently published in the newspapers descriptions of the works and navigations, but I shall only say, I never read one which gave me an adequate idea of the performances: they are really amazing, and greater, I believe, than were ever before attempted, much less achieved by an individual and a subject.

In 1772, still deeply impressed with all he could learn about canals, Reynolds pressed for an Act of Parliament for the making of the Severn towpath, but he was not successful at once. His son William, who was gradually relieving Richard Reynolds of some of the responsibilities of management, pressed on with the idea, and Telford says of him, when writing about 1780, of the improvement of the Severn, [2]

> . . . it is only necessary that a good towing path for horses should be formed along the banks of the river, and which will no doubt take place, if any scheme of general improvements should ever be adopted. In the meantime a laudable example has been shown by Mr. William Reynolds, of Ketley, who has formed a towing path for horses near to the new manufactories at Coalport, and has carried it on through his father's property to the iron bridge, a distance of about two miles: this being along some rugged banks, and over some of the worst fords which are on the river, proves beyond contradiction, that this sort of towing path is practicable at no extravagant expense, and besides, completely destroys the common objection of horse towing paths where many rapids or fords intervene.

In 1788 Richard Reynolds took a leading part in obtaining an Act of Parliament to allow the making of a navigable canal from the principal iron works in Shropshire to the river Severn, and this was almost his last public work connected with the development of the works. The Act being obtained, his son William became the moving spirit and to a large extent the designer of the canal, on which he introduced his most striking innovation, the inclined plane. Again, Telford's account of this cannot be bettered, and it has the merit of being an engineer's account, contemporary with the

[1] Letter from Ketley, 30th of Ninth Month, 1769, in Rathbone, H. M., *Letters of Richard Reynolds*, 1852, pp. 93–4.

[2] Telford's report in Plymley, J., *Agriculture of Shropshire*, 1803, p. 289.

construction, and by one who was partly responsible for many of the works in the area.[1]

The superior utility of navigable canals had by this time been pretty generally ascertained, and they were found to be more especially advantageous in the removal of heavy articles; it therefor became evident, that a navigable canal was the means by which coal and iron could be sent from such distances as the Oaken Gates and Ketley, so as to reach the market on terms of competition with the same sort of articles which are procured nearer to the river.

But how necessary soever a navigable canal might be for those purposes, it was for a long time deemed an impracticable project. The general summit over which it must pass, lying on that range which is considered as nearly the highest ground in the kingdom; this ground being also very rugged, and consisting of ridges which are insulated from the adjoining country, there was no prospect of procuring a sufficient quantity of water for the purposes of lockage, the only mode of conveying boats from a higher to a lower canal, which had at that time been practised in Britain.

These seemed insuperable difficulties, and most probably would have proved so for ages to come, had not Mr. William Reynolds of Ketley (whose character is too well known to need any eulogium) discovered the means of effecting this desirable object: for he, about this time, having occasion to improve the mode of conveying ironstone and coals, from the neighbourhood of the Oaken Gates to the iron-works at Ketley, these materials lying generally at the distance of about a mile and a half from the iron-works, and at 73 feet above their level; he made a navigable canal, and instead of descending in the usual way, by locks, continued to bring the canal forward to an abrupt part of the bank, the skirts of which terminated on a level with the iron-works. At the top of this bank he built a small lock, and from the bottom of the lock, and down the face of the bank he constructed an *inclined plane* with a double iron railway. He then erected an upright frame of timber, in which across the lock, was fixed a large wooden barrel; round this barrel a rope was passed, and was fixed to a moveable frame; this last frame was formed of a size sufficient to receive a canal boat, and the bottom upon which the boat rested, was preserved in nearly an horizontal position, by having two large wheels before and two small ones behind, varying as much in the diameters as the inclined plane varied from the horizontal plane. This frame was placed in the lock, the loaded boat was also brought from the upper canal into the lock, the lock-gates were shut, and on the water being drawn from the lock into a side pond, the boat settled upon the horizontal wooden frame, and as the bottom of the lock was formed with nearly the same declivity as the inclined plane, upon the lower gates being opened, the frame with the

[1] Telford's report in Plymley, J., *Agriculture of Shropshire*, 1803, pp. 290–9.

boat, passed down the iron railway, on the inclined plane, into the lower canal, which had been formed on a level with the Ketley iron-works, being a fall of 73 feet. Very little water was required to perform this operation because the lock was formed of no greater depth than the upper canal, except the addition of such a declivity as was sufficient for the loaded boat to move out of the lock; and in dry seasons, by the assistance of a small steam engine, the whole of the water drawn from the lock, was returned into the upper canal by means of a short pump.

A double railway being laid upon the inclined plane, the loaded boat in passing down, brought up another boat containing a load nearly equal to one-third part of that which passed down. The velocities of the boats were regulated by a brake acting upon a large wheel placed upon the axis on which the ropes connected with the carriage, were coiled.

It is proper to observe that Mr. Reynolds reduced the size of his canal boats, for instead of making use of boats of 70 feet in length, each carrying from 25 to 30 tons, he made them only 20 feet in length, 6 feet 4 inches in width, and 3 feet 10 inches deep; each capable of carrying eight tons. This inclined plane was completed in the year 1788.

Telford grasped the importance of these works possibly earlier than any other person, and his opinion must carry very considerable weight in any attempt to assess these inventions. The continuation of his report is equally important, and we cannot do better than quote it fairly fully.

As soon as the plan of ascending and descending by means of an inclined plane was fairly understood, every person was convinced that its principle was very applicable to the situation of the ground which lay between the Oaken Gates and the river Severn, and that this invention alone would obviate the difficulties which before had been considered insurmountable. Under this impression a subscription was entered into, and an act of parliament was obtained for the Shropshire Canal.

The general direction of this canal is nearly from North to South; it commences on the north side of the London road from Shrewsbury at a place called Donnington Wood, and proceeds about 100 yards on a level; it then ascends 120 feet by an inclined plane of 320 yards in length. From the top of this inclined part (which is the summit level of the canal) it passes on through the Wrockwardine and Snedhill coal and iron-stone works, and having passed Oaken Gates is joined by the Ketley Canal (before mentioned) from thence it goes on by the Holingswood iron-works, and having passed near the Old Park iron-works, proceeds to Southall-bank, where a branch striking off to the right, passes near to the Lightmoor and Horsehay iron-works, and terminates at Brierly-hill, near to Coalbrookdale. The main line of the canal turning to the left at

Southall-bank, goes on to the Windmill Farm, where it descends 126 feet, by an inclined plane 600 yards in length; from the bottom of this inclined plane it passes on to the east of Madeley, until it reaches the banks of the Severn, at about two miles below the iron bridge; here it descends 207 feet, by an inclined plane which is 350 yards in length. From the bottom of this inclined plane, and on a level above the reach of the floods, it passes parallel with the river, to Coal-port where it terminates.

The branch which turned off this canal at Southall Bank and which terminated at Brierly Hill was designed primarily for the carriage of coal and ironstone to the Coalbrookdale works and also for a certain amount of export coal to be carried to the Severn wharf. Limestone would be brought back up the canal for the use of the ironworks at Ketley and Oaken Gates. Brierly Hill is a very steep bank and for many years the connection between the canal on the summit level and the short branch to the Coalbrookdale works was made by a method very different from the inclined plane. The lower level was laid with a railway instead of a canal, and this line was carried by a tunnel into the hill to a point vertically beneath the termination of the canal. At the canal level, the boats were floated into an unloading dock, served by cranes, and the raw material was loaded in the boats in special crates which could be lifted bodily by the cranes. The cranes swung round over the vertical shafts alongside the canal, which descended to the railway tunnel. The crates arriving at the bottom of the shafts, fitted onto special bogies, and could be run out and into the works, along any of their existing sets of lines. Similarly, limestone and goods for the canal level were loaded on the Severn wharf in the special crates and run into the tunnel, to be lifted up the shafts and deposited, in the crate, in the canal boats. No power was used except that of gravity, the full crates on the crane either drawing up empties, regulated by a brake, or pulling up a lighter load of limestone. The shafts were 10 feet in diameter and 120 feet deep.[1] After some time, however, the inclined planes on canals proved their efficiency, and in 1792 it was decided that one should be substituted for the shafts and tunnel, and when this was completed some time after 1794, it was found possible to make the descent and ascent of the loaded boats in a shorter time than was taken for the transfer by cranes. Telford says, 'Boats pass these inclined planes with considerable expedition. Mr. Williams informs me, that he has known six boats passed down

[1] The cost of this scheme was £2,742.9.0.

and six taken up the windmill inclined plane, which is 600 yards long, and 126 feet of fall, in the course of an hour, and in the performing this, the steam engine and three men only, were employed.' This canal was finished and filled with water by 1792, and the water was maintained by two reservoirs; one was below the level of the canal, which could receive lockage water, and this water along with some from the drainage of the mines was pumped by a steam engine into the upper feeding reservoir. The canal was nearly eleven miles long, carried over old mining ground which was considered unsafe, along and over hill slopes, and with mines actually working under it; it cost £47,500 and was considered to give a complete demonstration of the cheapness and efficiency of this new method of transport, over the most difficult country. 'It has already paid at the rate of six per cent upon this capital; and if the navigation of the Severn and the other connexions were completer, there is reason to expect that this per centage would be considerably increased; so that, independent of every other consideration, there is a prospect of its becoming a valuable object, even as a distinct speculation.'

There is evidence that William Reynolds not only thought out these ideas for canal transport, but took a very active part in their translation into actual fact. There is fortunately one letter still extant, among the *Rathbone MSS.*, from him to his brother-in-law.

To William Rathbone Junr. Liverpool.

(Ketley) Bank
16 Jany. 11 oclock. 1788

Dear Brother,

. . . Please to give my dear love to my sister I have not forgot her as I often think of her tho' I never write to her. Indeed I have my hands full —we are making a canal from Oakengates to Ketley & have between 2 & 300 men at work upon it & as I am head and subschemer, Engineer & Director & have besides one in contemplation from the same place to the river wch I have been obliged to Levell & relevell, survey & resurvey I have had scarce time to do anything but think of them—I have not yet heard of the pig iron—as I expect some Cornish men here soon to attempt working mines shall be glad to have if they can be bo[t] of those thou mentions

40 Beds compleat	100 Flannel Drawers	50 pr Kendal Stockings
60 Hamacoes	100 Linnen Frocks	50 Do Leister
40 White Jackets	200 Trowsers	50 pr Shoes

thy affectionate Bro.
W Reynolds

This gives us a vivid picture of the energy of William, carrying out the surveying and clerk of works duties, dealing with two or three hundred men and supervising their work, and also buying in stores through his merchant brother-in-law, some to be used in the men's bunk houses, and possibly some to be sold to them through a truck shop. At the same time as this letter was written, we find William Reynolds busy in the management of the Ketley iron works and taking his part in the management of the Coalbrookdale concerns as well; truly he could have had no spare moments and the scientific experiments, which engaged much of his interest a few years earlier, must have been very much in abeyance during these more strenuous years. The letter, and other supporting evidence seen in various items of his letters, make one feel that the glowing testimony paid by Telford to Reynolds's activity is not in the least part undeserved.

The canals, though designed by William Reynolds, were undertaken by the Coalbrookdale Company and the Ketley Company, and in the Minutes of a meeting of the Directors in May 1794, instructions are given for their valuation. Half the original cost and subsequent improvements of the canal must in all cases be written off in the first eight years, and the remaining half of these costs was to be written off by a fractional proportion of the value for the time being, equal to the number of years which were still unexpired in the leases.

Besides the canals which were directly connected to the works, the Coalbrookdale Company had an active interest in two other schemes, the Shrewsbury Canal and the Ellesmere Canal. The Shrewsbury Canal connected with an extension of the Shropshire Canal which Reynolds had built from the foot of Wrockwardine Incline towards Ketley. This had been designed to carry the produce of the Wrockwardine mines to Donnington iron works and to give an outlet for their goods onto the Shropshire Canal. At the end of this branch canal the Shrewsbury Canal Company built an incline 223 yards long with 75 feet of fall. From there it goes by way of Eyton Mill, Long Lane, Roddington and Pimley to Shrewsbury. Telford reports that

There are several circumstances which are peculiar on this canal—one is that the communication between the higher and lower levels is partly by means of an inclined plane and partly by locks; a second is, that as small boats are used on the canal, the locks are so formed as to admit of either one, three or four boats passing at a time, without the loss of any more water than is just necessary to regulate the ascent or descent of the boat or boats that are then in the locks. This is accomplished by having gates that are drawn up and let down perpendicularly, instead of being worked horizontally; and each lock has three gates, one of which divides the body of the lock so as to admit one, three or four boats at a time. A third and perhaps the most striking circumstance is, that the canal passes over the valley of the Tern at Long, for a distance of 62 yards, upon an aqueduct made all of cast iron, excepting only the nuts and screws, which are wrought iron; and I believe this to be the first aqueduct for the purposes of a navigable canal, which has ever been composed of this metal. It has completely answered the intention, although it was foretold by some, that the effects of the different degrees of heat and cold would be such, as to cause expansion and contraction of the metal, which not being equal to extend or draw back the whole mass of the aqueduct, would operate upon the separate plates of iron, so as to tear off the flanches which connect the plates lengthwise, and break the joints. Others said that the expansion of freezing water would burst the sides and so break off the flanches which connect the sides with the bottom plates; but after the trial of a summer's heat and the very severe frost of the winter of 1796, no visible alteration has taken place, and no water passes through any of the side or bottom joints. After the frost had continued very severe for three or four days, and the water had not been drawn off (although there is the means of doing so), but it had stood in the aqueduct about the height of two feet six inches, the ice had then frozen to the thickness of an inch and a half, but instead of having forced out the sides, it was melted away from them, and quite loose upon the surface of the water.

The idea of having this aqueduct made of cast iron, was first suggested and recommended by Thomas Eyton Esq. then Chairman of the Committee; after due consideration it was approved by the Committee and the principals of construction, and the manner in which it should be executed, were refered to Mr. William Reynolds and the writer of this article [Telford], who, after several consultations and forming and considering various plans, at last determined upon that which is represented by the annexed engravings No. 3. The castings for the aqueduct were done at Ketley, and were removed to Long, a distance of five miles, partly by land and partly by water carriage.

This aqueduct was proposed in consequence of the great flood which happened in the beginning of the year 1795, and it was fixed complete in March, 1796.[1]

The success of this cast iron aqueduct led to a much larger venture. In 1793 Telford was appointed as engineer of the proposed Ellesmere Canal. In the course of this canal it was necessary to cross

[1] Telford's report in Plymley, J., *Agriculture of Shropshire*, 1803, p. 298.

the valleys of the rivers Dee and Ceriog at a high level. Telford, relying on the success of the Tern aqueduct just described, designed the two further examples with cast iron troughing, resting on cast iron arches. These were in turn carried by tall and slender stone piers. The two aqueducts built to this plan are the famous ones of Chirk and Pont Cysylte.[1]

The ironwork for the Pont Cysylte aqueduct was made by William Hazeldine at his Llangollen Foundry, which was the nearest iron works to the site. This marked the beginning of a long association between Telford and Hazeldine, and when Telford was planning the Menai Straits Suspension Bridge Hazeldine got the order for the chains 'of best hammered Shropshire iron.'

The modest cast iron aqueduct over the river Tern must however be regarded as the pioneer experiment and parent of the later and greater works. This first aqueduct maintains the Coalbrookdale Company's position as a pioneer in transport construction, and their list of achievements includes the first iron railway, the first iron bridge, the first canal incline, and the first cast iron canal aqueduct, all of which were followed by other applications of their principles to produce a healthy progeny of similar structures.

[1] Descriptions of these, with some detail, will be found in Smiles, S., *Lives of the Engineers*, 1862, vol. II, pp. 342–9, and Gibbs, A., *The Story of Telford*, 1935, pp. 27–35.

Chapter Eleven

THE IRON BRIDGE AND OTHER BRIDGES 1778–1863

AMONG the many achievements of the Darbys one which caught the popular imagination at the time of its inception and has held it ever since, was the Iron Bridge over the river Severn. This was the first iron bridge in the world to be built and as it still stands,[1] in everyday use after a hundred and seventy years of wear and tear, and of Severn floods, it rightly deserves being scheduled as a National Monument. Many misstatements are still made as to its origin and builders, and it is at last possible to correct these from original documents only recently recovered.[2]

Abraham Darby II had had it in mind to build a bridge over the Severn, between Madeley Wood and Benthall, as there was considerable expense and delay in ferrying stores of all kinds across the river for the use of the Coalbrookdale works. Among many articles which had to cross the river in his time, there were large quantities of limestone for flux, hearthstones and firestones for the furnaces, bricks, timber, and a certain amount of ironstone. During his lifetime, Darby did not get so far as a definite scheme, any detail of which has survived. Randall who had access to many of the manuscript sources now lost says that this Abraham had proceeded far with the idea. However that may be, the present bridge owes its inception to a group of proprietors of whom one of the most influential was Abraham Darby III.

By September 1775 a group of subscribers had been got together for the purpose of building a bridge and a first meeting was called at the house of Abraham Cannadine, in Broseley, on the 15th of the month. The minutes of this meeting are the first to be entered in the

[1] In October 1950, Mr. E. Rathbone, Chairman of the Trustees and a descendant of Hannah Darby, handed over the Iron Bridge to the Shropshire County Council, and the toll was abolished.

[2] During this year, 1950, Mr. J. Hobbs, of the Public Library, Shrewsbury, recognized, among the papers belonging to the Harries family, the Minute Book of the Proprietors of the Ironbridge, 1775–1798, which is now in the *Shrewsbury MSS.* No. 337a.

manuscript which survives, and the first minute is 'Mr. Abraham Darby of Coalbrookdale was chose Treasurer. And Thos. Adenbrooke Secretary.' It is clear that there had already been a good deal of preliminary discussion about the securing of an Act of Parliament to allow the construction of a bridge, and the subscribers were now called together into a formal group to study the securing of such an Act by a Petition. This first meeting discussed some details of the petition and decided to include no road scheme beyond the minimum necessary approaches to the bridge.

It was also agreed that Mr. Hamilton of Lincolns Inn Fields London, be employed as Solicitor to Obtain an Act for Erecting the said Bridge and making the said roads, and that he be desired to prepare the Heads of a Bill from the following instructions—

The Bridge to be Erected between Benthall and Madeley Wood, a road from the Bridge on Madeley side to lead to the Turnpike road near Lincoln Hill Through Lands belonging to Tho. Crumpton, Elizabeth Crumpton, Richard Crumpton, Samuel Crumpton, Elizabeth Watkiss, Robert Davis and the Waste land belonging to the Manour of Madeley, on the Benthall side a Road through some Land belonging to the Reverend Mr. Harris and the Person for the time being in possession of the Benthall Estate and his and their Tenants (in Consideration of Mr Harris giving up his Private road call'd Benthall rail and the Ferry) to be secured from all repairs of the said Road, and Tolls to the Severn, gates to be put up at the discretion of the Commissioners not exceeding one Gate on each side and side gates or Bars, the Tolls for Carriage Horses &c. on both sides the Severn that go only to the riverside, to be half what is paid for going over the Bridge, the full Tolls to be settled at a future meeting.

Agreed that Mr Thomas F. Pritchard and Mr Samuel Thomas be desired to prepare estimates of the said Bridge against the next meeting, when it is intended to fix upon a proper method to raise money to defray the Expence of Erecting the Bridge and makeing the Roads.

The adjourned meeting was held on 28 September and a scheme of tolls was worked out, in which a foot passenger was to be charged one halfpenny, going and returning, but not to pay toll more than twice in one day.

Mr. Harris of Middle Temple was eventually employed to obtain the Bill,[1] instead of Mr. Hamilton, and on the same day, 28 September, a call of £10 per cent. was made on the subscribers, the record of which is useful as a list of the originators.

[1] The Act was obtained in the next year. 16 George III. c. xvii, 1776.

John Wilkinson	£2. 0. 0	Abraham Darby	£5. 0. 0
Edward Blakeway	2. 0. 0	Edwd. Harries	5. 0. 0
Leonard Jennings	1. 0. 0	John Matthews	2. 0. 0
Thomas Slaughter	4. 2½	Sergeant Roden	10. 6
Robert Gilpin	4. 2½	John Guest	1. 0
John Morris	1. 0. 0	Charles Guest	1. 0. 0
John Thursfield	10. 6	John Corbel	10. 6
John Hartshorne	1. 1. 0	Daniel Boden	10. 6
John Nicholson	10. 6		

On 17 October 1775 it was agreed that the sum of £3,150 already subscribed be paid to Abraham Darby, 'he agreeing in consideration thereof to defray all the expences of erecting the intended bridge in a substantial manner, according to the plan this day produced by Mr. Thos. Farnolls Pritchard, or as near as may be for the best and safest manner, for making roads at both ends of the bridge and obtaining the Act of Parliament for it.' On 15 May 1776 this minute was rescinded so that an advertisement could be inserted in the Shrewsbury and Birmingham papers in three consecutive issues, asking for tenders for the construction of a bridge with a span of 120 feet, a width of 18 feet and the centre 35 feet above the low water level of the river, these tenders to be sent in before 28 June next.[1] A separate tender was asked for the stone and brick work of the bridge abutments and approaches. In July Pritchard was instructed to prepare a model of the bridge according to his plan, and to find out the proper stone and brick to be used in the bridge abutments but there is no evidence that this was ever done. On 18 October, it would appear that no alternative tenders had been submitted, as the meeting agreed to accept Darby's suggestions, for the bridge structure, and

the said Mr. Abraham Darby agreed to erect an Iron Bridge of one Arch one hundred and twenty feet span and the superstructure not less

[1] 15 May 1776, the following advertisement appeared in the *Shrewsbury Chronicle*.

A Bridge to be built.

Any person willing to undertake to build a bridge of one arch over the Severn from Benthall rail to the opposite shore in Madeley Wood, of stone, brick, or timber, the arch of 120 ft. span, the superstructure 18 ft. clear, the centre of the arch 35 ft. from low water.

Send proposals to Thomas Addenbrooke at Coalbrook Dale before 28th. June next and to attend a meeting of the proprietors at John Nicholson's on Friday 28th of same month at eleven o'clock in the forenoon.

than eighteen feet wide . . . to be completely furnished with roads and avenues leading to and from the same as described in the Act of Parliament, on or before the twenty fifth day of December one Thousand Seven Hundred and seventy eight . . .

There were many meetings of the proprietors to discuss minor matters of tolls, forms for the assignment of shares, letting the ferry tolls over the river, and so on, but it was not until 14 July 1777 that further money was called for. At that meeting it was decided to raise sixty-four shares, including the sixty already subscribed, these of £50 each, and that the holders of forty-six of the shares should make a free gift of £5 and the owners of the remaining eighteen a free gift of £2 10/–, to the funds. £10 per cent. was to be paid to Abraham Darby as soon as the abutments of the bridge were completed, and a further 10 per cent. of the capital, every three months after that; and when the bridge, approaches, toll gates, etc. were completed, the remainder of the money was to be paid him. The bridge plan had been altered by this time and it was now to be an iron bridge with a span of 90 feet, a roadway 24 feet wide, and a towing path under it. If the bridge were not completed by 25 December 1778, then Darby was to pay 5 per cent. interest per annum for any further money paid after that date.[1]

Very little business was done at subsequent meetings, except to agree to contracts let by Abraham Darby to contractors for making short portions of the approach roads, etc., and to let the ferry over the Severn.

The next note of progress is found in the *Shrewsbury Chronicle* on 10 July 1779:

[1] At this time the share list was—

Rev. Mr. Harries	10 shares	John Morris	2 shares
Abraham Darby	15	Charles Guest	2
John Wilkinson	12	Roger Kynnaston	1
Leonard Jennings	10	John Hartshorne	1
Samuel Darby	4	Sergeant Roden	1
Edward Blakeway	2	John Thursfield	1
Farnolls Pritchard	2	John Nicholson	1

At an earlier date, 1 October 1776, 'Mr. Jennings and Mr. Wilkinson agree to let Mr. Darby have their shares in consideration of his giving them Security that an Iron Bridge shall be erected from Madeley Wood to Benthall in Two Years from Christmas next and Mr Darby agrees to take the said shares on that condition.' This means that in actual fact Abraham Darby held 37 shares and his brother Samuel 4, giving the Darbys 41 out of 64 shares, and this disposes of many recent statements that the Iron Bridge was the work of, or financed by, John Wilkinson.

On Thursday and Friday the 1st and 2nd instant one main rib was put up over the River Severn at Madeley Wood and Benthall for the first arch of the iron bridge which spans 100 feet.

On 18 September the same year there is a further paragraph:

We have the satisfaction of informing the public that the new turnpike road, from Ternbridge to that amazing scene of business Coalbrook Dale, is now open to carriages of ease; by which a short and pleasant communication is also opened to a sight of that most singular curiosity the iron-bridge of one arch over the river Severn.

The actual erection of the iron structural members of the bridge occupied only three months and another fifteen months passed before the bridge was formally opened for traffic. The *Shrewsbury Chronicle* carried a notice in the issue for 20 January 1781 :

The cast iron bridge over the River Severn between Madeley Wood (near Coalbrook Dale) and Benthall was opened on New Year's Day last; since which time (considering the season of the year) great numbers of carriages, besides horses and foot passengers have daily passed over the said bridge, the roads leading to and from it being nearly completed.

The greatest part of the time was needed for the building of the abutments and the road approaches, to make which, many old buildings had to be cleared away or altered. The Proprietors had imposed a term of two years and two months for the completion and apart from minor detail, Darby was able to work within this limit, although hampered by many difficulties. At the site chosen the banks of the river are steep and they were heavily encumbered with old buildings and with the ferry landing and approaches. The river was liable to very severe floods and solid foundations were not easily to hand. Because of the depth of the gorge and the design of the bridge, the legs of the arch had to be backed up by masonry abutments over thirty feet high. The design and construction of this heavy masonry, and the problem of founding it securely on a steep bank of soft rock and in a swift-flowing river, took Darby longer than had been anticipated by the Proprietors. This part of the work along with the casting of the bridge members occupied him all 1777 and 1778 and it was not until mid 1779 that the erection of the ironwork was started.

The bridge members were cast at Coalbrookdale, probably during the winter of 1778–9, ready for erection in the summer of 1779. The dimensions cast were for a bridge with 100 feet 6 inches span, 40 feet high above the river, and with a width of 24 feet. In the final details of the design one of the Coalbrookdale workpeople, Thomas Gregory, foreman pattern-maker, was associated with Abraham Darby. In preparation for the casting of the bridge members, many alterations were made in the works arrangements. The Old Furnace was enlarged and remodelled to a new design. The capacity of the Old Furnace was far too small for the main rib castings which each weighed over five tons, although a few steam engine cylinders of similar weight had already been cast, and it is probable that the experience gained with them decided the nature of the principal alterations in the furnace and casting floor. The old beams above the tapping hole, with the initials and date 1658 were retained in their old position, but two larger and longer beams were added above them, those with the cast inscription 'ABRAHAM DARBY 1777.' As some of the ribs of the bridge were nearly eighty feet long and parts of a circular arc, a new moulding floor was made on the east side of the furnace, big enough to meet all the bridge requirements. Of the actual casting and handling of the ribs in the works, we have no documentary record, though traditions are still alive in the Dale. The only account which gives any detail is that prepared by Richard Gough for his edition and translation of Camden's *Britannia*.[1] The precision of this account is evidence of very close observation and of contact with someone actually conversant with the problems of the erection.

Coalbrookdale is one mile long, and the property of Mr. Reynolds and subscribers. Over the Severn in this Dale was laid 1779, a bridge of cast iron, the whole of which was cast in open sand, and a large scaffold being previously erected, each part of the rib was elevated to a proper height by strong ropes and chains, and then lowered till the ends met in the centre. All the principal parts were erected in three months without any accident to the work or workmen or the least obstruction to the navigation of the river. On the abutments of stone work are placed iron plates with mortices, in which stand two upright pillars of the same. Against the foot of the inner pillar the bottom of the main rib bears on the base plate. This rib consists of two pieces connected by a dovetail joint in an iron key, and fastened with screws. Each piece is 70 feet long. The

[1] *BRITANNIA: or a Chorographical Description of the flourishing Kingdoms of England, Scotland and Ireland, and the Islands adjacent; from the earliest Antiquity.* By William Camden Translated from the Edition published by the Author in MDCVII. Enlarged by the latest discoveries, by Richard Gough, 1789. Quotations are from the second edition, 4 vols. folio, 1806.

shorter ribs pass through the pillar at appertures left for that purpose, and are morticed into the top bearers and into the base plate and pillar, the back rib in like manner without coming down to the plate. The cross stays, braces, circle in the spandrils, and the brackets connect the larger pieces so as to keep the bridge perfectly steady, while a diagonal and cross stays and top plate connect the pillars and ribs together in opposite directions. The whole bridge is covered with top-plates of iron projecting over the ribs on each side, and on this projection stands the ballustrades of cast iron. The road over the bridge made of clay and iron slag is 24 feet wide, 1 foot deep: toll for carriages is 1s. The span of the arch is 100 feet 6 inches, and the height from the base line to the centre 40 feet. The weight of iron in the whole is 378 tons 10 cwt. Each piece of the long ribs weighs 5 tons 15 cwt. On the largest and exterior rib is inscribed in capitals THIS BRIDGE WAS CAST AT COALBROOK AND ERECTED IN THE YEAR 1779.[1]

This is the only mention of the remarkable manner of construction of the bridge. The members were so cast that the assembly was done by slotting some members through others at various points. The holes were large enough to allow the necessary considerable swing and movement during the placing in position and this play was taken up by cast iron wedges on completion. The joints are either held in position by cottar wedges or one member drops into a dovetail box on the other and is tightened up with a screw. The bridge is thus a stable structure 'interlocked' in every part and having no bolted or riveted joints. To design and erect such a bridge a model was essential and no doubt the one now in the Science Museum, for which the Royal Society of Arts granted Abraham Darby their Gold Medal in 1788, was made to try out and rehearse the method of erection.

It is not possible to state the total cost of the bridge, nor do we know how much Abraham Darby subscribed over and above the calls on the shares which he held, but there is a note in the Torrington Diaries which suggests that Darby took a large part of the cost on his own shoulders.

> But of the iron Bridge over the Severn, which we cross'd and where we stopp'd for half-an-hour, what shall I say? That it must be the admiration, as it is one of the wonders of the world. It was cast in the year 1778; the arch is 100 feet wide and 55 feet from the top of the water, the whole length is 100 yards; the country agreed with the founder to finish it for £6000; and have, meanly, made him suffer for his noble undertaking.[2]

[1] The inscription is on each side of the bridge, but the name is COALBROOK = DALE and the date is in Roman numerals MDCCLXXIX.

[2] *Torrington Diaries*, 1934, vol. I, p. 184.

The Minute Book of the Proprietors of the bridge completely ignores the erecting and opening of it to traffic, as it also does the cost. In May 1778 it is noted that 'Notes of hand were given to Abm Darby for the remainder due of their shares and the free gift [voluntary levy] of fifty shillings a share.' It is also minuted that Mr. Guest agreed to sell to Abraham Darby, one share. On 30 April 1779, the Ferry was let to Daniel Day for £42 a year from 1 May 1779 to 1780 or until the bridge should be completed, whichever date was the first. In September 1780 a call of 10 per cent. on all shares was paid to Darby and that was the last payment made to him.

By various purchases Darby had secured more than half of all the shares, and in 1782 he transferred most of them to Richard Reynolds, after whose death they were inherited by Hannah Mary Rathbone, his daughter, the widow of William Rathbone. The major part of the shares remained in the hands of the Rathbone family until the final closure of the Trust when the bridge was handed over to the ownership and care of the Shropshire County Council on 12 October 1950. Major M. P. Rathbone on behalf of the Trustees handed over the deeds with the remark that to execute the transfer it had been necessary to obtain the signatures of all the trustees, who were now living in all parts of the world. The deeds were accompanied by a cheque for £500, as a gift of the Trustees towards the reconditioning of the bridge. The halfpenny toll was abolished and the bridge freed to all users. One of the original share certificates, made out to Abraham Darby and signed, at the transfer dates by Joseph Rathbone and later by Joseph Reynolds, is illustrated in the plate facing p. 240.

The later business of the Proprietors was mainly concerned with tolls and dividends, and it included the completion of a Toll House. Tickets were printed as receipts for toll, and season tickets both for the bridge and for the use of the access roads to the river side were issued. A season ticket was made available to coach proprietors, the first being for Mr. John Rowlands for a coach, the Dilligence, running between London and Shrewsbury, and compounding for 3/– a month. Foot passengers could get a season ticket for a year for a guinea. The value of the tolls can be judged by the price for which they were let each year from 1782. In that year they fetched at auction a sum of £326.3.4 but rose steadily to £587 in 1792. The period of acute trade depression is reflected in the tolls which dropped to £561 in 1793 and the two following years and to £525 by 1799.

The dividend paid on the shares varied and increased as the bridge approaches were completed, being fairly steady about seven to nine guineas by 1792.

In 1784 there was the first hint of trouble with the abutment of the bridge on the Benthall side of the river, in a brief minute—'22 October 1784. Ordered that a cement of six parts sand and one part lime be put in the cracks in the arch on Benthall side to see if they get wider.' We get some hint of the source or aggravation of the trouble in March 1785 when the Proprietors had to order the making of drains and culverts to divert the water that was running down the road from the Benthall furnace, and getting to the bridge structure. Robert Stephenson in the article on Bridges which he contributed to the *Encyclopaedia Britannica*, 8th edition, says of the Iron Bridge, 'If we consider that the manipulation of cast-iron was then completely in its infancy, a bridge of such dimensions was doubtless a bold as well as an original undertaking, and the efficiency of the details is worthy of the boldness of the conception.' He says further that because of a defect in the abutment the foot of the arch of the bridge was thrust towards the river and the ribs were partly fractured. This however is a mistake. It was the appearance of cracks in the Benthall abutment that gave rise to the fear which Stephenson took as actual fact, and to prevent such a thrust the abutment was altered and two small land arches were substituted for the earth-filled approach. This was done about the year 1800 with the arches made of timber. In 1821 the engineer Joshua Field[1] saw the iron bridge and comments upon it as follows:

> The Iron bridge at Colebrookdale seems to stand very well; it was built 1784. The great arch only was of iron and 2 side arches of wood which are now so decay'd that iron arches are putting up in their place. The ribs of one half the bridge are up and the road contracted to half the width.

These are the two small arches of cast iron, similar in pattern to the main bridge, which are still part of the structure.

In June 1791 the Trustees decided that the 'Ironwork at the Bridge be improved by finishing out the back Iron Ribs to support the Crosspieces and Strengthen the Bridge under the direction of Serg[t] Roden.' This may have been their response to the appearance of cracks at the Benthall end, and a fear that the iron work might

[1] 'Joshua Field's diary of a Tour in 1821 through the Midlands.' Hall, J. W., *Trans. Newcomen Soc.*, vol. VI, 1925–6, pp. 1–41.

be strained to cracking point. These fears seem to have been groundless and the bridge stood up to all the trials of flood and usage laid upon it.

When Smiles was writing about the Darbys in 1863, he had correspondence with W. G. Norris the manager at the Coalbrookdale works, and with other local persons, about the bridge. One of his correspondents informed him: 'At the present time the bridge is undergoing repair; and special examination having been made, there is no appearance either that the abutments have moved, or that the ribs have been broken in the centre or are out of their proper right line. There has, it is true, been a strain on the land arches, and on the roadway plates, which, however, the main arch has been able effectually to resist.'[1]

Very few details have survived which throw light on the care and maintenance of the bridge. In 1788 the bridge railings were painted with a clear varnish prepared by the British Tar Company 'so that it may be afterwards painted with such Colour as the Trustees shall order at a future meeting.' The following year lightning conductors were added at each side, and were earthed in the river.

The Minute Book of the Proprietors finishes in 1799, and almost the last item of business was an order to let Richard Reynolds have the spare piece of land at the end of the bridge which had been a very untidy dumping ground for lime and other goods. He intended clearing this and providing on the space, a market for live stock. Abraham Darby, having completed the design and building of the bridge, and transferred his shares in it to the Rathbone and Reynolds families, took no further part in the bridge maintenance. The employees of the Coalbrookdale Company were allowed the free passage of the bridge to and from the works.

The Company seem to have had little further connection with constructional work until 1795 when they were called upon to build another iron bridge across the Severn, to the design of Telford. In Plymley's account of the Agriculture of Shropshire, Telford wrote a short description of this bridge and opens with a note on the first iron bridge.

> the making the bridge of iron, of one arch only, and admitting the towing path to pass within the archway. . . . This great improvement upon a navigable river was first put in practice near Coalbrookdale,

[1] Smiles, S., *Industrial Biography*, 1863, p. 92.

where the river is narrow and rapid. The arch is 100 feet 6 inches in the span and rises 45 feet. It was executed in the year 1777, by Mr Abraham Darby, of Coalbrookdale, and the iron-work is now [1802] quite as perfect as when it was first put up.

About two miles further up the river, at a place called Buildwas, there was formerly a stone bridge, consisting of narrow arches, which were a great obstruction to the navigation. This bridge was carried away by the high flood in 1795, and has been rebuilt of iron at the expense of the county, from a plan given by me as county surveyor. It was executed in a masterly manner by the Coalbrookdale Company, and finished in 1796. The span of the arch is 130 feet, and the rise is 24 feet; as the roadway could not with propriety be raised to a greater height, advantage was taken of the Schauffhausen principle by making the outer ribs rise to the top of the railing, and connecting them with the lower ribs by means of dove-tailed king-posts; this will best be seen by the drawing No. 4.

In the *Shrewsbury Chronicle* for Friday, 17 April 1795, there is a report:

The Magistrates at this Session agreed with the Coalbrookdale Company to erect a cast iron bridge, of one arch over the Severn at Buildwas, the span of which is to be 130 feet, the width of the passage way 18 feet, and to erect the same in nine months, for the sum of £3,700, being considerably lower than if the same had been erected of stone.

We hear that sixteen of the bridges in this county which were damaged by the late high floods were presented at this session.

The Buildwas Bridge was duly erected, at a cost of £6,034.13.3 but was not such a straightforward job as these brief notices might suggest. The contractors, who were to build the abutments and do all masonry work about the bridge, failed in their contract, and the Coalbrookdale Company had to take over their stock of tools and materials and complete the job themselves. There is an account for this in the Horsehay Journal (*Coalbrookdale MSS.* 2), entered in the settling period 1797 to 1798.

Buildwas Bridge Dr. to Scale & Smallman.

For the undermentioned Utensills etc. agreed to be taken by the Co on Scale & Co giving up their Contract for building the Abutments when they were in an unfinished state—vizt.

Then follows a long and detailed list of contractor's equipment, of which a few items will be sufficient to show the general nature of the account.

6 Iron bars etc. etc. barrows, planks, hacks, axes.
1 small Crane £5.1.0., wedges, shovels etc. etc.
Square masonry with old stone
do do do new do
Rubble masonry with old stone
do do do new do
Pumping, mkg coffer dams, getting out slips
valued by J Simpson £2092.2.11

Later in the Journal there is the closing item of the account

To Buildwas Bridge by this sum lost by the Erection of it £733.17.4

In July the reporter of the *Shrewsbury Chronicle* notes that 'there is now casting at Coalbrookdale in this county three iron bridges; one for Buildwas, of 130 feet,[1] one for Bridgwater, of 75 feet, and one for Counde, of 40 feet.' With these the Company were well launched on a new aspect of their work, that of structural iron castings, and other bridges, shortly after, were a regular part of their work. The new material they had given to the structural engineer was not always applied in the best way, and it was necessary to issue a warning and a disclaimer in the *Shrewsbury Chronicle* for Friday, 30 October 1795.

The several accounts which have appeared in many of the London and country papers, of the iron bridge erected over the River Team, at Stanford, Worcestershire, having fallen down, by which the public have been alarmed and some unfavourable impressions made, respecting the safety and utility of iron bridges; and it is supposed by many people that the bridge was cast at Coalbrookdale,——a correspondent informs us that the Coalbrookdale company had no concern whatever in planning, casting or erection of that bridge and that it was undertaken and erected by a person who is an entire stranger[2] . . . the plan and manner are entirely different from ironbridges cast at Coalbrookdale . . . abundant proof exhibited . . . the Ironbridge sustained accumulated shock without least damage when floods and frost last winter threw down many bridges on the Severn.

Telford described this great storm which is quoted as a thorough test of the original iron bridge.

[1] This bridge weighed 173 tons, and as compared with the Iron Bridge, 378 tons, represented a great economy in design.

[2] This bridge was built by John Nash for Sir Edward Winnington. There are no records of its design and construction.

This season has been severe beyond all precedent. The Storm of Frost and Snow kept accumualting for two Months, after which a very hasty Thaw caused a greater innundation than has ever been known in England. Much injury has been done by the various Rivers, and the Severn has not been behindhand; that and other Collateral Streams have demolished many Bridges in Shropshire, and I have now before me a Plan for one over the Severn at Bewdley in Worcestershire, which I have just prepared, and I am likewise drawing one for the town of Bridgnorth; in short I have been at it night and day.[1]

The next bridge work of which we have any detail is entered in the Horsehay *Settling Journal* under the heading of the Bristol Bridge and Dock. In 1805 a steam engine and many bridge parts were supplied, including material for the construction of cranes and other gear, but as there are no other accounts remaining for this venture we can say little about it; some of the details of material supplied may be of interest.

Bristol Bridge & Dock Dr. to Warehouse. 1805. 3mo.			
For a steam engine and Materials of 10 Horse Power deld. on Bristol Quay as pr. agreement			£500. 0. 0
193 ft sawn oak Timbers for the frame @ 4/6 deld.			43. 8. 6
Workmanship in framing			8.10. 0
Pit work see Engine Book			105.11. 4
various small items	£41.5.6		
A Broad Wheeled Waggon with iron arms			47. 0. 0
2 Pr Triangles (Wood & Workmanship)			9. 9. 0
Part of the Castings for the Bridge 212T.3.1.17	@ £9.18.0		2100. 9. 7½
Part of the covering plates for do. 90.5.1.3 @ £9			812. 7. 5½
4 Pieces of Oak timber	36 ft.		
round Oak timber	40 ft	@ 22/6	9.10. 0
32 packing blocks		@ 1/-	1.12. 0
Bristol Dock Co. 6th.mo. 1805			
48 Covering Plates			
680 Ballusters			
54 Screw Pins & burs, cast iron.			
3 long Bridge plates			
36 Balluster rails			
22 Balluster Balls in a cask			
etc. etc. (a large number of small items) total			£600.15. 4

[1] Letter from Telford, 18 March 1795, in Correspondence of Sir John Sinclair.

During the early part of 1806 John Tranter writing to Edmund Darby about a tender for iron pipe work, wonders 'whether on account of the Bridge castings to be done' they will be able to take on more casting work. In December of 1807 there is in the charges for transport down the Severn, an item for the carriage of a bridge for Jamaica, taken by Richard Ford from the works to Bristol Dock. The weight was 50½ tons and the charge for transport was £50. There are other references of a similar sort which show that the Company were from time to time casting bridge work among other more regular orders for engine items. Much later in the history of the Company a new bridge was designed by John Fowler, Civil Engineer, for the railway which crosses the river Severn about a mile above Ironbridge. This, the Albert Edward bridge, was cast and erected by the Coalbrookdale Company in 1863.

The introduction of cast iron in buildings, to replace wooden beams and columns, was only made at the end of the eighteenth century. Professor Bannister[1] has shown recently that at least three iron framed mills preceded the one built at Salford in 1801, for which Boulton and Watt cast the beams and columns. The first iron framed mill to be built was William Strutt's at Derby and, as it was fire-resisting to a larger extent than any previous mill, it attracted attention among other mill owners. In this as in some other early mills, the cast iron columns rested upon the wooden floor beams so that in case of fire, there was still some danger of collapse as the beams burnt away. An attempt was made to eliminate all possible timber by using cast iron floor beams as well as columns, thus making a structure which would not collapse in case of fire. After the Derby mill, the next cast iron framed building was that known as the Maltings at Ditherington, Shrewsbury, and this had iron floor beams as well as columns. It was built in 1796 for Messrs. Benyon, Bage and Marshall, as a flax-spinning mill and was only converted to a maltings in 1897. Bannister gives reasons for supposing that this mill was designed by Bage and some recently acquired letters from Bage to Strutt, now in the Shrewsbury Library, prove that these two designers were on intimate terms. Probably Charles Bage was inspired in the Shrewsbury design by Strutt's mill at Derby. Mr. S. Morley Tonkin is of the opinion that it is 'almost certain that the iron work was done in Shropshire and probably in the Dale [Coalbrookdale]

[1] Bannister, T. C., 'The First Iron-framed Buildings.' *Architectural Review*, vol. CVII, April 1950, pp. 231–46.

since I don't think Hazeldine of Shrewsbury would be in a position to have done the job in 1796, but he may have done it.'[1] If this supposition is right, then the Coalbrookdale Company may have been among the earliest pioneers of cast iron members for building purposes.

The books of the Company do not contain many references to cast iron structural members for buildings, but in 1810 an agreement was made for the rebuilding of their Liverpool Warehouse. The beams for this building were to be cast of sufficient strength to do without pillars. B. Sothern agreed on behalf of R. H. Bradshaw Esq. to pay the Company £12 per ton for the whole of their castings delivered at Liverpool, except the first floor castings, as this is now nearly completed. This had been charged at £11.10.0 and Dickinson, for the Company, agreed to take the pillars now cast for the second floor, and not wanted on account of the change of plan, for £5 per ton.[2]

Among the lighter elements for use in buildings such as window frames, a notable example is the half-domed roof which they cast at the beginning of the century. This roof was designed by John Nash for the picture gallery at Attingham Hall, near Shrewsbury, and is probably the earliest example in this country of the use of top-lighting in such a room. The roof is a large oblong lifted above the walls by a cast iron glazing grill of quarter-circle section, on all four sides. The proportions of the cast iron are such as to give an effect of lightness and delicacy. Nash paid several visits to the Coalbrookdale works during the design and casting of these frames, and also had many other architectural elements cast by them, for other of his buildings.

[1] Letter Morley Tonkin to A. Raistrick, 6 September 1950, in comment on an article 'This Shropshire Building is the oldest surviving Iron Framed one in Britain,' by Hobbs, J. L., Librarian, Shrewsbury Public Libraries. In *Shropshire Magazine*, No. 3, July 1950, pp. 43–4.

[2] Shropshire County Records MSS. *Coalbrookdale papers*. Letter No. 42.

Chapter Twelve

RICHARD DEARMAN, 1789–1803

THE death of Abraham Darby in 1789 at the early age of 39 years may have been hastened by the worry and overwork which must inevitably be associated with a period of violent fluctuations and depression such as he had experienced through the whole of his term of management. To carry on the business, start the canal building programme, install the new and larger Boulton and Watt engines and extend the collieries, had all taken capital, while the declared policy and consistent action of Darby and Reynolds had cut them off from the large profits which were being made by other firms during the war. Although precise information is lacking, we know that Abraham and his brother had mortgaged many of their shares with William and Joseph Rathbone and some of the partners in the Company, and the Dale Company had also received loans from Richard Reynolds. The Ketley works had been extended and were now held by William and Joseph Reynolds and the Dale Company jointly, the Dale Company having half the total stock.

The first evidence we have of the difficult position of the Darby family is seen in the minutes of a meeting of partners, held in October 1789, who on that occasion met as the firm of Joseph Rathbone and the Dale Company.[1] Minute 5 goes some way to explain the position of Joseph Rathbone, who is mentioned in the title of the Company on this one solitary occasion, and for the rest is referred to as Agent for the Company.

The minute notes that any matter in question among the partners shall be decided by a majority of votes, but that as the shares of Abraham and Samuel Darby are held in trust by Joseph Rathbone and his other partners as a security for money owing by Abraham and Samuel to the firm, Joseph Rathbone can only vote on any question by virtue of his own shares and not of those held in trust. By another minute the partners agree to give a joint bond to Richard Reynolds for the debt of £20,000 owing to him, at 5 per

[1] 'At a Meeting of the undersigned Partners in the Concerns carried on under the firm of Joseph Rathbone & Dale Co. held the 19th October 1789; it is concluded as follows:—' *Coalbrookdale MSS.* 3.

cent. interest, money which he had loaned to tide the Company over some of its more difficult years. No dividends had been paid for some time but the profits due to partners had been returned into the business as loans bearing 5 per cent. interest, and the interest was to be paid half yearly to Joseph Rathbone, Sarah Darby, William Reynolds and the trustees of Hannah Mary Rathbone. No profits were to be paid to any of the partners until all the debts were repaid, and in the meantime any profits made by William Reynolds and Company, *i.e.* the Ketley works, should be paid into the Warehouse Account of the Dale Company and not paid to individual partners. This is the clearest proof we have that the Ketley Company was never a separate and independent concern; though it was always in the management of the Reynolds family it was regarded as a member of the Coalbrookdale group.

The remaining minutes of this meeting relate to the affairs of Samuel Darby, Abraham's brother and partner in the debt to the Company. To make provision for his wife and for the education of his children, Joseph Rathbone as Agent of the Company was instructed to pay him £200 a year for three years, this to be charged against any profits arising from the Dale Company or from William Reynolds and Company. Towards the £200 Sarah Darby was to pay any surplus of rents arising from Samuel's private estate after paying interest and necessary charges upon them. Finally five shares in the Shropshire Canal, on which Samuel had not paid the calls, were taken over by the Company, but Samuel could redeem them whenever he could repay the money and interest. These minutes are signed by Joseph Rathbone, Sarah Darby, William Reynolds, and William Rathbone acting as the trustee for Hannah Mary Rathbone.

The next meeting of the partners was in June 1790 when a most important matter was discussed, that of the consolidation of the two Companies then known as the Dale Company and as William Reynolds & Company. 'The consolidation of the two Concerns having been spoken of it appears the opinion of all present that it would be desirable; but doubts arise whether the Executrix [Rebecca Darby] of the late Abm. Darby can legally make any change in the shares which belonged to him. The consideration of this matter is referred to a future discussion.' The complete consolidation so desired was not obtained, but at the next meeting in October, it was agreed that the parent firm was to be called the Coalbrookdale Company, and that the Agents for the two concerns were to make out a trial balance sheet at the end of each year, and copies of these were to be sent to all the partners of both companies, who were, in fact, the same people. A notice of the new Company was to be printed as a circular letter and sent out 'where needfull,' after being signed by all the partners.

In succeeding transactions the two Companies generally act as one; for instance, when William Reynolds reports that he has purchased the Chepstow property (Warehouse etc.) for the Companies equally. The Agent there was William Horton whose salary was raised to £120 and who was to manage the property for the Company. Among other business the partners decided to build a house for the Clerk on the south side of the offices, to build a new moulding room at the Lower Furnace in the Dale, with C. Hornblower and D. Rose to superintend its building, and finally to lease the Liverpool forge and warehouse to Fawcett & Burrow.

In November the Company decided to build proper stores at the Dale works, and to put people in charge of and responsible for different sections of the works. Charles Hornblower was made a superintendent, responsible for fuel and ore for the blast and air furnaces, and for the furnace and works buildings and repairs. He was also to have charge of the Company's dwelling houses, to see to the rents and repairs, and to keep full accounts for the bricks, lime and clay concerns of the Company. John Hornblower was made time-keeper, and was to be at the works at 6.0 a.m., 1.0 p.m. and 6.0 p.m. to see that all workmen were in their workplaces. The recording of all production and the oversight of smithies, carpenters and labourers as well as all teams carrying or working in the Dale, were in his charge. The general dispatcher from the warehouse, John Tranter, was given an assistant and more responsibility. These appointments mark a real change in the structure of the Company, as prior to this date everything had been the direct responsibility of the manager, with no one in the position of head of a department, to whom he could delegate oversight and decisions on running policy. It was in this reorganization that the partners invited Richard Dearman to become Agent-Manager of the Coalbrookdale Company and in September 1791 he was given full powers to deal with the business of the Company, with power of attorney for the recovery of debts.

Richard Dearman was already well experienced in the iron trade. He was born in 1732 and in 1761 was an ironmonger in

Whitehaven. In 1760 he had married Hannah Petty who died the following year, and two years later he married Elizabeth Freeth of the Birmingham family of Freeth,[1] ironmongers, and close friends and customers of the Dale Company. In 1784 he had succeeded to the management of the Eagle Foundry, Birmingham, then carried on as Dearman & Freeth. When he moved to the Dale in 1791 his son John Petty Dearman took the management of the Eagle Foundry and in the same year married Priscilla Fox of Plymouth. The Dearman family was of the old Quaker stock and, like so many others, was linked by marriages with many of the Quaker banking families, Lloyd, Pease, Backhouse, while in 1793 Richard Dearman's niece Deborah, the daughter of his brother John, was married to Joseph Reynolds of Ketley.

At the first meeting of the Company with Dearman acting as Agent, in October 1791, an attorney's opinion was given that Rebecca Darby, as administrator of her late husband Abraham, and Samuel Darby, notwithstanding the mortgage of their shares, were entitled to vote in proportion to those shares, and from this decision being accepted, Sarah, Samuel and Rebecca Darby resumed an active part in the discussions and decisions of the partners. Among much other business, two items are worth special note, first the Company bought a sixth share in the Lloyds coal mines near the foot of the Dale, and secondly it was reported that John Davies, the brick maker, was asking increased prices for his bricks and wanted to get coals for the kilns in the Company's ground. The Company decided to take over the manufacture of bricks, tiles, pots and other clay goods from Davies, as part of the general concern, and this eventually became an important part of their work.

In the next year, 1792, there is much business concerning properties, and the Company decide to build forty workmen's houses near Ketley. There are now no minutes until December 1793 and at the meeting then held a serious review of the concerns was made. The partners decided however that it appeared expedient to have an inclined plane from the canal at the top of Brierly Hill with a railway thence to a point on Lincoln Hill near the Lower Forge, and a further incline and railway thence to the wharf at Severnside. The construction of this incline was authorized.[2] The forge held by the

[1] The family in which Abraham Darby I spent his apprenticeship.

[2] By 1800 this railway and incline was carrying about 450 tons of goods a month from Horsehay to the Severn Wharf.

Company at Liverpool was valued and then sold to William Fawcett for £2,300. Soon after taking over the management, Richard Dearman had been sent to Cornwall to collect outstanding debts; but many had to be wiped off, and to tide over a shortage of actual cash, Richard Reynolds had loaned a further sum of £4,000 to be repaid as soon as possible. The Company was still very unhappy and Richard Dearman and William Reynolds, in view of the unsatisfactory condition of the Coalbrookdale concerns, were asked to examine them in detail and see if any part could be sold or disposed of to advantage. Two months later, on the strength of the report which they made, the partners decided to sell Madeley Fields, Lloyds, and the Madeley Wood concern, and to let the Bridgnorth Forge and property on lease. The Lincoln Hill lime works was sold to Richard Reynolds.

About this time Mary Rathbone and Sarah Darby wished to exonerate Abraham and Samuel Darby of their debt to the Company, and informed the partners that they were willing to transfer to the Coalbrookdale Company £6,400 each out of the money owing to them by the Company, and also to transfer their shares of a dividend of £50,000 out of the capital or stock of the Coalbrookdale concern, to the partners, proportional to their shares. Four-fifths of the £50,000 and the £12,800 first mentioned would discharge the debts to the Company of Abraham and Samuel (except a remaining balance of £1,682.19.8¼ which it was proposed to transfer to debit of Stock); therefore it was agreed that the following entries be made in the books:

Stock to Sundry Accounts Dr.	
Mary Rathbone for her 1/5 of £50,000 divided among the several partners	£10,000
Sarah Darby the like	10,000
Abraham Darby 2/5 do	20,000
William Reynolds 1/10 do	5,000
Trustees of Hannah Mary Rathbone 1/10 do	5,000
	50,000
Abm & Saml Darby for this sum which makes the remaining balance of their debt which the Cdale Co agree to give up as well the Principal as the Interest	1,692.19. 8½
	51,692.19. 8½

Abraham & Samuel Darby to Sundry Accounts Dr.	
Estate of the late Abraham Darby for the balance due from it	1,142.16.10½
Samuel Darby for the balance due from him	1,525. 4. 3
	2,668. 1. 1½

Sundry Accounts to Abm & Saml Darby Drs Mary Rathbone for this sum transfered by her direction	16,400. 0. 0
Sarah Darby for the like	16,400. 0. 0
	32,800. 0. 0

Samuel Darby signed a deed of trust of his shares with all the partners of the Company, by which they were to apply the money they received as follows—

£300 per ann. for himself and family
£3400 and interest retained as their own property
£13,000 to be placed out at interest for the benefit of Samuel Darby and family
Samuel Darby to take the clear profit of what may remain for his own use.

From these transactions we see that the Coalbrookdale Company was essentially the Darby family concern, as Abraham, Samuel, Sarah and Mary (Rathbone), the children of Abraham Darby II, had four-fifths of the interest and only one-fifth had gone to Richard Reynolds, via his wife Hannah, Abraham Darby II's eldest child, and from him to his son and daughter, William and Hannah Mary. The state of the Companies was therefore as follows—Coalbrookdale Company: four-fifths Darby; one fifth Reynolds-Rathbone. Ketley Company: half Reynolds; half Coalbrookdale Company. Richard Reynolds was still the sole party to the Articles of Partnership for the Ketley Company, for half the concern, so he now vested all his share in his two sons William and Joseph, equally.

The condition of the Ketley works was much better than that of the Dale, largely because they had the newer, larger furnaces and more efficient Boulton and Watt engines for the blast. Their premises were compact, and they were concentrating their trade almost solely on pig iron for the forges and on forge work. A railway was needed from the New Work Collieries to Horsehay, but the finances of the Coalbrookdale Company made it inconvenient to undertake it just then, so William Reynolds and Company offered to build it at their own expense on condition that 2d. per ton per mile was paid for all material travelling upon it. Richard Reynolds by his purchases owned much of the coal and ironstone royalties, and through his connections with the growing tin plate industry in South Wales and the merchant's companies in Bristol, had become a man of very great wealth, able to keep Ketley works in the best of condition. He was generous towards the Dale Company, as is shown in a minute of the meeting of partners in February 1794. The general declining state of the Coalbrookdale Company and the heavy capital employed, the large debts owing on interest and loss on Madeley Field, having come to the knowledge of Richard Reynolds, he had voluntarily proposed to abate £1,000 per annum from the rents now payable, and as some alterations had taken place since the first lease was made, proposed to have a new lease with the new rent. It was decided at the next month's meeting that it would lessen the Coalbrookdale concern if the large coal and ironstone leases, held from Richard Reynolds as lord of the Manor of Madeley, could be divided so that someone else could take part and open collieries in new ground near the Hay Brook. The Madeley Wood furnaces were proposed to form part of a second division, which would contain enough coal and ironstone for their needs, and Coalbrookdale Company would keep the third portion which was to be big enough for their demands. This was done and the Madeley Wood furnaces and mines, built and opened by the Dale Company in 1766, were eventually partly bought by William Reynolds, and partly leased to him by his father. The Coalbrookdale Company blew out these furnaces and reduced their coal and ironstone undertakings in the Lloyds and Madeley field, to what was needed for only one furnace. To facilitate discussion of the concern, a valuation was ordered to be made and this was returned at £62,574.13.3½, but on advice, many articles were depreciated and a net value agreed upon of £39,858.11.5½. Without giving all the details of this valuation, the totals are as shown on the opposite page.

The Inventory No. 20 has not survived so we do not know the full nature of the debts, though a considerable fraction were due to Richard Reynolds.

Following this valuation, the partners asked for a similar valuation of the Ketley concerns of William Reynolds and Company, and this was returned up to 20 December 1793, of £138,067.8.4.

PLATE XXI *A view looking east along the River Severn in 1803 with the glow from coking ovens throwing into relief the domestic buildings on the left and Bedlam Furnaces in the centre. These furnaces of the Madeley Wood Company were situated less than half a mile from the Iron Bridge.*

PLATE XXII *The River Severn was the main artery for materials and goods entering and leaving the area. Hundreds of vessels plied between the Gorge and Bristol, and in this view Severn Trows are being loaded at the Severn Wharf, Ironbridge, where in the 1840's the Coalbrookdale Company built its gothic-style warehouse* (see PLATE XXXII).

	£ s. d.
Coalbrookdale Foundry	62,001.18. 8½
do Forges	4,859.11. 4
Madeley Field Co.	4,430. 6. 9
do Lloyds	2,620. 4. 1
Madeley Wood Co.	4,909.14. 8
Lincoln Hill Invtry	29. 9. 6
Brierly Hill Inclined Plane	197. 2. 4
Railway from Lincoln Hill	1,440. 9. 4
Bridgnorth Corn Mill	785.12.10½
do Forge	632. 1. 9
New Work Co. (collieries)	1,082. 7. 8
Lawley & Dawley Co. (collieries)	5,678.17.10
Chepstow Premises	1,736.17. 6
	90,404.14. 4
Deduct the Amount of Debts owing by the Coalbrookdale Co. as per Inventory No. 20	50,546. 2.10½
Neat value of the Coalbrookdale Co.	£39,858.11. 5½

This was examined and subjected to the same objections as the Coalbrookdale one, that little or no allowance for depreciation of materials and tools had been made, so a revaluation was called for and lengthy rules for the valuation of different kinds of property were laid down.

Richard Dearman reported to the partners that he had received two letters, one from William Reynolds and one from Mark Gilpin who was a trustee for the marriage settlement of Hannah Mary Rathbone, each asking that the Coalbrookdale Company should buy in the shares in the Coalbrookdale concern which were held by William Reynolds and Hannah Mary Rathbone's trustees. The shares, each of one-tenth, were offered to the partners for the due proportion of the valuation of £39,858.11.5. This offer was declined, but William Reynolds then made a new suggestion, that payment for the shares should be made by transferring to him some of the appendages which could most conveniently be spared from the Coalbrookdale works, and which the partners had already agreed might be disposed of. This was accepted in principle, and Reynolds then proposed that the shares should be estimated as two-tenths of a round figure, £40,000, that is £8,000. For this he would take the Coalbrookdale share of the Chepstow premises; the tools and materials at the Lincoln Hill lime works and the re-lease of these works direct from his father; the inclined plane at Brierly Hill with the railway to the Severn, except the Brierly Hill tunnels, when the partners had completed the work contemplated upon it; he would also take all the waggons made for the inclined plane, 57 used ones and 45 unfinished ones to be finished off, at £4.15.7 each; and Bridgnorth Mills and Forge, with the pool and tools, at a valuation. If necessary he would take also the reversion of the Nailers Row lease, and the final total could be adjusted either way to £8,000.

The partners declined this suggestion and instead offered the Madeley Wood and Madeley Fields concerns, the price of which would be much in excess, but the £8,000 could be taken from the price and then the rest used to repay debts owing either to William Reynolds or to Richard Reynolds. After further discussion of details this was accepted by both parties, and the Madeley Wood and Madeley Fields concerns were sold to William Reynolds and the Trustees for Hannah Mary Reynolds, at a valuation of £14,000. In this way, the Reynolds-Rathbone shares in the Coalbrookdale Company were bought back and the Company now became a compact family holding with four shareholders, Rebecca, Sarah, Samuel and Mary (Rathbone) Darby. The two concerns of Coalbrookdale and Ketley were becoming a little less involved in one another, but Coalbrookdale still held half the shares in Ketley. The clearing of this was the next great task, and William Reynolds offered to buy this half-share giving the Coalbrookdale partners the shares he had in the Horsehay works as part payment, or to buy outright. In the end, the Ketley valuation was completed at £105,279.9.1 and this was accepted as the basic figure for reckoning the sale and transfers. The Donnington Wood works were sold to John Bishton, and the Ketley part of this sale price was brought into the accounting.

In July 1796 the agreements were signed, and in February 1797 the partners met as 'the late Partners in the Concern carried on under the firm of Wm. Reynolds & Co' to adjust differences in the value of leases as between Ketley and Horsehay and also to make arrangements about the repayment of debts to William Rathbone and Richard Reynolds.

The final meeting of these partners in the two concerns was in the next month.

At a Meeting of the late partners in the Ketley Company held the 13th day of March 1797. Richard Dearman & Egerton Leek having taken the matter refered to them by the preceding resolution into consideration, the following accounts are agreed to:—

Dr. the Stock Account of William Reynolds & Co.

To Sundry overcharges in the Inventory and errors in the summary at Ketley		539.19. 9
To do. at Horsehay		162. 1. 4
To Allowance of £1 per cent for collecting outstanding debts (first deducting Donnington Co.) being 20463.15.8		204.12. 9
To further allowances on Debts, Machinery, Buildings, Risks, etc. and the difference between Ketley & Horsehay leases		5074.16. 4
To Wm & Joseph Reynolds for the net amount of Ketley Stock		86000. 0. 0
To Coalbrookdale Co. for net amt. of the Stock at Horsehay		14000. 0. 0
		105981.10. 2
Cr.		
By amt of Sundries at Ketley as per summary		90935.19. 8
By do of Sundries undercast and underadded in Ketley Concern		434.13. 8
By 12:20th of £638.7.5 being the difference between £1000 agreed to be added to the amount of the stock for omissions etc. & difference of errors		383. 0. 6
		91753.13.10
By amt of Sundries at H. Hay as pr summary	£13343. 9. 5	
By Sunds omitted & undercast in the Inventories	629. 0. 0	
By 8:20ths of £638.7.5 agreed to be added in lieu of omissions	255. 6.11	
		14227.16. 4
		105981.10. 2

We the undersigned having perused the above accounts approve them and it is resolved that the necessary assignments be prepared as soon as may be in order to assign the concerns at Horsehay to the Coalbrookdale

Company and the Concerns at Ketley to Messrs William Reynolds and Joseph Reynolds.

Signed in the presence of

Egerton Leek
Richd. Dearman.

William Reynolds
Joseph Reynolds
Rebecca Darby
Mary Rathbone
Sarah Darby

We agree to the above as Trustees for our late brother Samuel Darby—
Mary Rathbone
Sarah Darby.

These assignments were notified to the public by advertisements in the papers, those in the *Shrewsbury Chronicle of* 10 May 1797, being as follows:—

Notice is hereby given that the partnership lately subsisting between Samuel Darby deceased, Rebecca Darby, Mary Rathbone, Sarah Darby, William Reynolds and Hannah Mary Rathbone of Coalbrookdale in the County of Salop, Ironfounders under the firm of the Coalbrook Dale Company, is dissolved by mutual consent: And that the business is now carried on by the said Rebecca Darby, Mary Rathbone, Sarah Darby and by the said Mary Rathbone and Sarah Darby as trustees for the said Samuel Darby, deceased under the firm of the Coalbrook Dale Company. Dated the 6th day of February 1797.

Notice is hereby given that the partnership lately subsisting between William Reynolds, Joseph Reynolds, Samuel Darby deceased, Rebecca Darby, Mary Rathbone and Sarah Darby of Ketley in the County of Salop, Ironfounders, under the firm of William Reynolds and Co. is dissolved by mutual consent: And the business is now carried on by the said William Reynolds and Joseph Reynolds under the firm of W. Reynolds and Company. Dated the 6th day of February 1797.

The separation of the Coalbrookdale and Ketley works was not in actual practice so great as these assignments might suggest. The Day Book for Horsehay (*Shrewsbury MSS.* 334) shows a regular, almost daily exchange of material and work between Horsehay, Ketley and Coalbrookdale. It would appear from the items of this manuscript that there had been a certain amount of specialization at these three works: Horsehay was primarily developed as forge and rolling mill, with its own and the Lightmoor furnaces to provide common iron; Ketley was producing pig iron and in its forge was working this into 'tough grey half blooms' which were sent to Horsehay to be rolled and returned mainly as 'tough mill iron bars'; this was a firmly established weekly exchange of products. Ketley had a machine shop and most of the grooved rolls for the mills both at Coalbrookdale and Horsehay were made at Ketley and from time to time were sent back to be turned and trued, though repairs to stocks and other plant about the mills at either works were sent to Coalbrookdale.

Horsehay further specialized in rolling boiler plates and making boilers, while Ketley and Coalbrookdale made engine parts. Coalbrookdale apparently continued as the general foundry where pipes and cylinders as well as many other products were cast. Railway waggons for all the lines about the several works were built at Ketley, Coalbrookdale supplied timber to all of them, and there was a brick yard attached to Horsehay which made both building bricks and fire and furnace bricks for all. The general picture is therefore one of a group of works which together make a well balanced ensemble, with a large volume of material and work moving among them, the charges for most of which could be adjusted by book-keeping entries with very little call for cash payments.

Before the death of Abraham Darby, William Reynolds had received a good training in all three of the works, and had assumed a responsible position as is evidenced by his negotiations, on behalf of the Company, with Boulton and Watt from 1780 onwards. After the death of Darby and until the separation of the Companies in 1797 he remained in effect the technical manager and adviser, and in fact, until his death in 1803, his was the scientific mind behind most of the developments. Among the ironmasters of his period he was possibly the best informed and had the widest scientific interests. He read extensively both in the English and French scientific journals and his note books contained transcripts of a variety of papers from the Philosophical Transactions and other sources.[1] At his home at Tuckies, Broseley, he maintained a well designed and equipped laboratory and was an experimenter of considerable skill. In 1799 he secured a patent for the making of manganese steel, thus anticipating a much later development.[2]

[1] Randall, J., *History of Madeley*, 1880, p. 90–1.

[2] Patent No. 2363. December 1799. Preparing Iron for the conversion thereof into steel. '. . . My method or invention consists in mixing the oxyde of manganese, or manganese, either with the materials from which I procure the pig or cast iron or with the cast iron in any of the processes used or to be used for the conversion of cast iron into natured or malleable iron, whether in the finery, bloomery, puddling or other furnace.'

Notice is hereby Given,

THAT the Coalbrook-Dale Company have ordered a Supply of Coals to be kept at the Pen near the Machine-Houſe on the Upper Hearths, to be Sold in ſmall Quantities.

And whereas many People have of late feloniouſly taken Coals from off the Hearths and out of the Waggons and Crates, alſo from the Incline-Plane, and that ſome Workmen carry away Coals covered with Cinders or ſmall Brays, others cut Ends off Boards and other uſeful Stuff into Chips and carry the ſame Home, and ſome Waggoners ſell, or give Coals from off the Waggons, on the Road betwixt the Pits and the Coak-Hearths.

The Company therefore give Notice, that if any Workman, Waggoner, or any of their Families, ſhall be found ſtealing, ſelling or clandeſtinely carrying away Coals, Iron, Tools, Ends of Boards, or other uſeful Stuff, they ſhall pay a Fine of Five Shillings for every ſuch Offence, and that one half of ſuch Fine ſhall be given to ſuch Perſon or Perſons who ſhall give Information and ſatisfactory Proof thereof to the ſaid Company.

And every other Perſon or Perſons (who are not in the Company's Employ) being found guilty of any of the above Practices, will be Proſecuted as the Law directs, and the ſame Reward given to any Perſon giving Information, upon their being Convicted thereof.

RICHARD DEARMAN, for
The Coalbrook-Dale Co.

26th March, 1796.

In philanthropy and in the relations with his workpeople he followed in the direct line with his father and the Darbys.

The Coalbrookdale area was, like most other parts of Britain, sorely distressed by the financial instability and the high price and scarcity of food in 1795 and 1796. On 24 July 1795 an advertisement appeared in the *Shrewsbury Chronicle* noting a meeting held at the Tontine Inn, Ironbridge, at which a subscription was raised for the relief of the poor. The subscribers include Richard Reynolds and the Coalbrookdale Company, a hundred guineas each, Thomas Botfield twenty guineas, Richard Dearman and R. Chamberlain ten guineas each and Sergeant Roden five guineas. As the food shortage increased the Company decided to purchase stocks of rice and corn which were to be sold to their workpeople at three-quarters of the cost price, and the scheme soon developed so that in 1796 the subscribers were

Messrs Bishton & Co. (Snedshill Furnace)	£1,500
Mr. Botfield for Old Park Co.	1,500
Mr. Jas. Reynolds for Ketley Co.	2,000
Mr. R. Dearman for Coalbrookdale Co.	1,500
Mr. William Reynolds for Madeley Co.	1,000

These were supplemented by many private subscriptions and, along with the maintenance of work, the scheme helped the population to tide over a disastrous time and avoided the food riots which affected most parts of the country.[1] The general financial situation was such that on 2 March 1797, a special meeting was called in Shrewsbury to uphold public credit, particularly the credit of the Shrewsbury Bank; at this meeting the Coalbrookdale Company, represented by William Reynolds, subscribed a large sum of money which, with others, enabled the bank to continue its payments.

The precarious position of the local bank only reflected and was developed from the position of the Bank of England. In the preceding month the Directors of the Bank of England had been compelled to curtail their issues following the run on the Newcastle banks in December 1796 which rapidly spread to other Country banks throughout the Kingdom.

The famine was not so severely felt in the Madeley parish as in some others, because of Richard Reynolds's policy, after his purchase

[1] A clear statement of the facts will be found in a letter from Reynolds to J. Smitheman, 14. 7mo. 1795, printed in *Letters of Richard Reynolds*, Rathbone, H. M., 1852, pp. 270–2.

of Madeley Manor in 1782, of offering the workpeople allotments and small holdings on which they were able to grow at least some of their food requirements. One writer lays the blame for some of the wheat scarcity on the improved standard of living and on the habit of tea-drinking! He says 'I find, July 29th, 1795 that in the parish of Madeley, Salop, there are 924 families; and since the use of Tea is becomming so prevalent, on a moderate calculation each family consumes three and a half pounds of flour each week more than formerly, by instituting a fourth meal each day. In days of yore, Breakfast, Dinner & Supper were esteemed sufficient, but now it must be Breakfast, Dinner, *Tea* & Supper, which wastes both Meal and Time and makes a difference each week in the parish of Madeley of 3234 lbs. of flour.' This new habit may have aggravated the demand for wheat but the causes of the shortage were more widespread than any such change of custom. The deficient harvests of 1795 were experienced in other countries besides this, while our relations with France and Holland cut us off from some European supplies that otherwise might have afforded considerable relief.

During this very difficult period there are a few events which relieve the gloom. The Company was experimenting with new types of engines such as Sadler's and Heslop's, developing their boiler shop and extending forges and rolling mills to be in a good position to benefit by any revival of trade. Their good reputation was widely known and in 1796 they had among their many visitors the Prince and Princess of Orange. On 12 August they visited the Coalbrookdale works, and also walked for two hours in the walks made by Richard Reynolds over the Lincoln Hill properties.

Samuel Darby died on 9 September 1796, and the Company was carried on by his widow Deborah, his sister Sarah, and Rebecca the widow of Abraham Darby, with Richard Dearman as works manager and William Reynolds always at hand for help and advice. The Darby wives were a remarkable group of women, all of them active in the work of the Society of Friends, and all ready at any time to take an interest in the business management and in the actual working of the Company. Of this present group, Deborah is probably the best known as a preacher, being of a 'naturally sweet and amiable temper,' with a 'fine presence that never failed to keep hold of her audience, whether felons in prison, soldiers on parade, the rough back-woodsmen, or the cultivated dwellers in large cities.' She was said to be 'as bold as a lion in the Cause of Christ, but gentle as a lamb in suffering for His Name, comly in person and active in ministry.' In 1793 she felt called to travel to America with her friend Rebecca Young. They visited families of Friends in New York and Philadelphia, crossed the Alleghanies, and did much for the welfare and relief of the Negro slaves. She visited nearly a thousand families before her return to England in 1795, and after that still travelled much in the ministry in this country. Of the many contacts of her earnest life probably the best known is that with Elizabeth Gurney, who became the great Quaker philanthropist, Elizabeth Fry.

Elizabeth Gurney as a girl was very much troubled by the conflict between the gay life around her and the inclination she had towards a more serious and devoted life. Friends at that time were somewhat divided, or rather differentiated, between 'plain Friends' who maintained a primitive simplicity in their life and habits, along with the use of the plain speech of thee and thou and the simple Quaker fashion in dress, and the 'gay Friends' who conformed much more to the current fashions of the world. The Darbys were among the plain Friends. In the summer of 1798, John Gurney the banker took his seven daughters on a long journey through the south of England and into Wales, and then to Coalbrookdale. Elizabeth, who was far from well, was left there to stay a short time with her cousin Priscilla Hannah Gurney, the friend of Richard Reynolds, of whom it is said that 'she had become a plain Friend and a Minister, left her mother in Bath and found a congenial retreat for many years in Coalbrookdale.' It is also said of Coalbrookdale, and of the visit of Elizabeth Gurney.[1] A place more suited to her state of mind 'could not have been found, than Coalbrookdale and the residents there. Richard Reynolds at that time advanced in years was as a patriarch among his family, his friends and dependents. . . . Several valuable Friends resided at Coalbrookdale, connected with each other in business or by marriage, or the stronger bond of similarity of taste and principle. They were a happy band, Christian love prevailing among themselves and towards others.'

Elizabeth took breakfast with the Darbys and, as was so often the custom, immediately after breakfast one or other would speak a few words that lay on their mind and spirit. On one occasion Deborah Darby preached and Elizabeth says that she was spoken to particularly and that Deborah 'expressed first that I was and am sick of the world, which is true indeed.' 'This afternoon I was at the

[1] *Memoir of the Life of Elizabeth Fry*, by two of her daughters, 1847, vol. I, p. 52.

Darbys and the love they all express for me is great.' On 4 September her journal tells us that

> after tea we went to the Darbys, accompanied by my dear friend Richard Reynolds, and still dearer Priscilla Gurney. We spent a pleasant evening, when my heart began to feel itself silenced before God; without looking at others I felt myself under the shadow of the wing of God, and soon I found the rest drop't into the same state. . . . After sitting a time in awful silence, Rebecca Young did speak most beautifully. She did reach my heart. D. D. then spoke—I only fear she says too much of what I am to be—a light to the blind, speach to the dumb and feet to the lame. Can it be? After the meeting my heart felt really light and as I walked home by starlight I looked through nature to nature's God. Here I am now in Cousin Prissy's little room—never to forget this day while life is in my body. I know now what the mountain is I have to climb. I am to be a Quaker.

Again and again she speaks of these vital days which launched her on her life's task of reform and reconciliation, and made her one of the most courageous as well as gentle of women.

It is perhaps well to remember that these people who gave her such unstinted love, this community in which she found her spiritual home, was set in the midst of the furnaces and forges of the Dale. From the windows of the Darby's house and from the Friends Meeting House close by, she could look out into the works. The group of Friends who were so powerful to influence her were the same who were struggling to keep together the iron works through a period of utmost difficulty, who as widows were carrying the affairs of the Company until the sons were old enough to take up the burden. Many of the workmen in and about the works were Friends, and gathered in complete unity of spirit and equality before God, with the Darby, Reynolds, Dearman, Luccock and other Quaker families who for a century had lived together in the Dale and striven in the making of iron. The power of the Darbys to face every kind of economic difficulty and to keep going on with faith, owed much to their capacity to fall naturally into a silence such as Elizabeth Gurney experienced, in which they felt a renewing of strength and revitalizing of the spirit. It is not possible in this first century of the Company, to separate, in any of its leaders, their character and habit as Friends from their outlook and actions as employers and works managers. There was a striking unity and simplicity of life, which was their strength.

Chapter Thirteen

EDMUND DARBY, 1803–1810
BARNARD DICKINSON, 1810–1827

IN the earlier sections of this book, very little has been said about the forges, and it is time that that side of the Company's activities was given some notice. This would appear to be the appropriate place, where the earlier development of the forges can form an introduction to the closer study of the Horsehay section of the works, which in the early part of the nineteenth century was said for a time to be the leading forge in the country.

The beginnings of the forge development lie in the experiments of Abraham Darby II which aimed at producing a pig iron suitable for further work in the finery and chafery, for conversion into good wrought iron bar. By 1750 Darby was selling an acceptable pig iron to some of the Midland forges and a small quantity was being used in his own forges in Coalbrookdale. Soon after 1750 the forges were making small boiler plates of up to 40 or 50 lb. in weight, these being made under a plating hammer from slabs or moulds prepared in the forges. The forges also made some engine parts, an occasional note being entered in the books for a piston rod forged, or for some other such work.

The forges had to face two adverse factors, one, the increasing cost and scarcity of charcoal, and the other, the slowness and the labour involved in the old method of work in finery and chafery. In 1766 Richard Reynolds secured a patent on behalf of Thomas and George Cranage for their invention of a method of making iron in a reverberatory furnace with raw coal as fuel, and in the following year the Coalbrookdale Company were selling iron 'made in the new way.' By this time the Company had forges at Bridgnorth and Liverpool, though they never became very important. With the patents taken out by Onions in 1784 and by Cort in 1785, the Cranage method of making iron was entirely superseded and the Cort puddling furnace and rollers were adopted both at the Dale and at Horsehay. Percy (*Metallurgy of Iron*, 1864, p. 636) says that Cort saw a demonstration of his method at Coalbrookdale in 1784. The advantage of the new methods is clearly shown by the amount of labour taken in the production of the iron bars. Prior to the introduction of Cort's method, one ton of iron bars could be produced by twelve hours work, but using Cort's process twelve hours was sufficient to make five tons of small or fifteen tons of large iron bars. This great gain in time and productivity encouraged the Company to develop large bar and rod mills at Horsehay and to enter into the bar iron trade in a large way.

The development of Boulton and Watt's rotative engine in 1782 led Horsehay forge to try it almost at once, and in 1783 such an engine was installed to work the forge hammers, in place of the water wheels which had previously done this work. Two other engines for the forge hammers were put in, at Horsehay in 1784 and at Ketley in 1787, and all gave great satisfaction in their working. While these developments were taking place at Horsehay and Ketley, the forge at Coalbrookdale was being developed in the same way with a rotative engine for the hammers, put in in 1785. Richard Reynolds in a letter of that year says that the Coalbrookdale Company now had sixteen fire engines, eight furnaces and nine forges; the furnaces would be two each at Coalbrookdale, Horsehay, Ketley and Madeley Wood; the forges included three at Coalbrookdale. The Coalbrookdale forge was already looking to the rolling mill as a natural development in 1784. Boulton and Watt had no experience of designing an engine for such work, but two years later informed the Company that Wilkinson had harnessed one of their engines to a rolling and slitting mill. Coalbrookdale made their rolling mill about the same time and it proved most satisfactory and in 1789 others were built at Ketley and Horsehay forges, the one at Ketley being used mainly to roll square sections from three inches to three-quarters of an inch side.

Within the next few years Horsehay rapidly took the leading place and began to be developed as the principal forge unit of the Company. This was particularly the case after the separation of Ketley in 1796. By the beginning of the nineteenth century the works had sorted themselves out very much as follows.

Coalbrookdale—small furnaces, foundry, light rolling mill and forge, engine shops and timber yard.

Horsehay—larger furnaces, heavy rolling mill and forge, boiler shop and brick yard.

Ketley—furnaces, foundry, light rolling mill, engine and waggon shops.

Madeley Wood—furnaces.

Associated with these were also the furnaces at Lilleshall and at Donnington Wood, both of which sent in pig iron to the forges at Ketley and Horsehay.

At the beginning of the new century the Coalbrookdale forge had a serious set-back through an explosion at the furnaces. On Sunday, 6 September 1801, a cloud-burst caused a flood which burst the pool dam and poured into the Old Furnace, causing a great explosion when it reached the molten metal. The flood also wrecked many of the workshops. Adam Luccock who was present, and who lived to the age of a hundred and three years (1728–1831), gave a verbal account to the historian Randall, some years later. He said that the flood occurred while the Darby family were in meeting, which broke up on hearing the noise of the explosion.

> 'Is anyone hurt ?' That was the first question asked by Miss Darby (now Rathbone). She was an angel of a woman, indeed everyone of the Miss Darbys have been so. 'Is there anyone hurt, Adam' she said; I said 'No ma'am, theres nobody hurt but the furnace and blowing mill, the pool dam and the buildings are all gone.' 'Oh, I am so thankful' she said 'never mind the buildings so no one's hurt' and they all looked as pleased, if you'll believe me, as if they had found a new vein of coal in the Dawley Fields instead of having lost an estate in Coalbrookdale.

The damage was repaired in the next year and the opportunity was taken to make some improvements in the general lay-out. The development of the works was affected by changes in the personnel during the next few years. William Reynolds, of the Ketley Company, died 10 June 1803, and Richard Dearman, manager of Coalbrookdale and Horsehay died 12 October 1804. The works at Ketley were carried on by William's brother Joseph, who had been associated with him in the works as an equal partner but had not his brilliance and inventive genius in engineering. In 1805 Joseph Reynolds started a bank at Wellington[1] and put Ketley in charge of a manager. After the death of William there was little further change at Ketley, but it continued to maintain its close links with Coalbrookdale and share a good deal of work with them. The management at Coalbrookdale fell to Edmund Darby the son of Samuel, brother of Abraham Darby III. With him in the Company were Francis, the son of Abraham III, Abraham's widow Rebecca, and Abraham's sister Sarah. All these took an active interest in the works, with Edmund as the manager until his death in 1810, when Barnard

[1] The bank of Eyton, Reynolds and Wilkinson, Wellington.

Dickinson, his brother-in-law, the husband of Anne Darby, was appointed the manager. Mary Rathbone and Samuel Darby died in 1808 and Richard and Hannah Darby joined their brother Francis, Richard taking an active part in the works.

Edmund Darby was 21 in 1803 and in that year he married Lucy Burlingham and built a house near the works. His training had started in the works some years earlier, and he was competent to take over the management at Dearman's death, although he was only a young man. He had assumed some responsibility in 1803 as there is still extant an indenture of that year, by which he took George Fletcher, clockmaker in Coalbrookdale, as an articled clerk for four years, to learn to manage forges, mills, furnaces and foundries, and to keep accounts, yield books and day books. Fletcher's wages were to be £46.16.0, £54.12.0, £62.8.0 and £70.4.0 in the four successive years. When he took over the management Edmund's salary was at first at £200 a year, with an allowance of £100 a year towards the expense of entertaining customers and people coming to the works. This was later raised to a salary of £400 with the £100 allowance extra.

Richard Dearman had planned some alterations and improvements for both Horsehay and Coalbrookdale and with Edmund Darby assisting him these had been started in 1801 and 1802 following the disastrous flood. Dearman's death thus left Edmund with these schemes well under way, and with a good working knowledge of what Dearman had intended to do. The blast engines at Horsehay were now getting old and worn and a new one was planned for the No. 3 furnace, for which two boilers were made and installed. Some of the older property was renovated or altered and new buildings which were put up include a brewery at Poolhill and a properly arranged and efficiently designed warehouse for the iron and forge products. It was the custom throughout the works to make an allowance of beer to the workmen, according to the nature of their job, and the beer was brewed by the Company. Abiah Darby for many years provided the malt from the Malt House which had been started by Abraham I, and carried on as a small family business within the Darby family for nearly a hundred years. The business was now carried on by Sarah Darby who supplied malt to the brew house, but had no part in the actual brewing. The quantity of beer provided can be gleaned occasionally from the accounts, usually appearing under separated items. In 1803, some of these were as follows. 'Ale as given to Sundries from 23.7mo.1802 to 23.7mo. 1803. to Forges 5317 quarts, £117.18.8.' Similar entries for some of the other sections of the works are, rolling mill, 1,458 quarts, blast engines 1,956 quarts, farm 83 quarts, general Warehouse 353 quarts, Horsehay furnaces 5,281 quarts, Coalbrookdale foundry 179 quarts. The heaviest consumption was naturally at the puddling furnaces. An allowance for lodgings and ale was generally made to men who were away from the works on an outside job; for instance, three men were out with a boiler, three and a half weeks, and received an allowance of 1/- a week each for lodging and 2 quarts of ale each per day for 23 days.

The iron warehouse was part of a general scheme to keep a better check on materials, which had been proposed by John Tranter when he became general store keeper and dispatcher. He found by experience that there was a rather lax system of checking the movement of material from one shop to another while being processed, and appealed for a better method. Some changes were made, but in 1808 he wrote to Edmund Darby complaining again of laxity, and stating a little of the history of his plea. 'When I came to the Works and for some years after, the Workmen's own accounts were taken for their work till J Tranter [himself] after repeated applications prevailed upon the Co. to appoint someone to take an account of the Moulders work in particular and he also acted at something being done in taking an Acct. of the Work from the Fitting up Shops but this has been but partially done. . . .' His proposal was for the appointment of a specially trustworthy person, to have a small office at the foot of the incline near the furnaces, to be on duty from 6 a.m. to 6 p.m. His duty was to be to take account of all work done in the shops, of castings taken from the moulding rooms to the fitting shops, and of all other movements of materials within the Coalbrookdale works. Presumably he would himself do the same at Horsehay. These reforms were carried out soon after this letter was sent and at Horsehay the careful regulation of the new iron warehouse was extended over the whole works.

The Company during this first decade of the nineteenth century was active along many different lines. The rolling mills were producing an amazingly wide range of bar sections and plates at both mills, with a steady output of boilers, mainly from Horsehay. Many of the boilers were made to drawings supplied by the customer, and some were of large size. Coalbrookdale foundry cast engine and structural parts, and it is noted that on 19 May 1803, they cast a large shaft weighing 212 cwt.[1] In 1806 Tranter discussed with Edmund Darby a price to tender for the cast iron water pipes asked for by the East London Water Company, but says, 'Whether on account of the Bridge castings to be done you will see it right to offer prices at all or not for the pipes, is what we cannot determine but will observe that an order for pipes of such strength is very tempting provided the payment is alike so.'[1]

It is possible to recover something about the staff of the Company from the items in the Settling Journal (*Coalbrookdale MSS.* 2) at the beginning of the century. In 1800 Richard Dearman as manager had a salary of £400 with the allowance for entertaining visitors. The 'clerk' or chief accountant was John Ford at £100 a year, with an assistant Mark Gilpin also with a salary of £100. John Tranter had £90 a year with an allowance of one guinea for taxes and an allowance for house and coal. John Hornblower had £50 a year as general timekeeper and Charles Hornblower was responsible for the furnaces and their fuel and ore supplies, and for all buildings. His salary is itemized as £40 plus £10 for his attendance in the coal fields and £10 for finding his own house coals. These appointments were for the whole concern including Horsehay, the coal fields and outlying properties. The Company owned large estates in which there were two farms partly worked by direct labour and partly rented by Sarah Darby. The Dale Farm was 67 acres in extent with a rental of £73.8.11, and the extra land rented by Sarah Darby totalled about £40 in rent. The Company's horses were kept on the Dale farm, while Sarah Darby also kept a team of horses and contracted with the Company for team work and for haulage and carriage of materials. A typical haulage account is:

Dale Farm Horses, for Team work;
4 Horses 318 Days at 10/–, 5 horses Jinneying 312 days at 12/6, 2 horses drawing cinders etc. 182 days at 5/–, 1 horse 182 days at 2/6. Vetches and grasses for Hackneys £5. £427.5.0

Horsehay Farm was leased by the Company and on this a few of the horses for transport and carriage use were kept, and the surplus of fodder and vetches grown was returned to the warehouse. The rent of this farm was £26 a year and for a time it was let to Mary

[1] Salop County Archives. *Coalbrookdale papers.* No. 20, 10 April 1808. Letter from John Tranter to Edmund Darby in London.

Machin who contracted for much of the haulage, particularly team work such as carrying boilers or massive castings to inland places, or occasionally taking special loads to Coalport, *e.g.* '6 Horses going down to CPort with a Load of Iron from Severn Warehouse ½ Days @ 18/-.'

Among the ancillary concerns there was also the Dale Corn Mill, which purchased grain, ground it and sold the flour to the workpeople.[1] The cost of running the mill for the year was £53.9.4 made up as follows:—

> Geo. Morgan's Attendance 337½ days at 2/-
> Jas. Perry 52 days at 2/-; 3 Gal. of Oil at 4/-
> 30 lbs Candles @ 10d.; 3 Brass Brasses 8 lbs. at 1/8d.
> 1 Yrs. Use of Buildings & Machinery £12.

During the opening years of the century there seems to have been a change in function as between Horsehay and Coalbrookdale. Prior to 1800 Horsehay was sending away large quantities of bar iron and other products, by canal, to customers in the Midlands, as well as to Stourport. Then from 1802 almost all this trade was dropped and the bulk of the bar iron was taken to Coalbrookdale, but the pig iron trade remained. The freightage on goods was variable; pig iron from Horsehay to Stourport cost 4/- a ton carriage, to Wrens Nest 3/-, but iron goods were often 6/- a ton to Stourport and 9/- to Gloucester. In the year 1802–3 taken as a sample, there was a charge of freightage on 1,035 tons of goods sent to Bristol, at 14/6 a ton. On the river the Company now had several boats of their own, which are described as 2 Trows, *Friends* and *Trial*, 1 Deal flat, *Victory*, 2 barges, *Mary* and *William*, and a frigate, *Hermaphrodite*, valued together at £1,439.0.0. The Company's canal boats were valued at £1,656.2.6, without being specified in detail. Carriage from the works to the river wharf was mainly over the Company's own railway lines, but some of the ore and coal brought to the furnaces travelled over lines belonging to the Ketley Company and a way leave based upon tonnage rates was paid for this use. With the completion of the various canal schemes in the early years of the nineteenth century, much of the produce of Horsehay furnaces and forges was sent to Stourport by canal and there could be transhipped either onto the inland canals for the Midlands, or onto barges on the Severn

[1] A visitor to the Dale in the 1850's says the mill was then grinding corn for 3,000 employees of the Company.

for Bristol. Some part of the Coalbrookdale output also, now travelled down the river to Stourport to enter the canal network there, for which Stourport was rapidly become an important collecting centre.

Production was at a high level in these years, as may be judged by the pig iron made at the furnaces. In 1801 the Horsehay furnaces Nos. 1 and 2 made an average of 66 tons a week throughout the year, a total of nearly 3,500 tons. In 1807 the average make was well over 80 tons a week, while at Coalbrookdale, a figure given to the Board of Excise for 1805 was a make of 2,765 tons in the two furnaces. In addition to the local make, some pig iron was sent to Horsehay forges from the furnaces at Lilleshall and Donnington Wood, so that the make of bar iron, rod iron and plate was a little in excess of the pig iron figures. The year from July 1802 to July 1803 is quite typical of this period, when the produce disposed of from Horsehay was 1,993 tons of pig iron, nearly all of it described as grey forge pig, and 1,731 tons of bar, rod and plate iron from the forges. The principal customers were, for the pig iron, Joseph Jesson & Co. of Wrens Nest, and John Knight, and for the bar iron, the Coalbrookdale forge. The iron taken by the Coalbrookdale forge, often as much as a hundred tons in a month, was Common Merchant iron, Common Tire iron, Best Tough, and Common Rod iron, with occasionally a few half blooms of Best Tough iron and a few boiler plates. The pig iron was sold at £6.10.0 a ton and the bar iron, Common from £14 to £16 a ton, and Tough from £17 to £22 a ton.

The boilers made within the year quoted weighed 27 tons 7 cwt. and were charged £943.11.6 or nearly £34 a ton average, The rolling mill at Horsehay did a certain amount of outside work. mostly in rolling plate from slabs sent by neighbouring works. The Snedshill and Old Park Companies from time to time sent in parcels of slabs, ten tons or more, to be rolled to specified sizes of plate or boiler plate. It is not very clear what was being done at the Coalbrookdale forge, beyond rolling some of the bar to smaller sizes, and acting as a main outlet and warehouse to Horsehay. The sale of bar iron from Horsehay, other than to Coalbrookdale, was small and local, whereas Coalbrookdale handled a very considerable trade with Stourport and Bristol.

With the death of Richard Dearman in 1804, Edmund Darby was left to manage the whole of the works with Francis Darby to assist him. Within the next few years Edmund had to face several difficulties at the same time that he was planning the remodelling of part of the forge. In 1806 the threatened tax on pig iron drew strong protests from the ironmasters, and Edmund Darby was active in these. In April 1806, Richard Swallow of Sheffield,[1] wrote to Edmund that meetings were to be held in Sheffield and Wakefield to organize the opposition to the tax, and expressing the hope that similar meetings would be held in Birmingham, Wolverhampton, Dudley, Stourport and other towns. Edmund responded to this letter and went to London to take part in further deliberations there, and was kept for a few weeks. The works were affected slightly, as some of the customers were hesitant about contracting for quantities of iron until the matter of the tax was settled. Harvey & Co., good customers at Bristol, wrote to Edmund Darby on 17 April, that they do not like making provisional agreement for iron, but will take as much of their order, not above 125 tons, as Darby can supply, before the tax is determined, at £16 a ton, delivered at Bristol, with 10/– a ton discount for prompt payment.

In May of the same year, Horsehay furnace cast twelve tons of hammers and anvils, and many other goods with a note in the Day Book, 'the above castings was Cast on acco^{t} of the Tax as was Proposed on Iron.' It may be the same cause which encouraged Edmund at this time to enter upon a rebuilding of the forge furnaces, for which many castings were made for use in the framing of new rolling and slitting mill furnaces. No. 1. blast furnace also was partly rebuilt and many new castings made particularly new pipes for the blast, and plates and beams for a new bridge to the furnace.

In the latter part of the same year, the first signs of a keen price war were visible. Underwood & Sons, of Coaley Mills, near Dursley, Gloucester, were buying iron delivered at Bristol at £19 a ton, and say in a letter to Darby, that there is not better iron in this country than what they are now working. They place an order with Darby for five tons of iron to give it a trial, and evidently are satisfied, as from that date they appear in the books as regular customers. In May 1807, William Underwood wrote to Darby from Bristol that Mr. Harvey informs him that their price for roll iron is £14 per ton at Cardiff and £14.5.0 at Bristol. 'I beg leave to ask you what is to be done and what is the cause of this continual reduction in the price? I hope you will not suffer the Welch Gentlemen to shut you out of this Market.' Two months later another important customer, John

[1] Richard Swallow was adopted by John Fell of Attercliffe Forge, and inherited this and Fell's share in other Yorkshire iron works.

Bradley of Stourbridge, wrote to Edmund Darby that Customers in London want a further and impossible reduction in the price of bars.

They cannot afford to give me more than £14 which price you must be sensible is utterly out of our power to conform to at the present price of materials and God only knows what is to be the end of it or what plan is to be pursued, I have only to repeat what I have before remarked to you, that it is my disposition to do the whole of my business with your House so long that the same can be done mutually pleasant . . . and trust such arrangements may yet be made that would preserve us to you and enable us to meet the Welch Gentlemen, it cannot, I think, last long and though my efforts to resist the attacks of these gentlemen are very weak and feeble compared to yours, I am content to say that to enable me to keep my connections, I shall with pleasure sell Iron for no profit for a year if I can at the Years end secure myself and Company from absolutely running out.

The matter of price cutting was now becoming an earnest problem for the Ironmasters' Association, and at its meeting at Newport on 14 January 1808, they proposed that the price of bar iron should be stabilized at £15 per ton. The price however continued to fall, the rivalry being chiefly between the Bristol merchants and Crawshay of Cyfarthfa. In July 1809, Crawshay replied to a letter from Edmund Darby which had asked for his prices, in very strong terms.

By what authority or prescriptive right are you to sell 5s. a ton in Bristol lower than me, iron made by my Invention[1] to bring forward which I risq'd a handsome fortune (but no patent), everyone is free to work in my way—and give away the iron if they please—but not to demand of me to sell at 5s. a ton above them and thereby give up my customers to you or anyone, my wish is to have a good profit to everybody but I will not be undersold, if you fall 5s. more you will be followed by your respectful Friend Richd Crawshay.

The prices were still falling in the next year, and Darby had to take a firm line with some customers who were asking for further reductions. Underwood & Co. had been making such a request and Edmund Darby replied to them:

With regard to Merchant Iron, we have not sold any into Bristol for less than £13.0.0 as yet and in the present state of the Trade it will not be possible for the manufacturer to render it low enough for the middle man to gain as much as he used to do, for the manufacturers are losing by all the Bar Iron they make, at least in our part of the Kingdom.

[1] Probably referring to the pre-heating of iron in a coke refining furnace before puddling, sometimes called the Welsh method, and claimed by Homfray.

He was prepared to accept orders at £13 a ton at Bristol, or £12.10.0 at Stourport.

The decline in price still continued, and in 1813 we find Darby's successor, Barnard Dickinson facing up to the same problem. Joseph Reynolds of Ketley Company sent Dickinson a copy of a letter from Richard Fothergill of the Tredegar Works, who was promoting a meeting of ironmasters at Gloucester to discuss the price of iron. Fothergill had had no answers from the Staffordshire ironmasters so supposes that there can be no meeting now before the regular quarterly one. The Bristol houses confirmed the price of £11.10.0 and as this agreed closely with the Coalbrookdale price, the London merchants determined to fall in with it. Reynolds proposed to the March meeting of ironmasters at Gloucester that there should be a restriction of output to raise the price of iron and prevent some firms having to close altogether. Fothergill endorsed this: 'I join in your Ideas that reducing the make (if it could be adopted) will alone be effectual in getting up the price of bars, however, the difficulties are such as to induce me to think that it will not be submitted to till many have had a Bellyful of this £11.10.0.' The Bristol houses are underselling the others and will bring the price down to £11. 'I am glad that you and the Coalbrookdale Co. see the propriety of disapproving these proceedings.'

During this long struggle against falling prices there were some very careful investigations of the actual cost of making iron, and some such determinations have survived from 1810 and 1813. In 1810 the Dawley Castle furnaces had been brought into blast and were supplying pig iron to Horsehay forge and Coalbrookdale, so that it was convenient to compare its costs with those of the older furnaces. At Horsehay the cost of making a ton of iron was reckoned as follows:—

Originally 3.1 tns of coal made 1 tn of coke, now reduced to 2½ tns of coal per ton of coke.

34 cwts of coke per ton of iron cost at Horsehay—	
Coals 5 tons @ 6/6 per ton long weight	1.12. 6
Mine—2 tns 4 cwts @ 15/– long weight	1.13. 0
Limestone—18½ cwts @ 7/6 long weight	6.11
Labour and drink	10. 0
Use of tools at furnaces, sand, etc.	2. 0
Blast	3. 7
New Hearths and Agency	2. 0
Cost per ton long weight at Horsehay	£4.10. 0

At Dawley Castle coal was better and carriage from the mines less, so cost was £4. 4. 0

Coversion costs in next few years.

Pig iron cost £4. 0.0 to £4.15.0
Refined iron £5. 4.2 to £6.1.0
'half blooms'£6.15.6 to £8.15.1
Merchant bar £8.7.0. to £10.3.0

The calculations of costs in 1813 are in greater detail than this, and give a very complete picture of the processes and of the method of costing.

1.mo. 12th 1813. HHay Ironworks.

Coals	$4\frac{3}{4}$ tons @ 6/6	1.10.10	
Mine	$2\frac{1}{4}$ tons @ 16/–	1.16. 0	
Limestone	$18\frac{1}{2}$ cw. @ 8/–	7. 3	
			3.14. 1
Coakers 2/– Drawg up Coaks 7d Drawg up Mine 5d Breakg L Stone 6d. Fillers 10d Keepers, Fness Labour & Twia Boys 1/6. Gettg out Cinders 1/– Smiths 4d. Carpenter 4d. Coak filling 6d. Oilg Cares Collect Mine & Machine man 5d. Damages Sand & Taxes 2d. Inspect Coakers Changg rails & leadg into Hearth 5d. Labourer doing sundries 6d Casting Timps, Cinder plates, Plates for Bridge House Soughs etc. for Hearth 5d. Drink 6d. Coal to Workmen's Houses 6d.		10.11	
Use tools at Furnace & Hearth wth sand		2. 0	
Blast		4. 0	
New hearth & agency		2. 6	
General charge			19. 5
Incidental expences			1. 6
Pig iron per ton lo.wt. at HHay			£4.15. 0
Pigs to metal lo.wt. 22cw.3.0. @ £4.15.0 p ton			5. 8. 0
Coal 17cw @ 5/6 Coaks 6d.			5. 1
Wear & tear of finery & use of tools, sand etc.			2. 6
Blast			2. 0
Getting away rubbish			3
Refining 2/6 Stocking 6d.			3. 0
Carriage to Forge			2
Refined iron lo.wt. at HHay			£6. 1. 0

Refined iron for Blms 22c.3.0.lo.wt. @ £6.1.0	6.17. 7
Coals 35cw @ 5/6 Puddling 10/3	19.10
Castings Brasses Tools & wear & tear of furnaces	7. 0
Engine 2/– Sand 9d	2. 9
Gettg away rubbish 6d. Stocking 9d.	1. 3
Shingling 3/4 Staffs 2/–	5. 4
Coals to Workmens houses 6d Agency 6d	1. 0
Carriage to Mill 4d.	4
Cost of Blooms at HHay lo. wt.	8.15. 1
,, ,, ,, ,, ,, ,, sht. wt	£8. 3. 5
Half Blm to Bars 22cw. sht.wt. @ £8.3.5	8.19. 9
Coals 17cw. @ 5/6	4. 7
Sand 3d Rolling 4/6. Stocking 1/6	6. 3
Mason & Bricks 1/6 Tools 6d.	2. 0
New castings. Brasses & Grease	2. 0
Working over crop ends & cracked bars	2. 0
Engine expences	4. 0
Agency, carpenters, & rise turning	2. 0
Gettg away rubbish, unlodg coal. chargg mill	5
Cost of Mcht Iron sht wt at HHay	10. 3. 0
Freight to Stourport	7. 0
Cost Mcht Bars deld at Stourport	£10.10. 0

With the manufacturing costs at this level and the market price of iron still falling to within a few shillings of it, it was clear that some economy must be made in the works if the firm were to continue. In this search for economy, Dickinson introduced boilers to use the waste heat from the puddling furnaces, and found that they were very successful. His estimate of cost is given on page 238.[1]

This scheme for waste heat boilers was a very important advance. H. W. Dickinson in his recent account of the utilization of waste heat from industrial operations,[2] says when speaking of puddling furnaces, 'The waste of heat from them, more noticeable at some stages of the process than at others, is so obvious that many persons must have thought of its recovery. The difficulties in the way seem to have been first overcome by John U. Rastrick, about 1827, by his application of the heat to raising steam.' It would appear that

[1] MSS. *Iron & Steel Institute*, No. 2, which is a continuation of the costs of making iron, just quoted.

[2] Dickinson, H. W., paper under that title, *Trans. Newcomen Soc.*, vol. XXIV, 1944–5, pp. 1–11.

Calculations of the expences of Putting up one Boiler to heat from Puddling Furnaces and savings thereon. 1mo.12.1813.

Boiler with tubes 6tn.18cw. @ £25 pr. ton		172.10. 0
Cast iron buckstaves & binders 1tn. 9 @ 8/-		15.12. 0
Wrt Iron Hoops & Cramps etc.	10 @ 18/-	9. 0. 0
Pipes Cisterns etc.		15. 0. 0
63 m. common bricks /3 Brick ends	14/-	44. 2. 0
7 m. White bricks	33/-	11.11. 0
740 Bushels Lime @ 6d.		18.10. 0
2½ tns Clay @ 6/-		15. 0
Mason work		32.10. 0
Sand 10 ton at 5/-		2.10. 0
Cast iron dampers	2cw. @ 8/-	16. 0
erection of boiler complete		£322.16. 0

It is supposed that one boiler will get Steam equal to 20 ton Coal p week on 50 uses is 1000 Tons @ 5/6 — 275. 0. 0

Deduct		
Interest on £322 p Ann	£16.2.0	
Wear & tear of boiler do	16.2.0	32. 4. 0
Saved by One Boiler per Ann.		242.16. 0

which is £75 p Cent on Money expended. And the concern will admit of at least six such boilers to be erected.

Dickinson had long anticipated the work of Rastrick, in his boiler at Horsehay. Rastrick's boiler contained a tube through which the waste gases from the furnaces were passed, and though we have no other specification, Dickinson's boiler contained tubes, as evidenced in the costing of it.

Whatever economies were practised, they were not sufficient to neutralize the general fall of prices and disruption of trade which followed the Napoleonic wars. The depression had been growing steadily from 1810, and in 1812 the Company blew out one furnace at Horsehay. Conditions steadily became worse and, according to the Annual Register for 1816, there were in that year 24 furnaces out of blast in Shropshire, and only 10 still making iron. Joseph Reynolds had been unable to meet the declining business and in that year closed down and dismantled the Ketley works. Coalbrookdale had closed down two furnaces, leaving two at Horsehay and two at

Dawley Castle in blast. The furnaces which had closed down had consumed 8,000 tons of coals a week and a corresponding number of colliers were thrown out of work. There was acute distress all over the area.

Reynolds had transferred most of his energies to the new bank at Wellington, and offered to sell part of the plant at Ketley to Dickinson, on behalf of the Coalbrookdale Company. His principal offer was the Ketley rolling mill and engine and for this he asked £1,200, rating it only in accordance with the current price of pig iron. Dickinson rejected the offer, but Reynolds was very persistent. In November of 1816 Dickinson in reply to further offers by Reynolds made a statement which is significant of the uncertain state of trade: 'If we should continue to make Bar Iron at Horsehay for 5 Months longer, we would have no objection to agree that at the expiration of that time we would take the materials specified in the Inventory sent us at the price of Shropshire Forge pigs at Stourport, less the Freight from Ketley thither. . . .' Even with trade in a better condition it would have been little advantage to purchase this mill and engine, which had been built about 1790, and was old-fashioned and worn in comparison with the newer mill at Horsehay. This new mill, which replaced the contemporary of the Ketley mill, had been designed by Edmund Darby in 1806 and built under his supervision by Messrs. Wetickless and Sons of Ironbridge, and it was considered by all who inspected it to be far in advance of the neighbouring mills at Old Park and Ketley iron works.

The furnaces at Madeley Wood, which were taken over with Ketley forge at the time of the separation of the Companies, were managed for Reynolds by Mr. Anstice and were leased from Richard Reynolds. These furnaces continued in full production up to 1816, although in 1816 they were reported to be storing much of their produce, having 3,000 tons of pig in stock.

In September 1815 they were visited by Thomas Butler of the Kirkstall Forge, Leeds, who entered in his diary,

> Went to Madeley Wood—3 blast furnaces. Owners Reynolds and Anstice. Probably the most prosperous Iron Concern in the Kingdom. Prices of their pig iron:—No. 1. Super, £9.5.0. No. 2. £8.15.0. No. 3. £7.10.0. Melting. No. 4. Forge, £6.5.0. All delivered at Stourport.

The various economies and technical readjustments enabled Dickinson to keep Horsehay and Coalbrookdale at work, but the price of iron still remained unsettled for many years, and the ironmasters were finding it difficult to dispose of all their produce at a reasonable price. In 1821 this problem was still under discussion and Mr. Botfield of the Snedshill furnaces, as Chairman of the Shropshire Ironmasters, said: 'They consider the present depressed state of the Iron Trade has been produced by the late increased make which has done serious injury to the trade in general and very little ultimate good to the parties. A reduction in make is absolutely necessary and ought to take place.' The principal problem for the Shropshire ironmasters was still the strong rivalry of the Welsh dealers in the Bristol market and this seemed incapable of settlement. The great iron works of Merthyr Tydfil, Cyfarthfa, Tredegar and others of the Welsh valleys, were now feeling their strength and increasing production at a great rate, with two principal outlets, Cardiff and Bristol. In 1823 Dickinson agreed to maintain the fixed Shropshire prices for bar iron, 'except where we meet the Welch: allowances then may not be necessary in every instance.' In 1826 William Crawshay of Cyfarthfa declared his intention of selling iron at £9 per ton, and declines any further discussion with anyone. In 1830 the Ironmasters' meetings were still calling attention to the harm done by a too heavy make of iron, but individuals were advised to do something about it, without the meeting's trying to impose any regulation upon its members. They still hoped for individual effort and shied away from collective action. The output of the Welsh works was sufficient to dominate the Bristol market, and the Shropshire iron works were compelled to regulate their prices by that of Welsh iron.

During this time of extreme difficulty a great variety of work was carried on at Horsehay and Coalbrookdale, as can be seen by a list of prices which were agreed for the work being done.[1] This list was drawn up by a foreman in the works to enable him to regulate the wages of the various men employed in the forge. Some of the prices agreed upon are as follows:

Fitting up a nozzle with Racks & Sectors for 24 Ins. Cylinder £4.4.0
Turning cast iron cranks for beamless engine[2] 10.6

[1] The list *in extenso* is in a small note book among the manuscripts of the Iron & Steel Institute, and is reproduced with their permission. It contains details of prices for many kinds of work.

[2] This beamless engine, is of course the 'engine after Trevithick's plan,' numbers of which were made at Coalbrookdale and Ketley.

A Cylinder 24 Ins Diameter and 3 ft long may be bored in 4 Turns 12 Hours each.

A Cylinder 5 ft long 30 Ins diameter 7 Turns in boring.

Set of working gears for Mr Boulton & Watts Engine, say the Forge Hammr. Engine, will take a Man a Month to compleat them.

Price given for making a Set of working gears for Boulton and Watts Engine £2.2.0

Set of working gears for Adam Heslop's engine will take a man 3 weeks to finish them.

It is thus evident that all three types of engine were still being made, Boulton & Watt, Trevithick, and Heslop.

Prices are given for different castings:

open sand castings	10/–	a ton short weight
Flask	15/–	
Dry sand	20/–	
Lome	30/–	
Brass	30/–	

Pipes and cylinders of all lengths and sizes, @ 1/– for every inch in diameter whether long or short.

Other notes for smiths relate mainly to boiler making, with one item for '16/– making a good set of stocks and screws from ½ inch up to inch about of a price.'

3 Men will make a Boiler 9 ft in diam. in a fortnight and follow the work up close.

3 men will complete a 7 ft boiler in 9 days

3 men will complete a 10 ft boiler in 18 days

Boiler making—the rivet Holes in the Boiler Bottom & Flue Plates should be ½ & 1/16 ins. diam. & 1¾ from Centre to Centre.

The rivet holes in the Top should be ½ ins. dia. and 1½ ins centre to centre.

One other product of Coalbrookdale at this time was connected with the rapidly growing sugar industry abroad, the casting of sugar boiling pans and furnaces, and the making of sugar rolls. The cast furnaces were mainly sent to the closely connected firm of Fawcett, Preston & Co., Liverpool, who were the principal makers of sugar cane roller mills.[1] During the period 1813–17 they had orders for

[1] Deerr, N. and Brooks, A., 'Evolution of the Sugar Cane Mill.' *Trans. Newcomen Soc.*, XXI, 1940–1, p. 5.

sixty-three horizontal and eleven vertical sugar mills. The price for turning sugar rolls at Coalbrookdale is stated to be 5/– each, the rolls being about three feet long and two feet in diameter.

Although the second decade of the century was so disastrous as far as the prices of iron were concerned, and was marked by the closing of many furnaces, the Coalbrookdale Company maintained the Dawley Castle furnaces and two of the Horsehay furnaces in blast. There is a glimpse of improving conditions in the profits of Dawley furnaces, the bulk of the pig iron produced being sent to the Horsehay and Coalbrookdale forges. The output for the year 1819 was 2,759 tons of pig iron, sold at £4 a ton. With Horsehay furnaces the total make for the year would be above 6,000 tons.

There is no doubt that the Coalbrookdale works had been sadly neglected during this period, and we have a picture of its condition in the diary kept by an engineer, Joshua Field,[1] who spent some time visiting the various engineering works in the Midlands. In August 1821 he was at Coalbrookdale, and his comments are somewhat depressing.

> . . . in the evening went in a Chaise to Colnbrookdale, at which place we arrive at ½ past 10 at night. When we descended the hill the numerous furnaces below seemed to fill the whole valley with fire & produced an effect dreadfull & grand.
>
> Walked through the dale works which are in a great measure deserted, the lease being nearly out, the Company are at little pains to keep them up. The Blast furnaces are not worked and nothing is doing here but some castings and a little bad mill work. A wretched bad sugar mill is making from drawings sent from the west indies from which they cannot alter anything. The foreman does not know how the thing is to perform, it is with three horizontal rollers; a small forge or 2 is working from the stream of water which originally led to ironworks being established here but the great engine which supplied the deficiency of this stream is now taken partly down and the Furnaces are all removed to where the ironstone coal etc. are found and the furnaces blown by steam.

It is perhaps fair to comment that the visit was made on a Sunday, when there were no workmen on the place except his guide, and the emptiness of the place would be more striking than on a working day. The removal of the furnaces refers to the development of those at

[1] Hall, J. W., 'Joshua Field's diary of a Tour in 1821 through the Midlands.' *Trans. Newcomen Soc.*, vol. VI, 1925–6, pp. 1–41.

Dawley Castle and Lightmoor, which became the main sources of supply of the pig iron used at Coalbrookdale.

We walked on to the Horshays one of the Company's works. Here are three Blast Furnaces 2 at work and a large rolling mill of 60 HP. tolerably good but old & dirty, The rolls & fly work very fast, stroke 7 feet, spur wheel 15 ft, pinion on rolers 3 feet, fly wheel 18 ft, shears &c, but no hammers.

Another engine of abt 50 H P drives 2 hammers but only one at a time which is a very common method so the engine must work the contrary way to work the other hammer. There are hammers also driven by a water wheel from a great Pond in which the condensing water cools and which is partly lifted up again by a pump attached to the blast engine which is a very rough one working horse heads chains &c. They have a pair of rolls for passing the balls through without hammering at all and send the blooms only to the mill.

The furnaces are situated by the side of a hill so that the filling houses are level with the tops of the furnaces; this is a general way in Shropshire tho not in Staffordshire. A foundry is attached to one of the blast furnaces in which furnace they always make better iron than in the other, for some of it goes in castings.

Mon. Aug. 27th. We went to the Lightmoor works belonging to the Company about 3 miles from the Iron bridge; this is a large works for making pig iron, esteemed a good sort of Shropshire pig. They have 3 furnaces 2 in & 1 repairing into which we went.

They have a fining hearth to refine all the broken pigs and odd pieces and send none but good pigs to the market. Manby uses much of this iron. The Manager is a very intelligent man & told us many things respecting the works. The old parks work are near here but we could not go having taken part of a chaise on to Shrewsbury. The blowing engine at this work was a tolerably good one: 2 fly pistons and water regulator, cylinder 42 in. & blast cylinder 6f.10″ these we measured stroke 7 feet is capable of blowing three furnaces. The Boilers of these kind of engines are generally round about 18 feet diam and mostly 2 in use. The quality of coal they know nothing of. They are in general kept in good order and seldom stop night or day, some time an hour or 2 to pack the piston. At Horsly Mr. Davis told us the large engine had not stopd a whole day for 3 years and they sometimes pack'd the piston in ½ a hour.

The reference in this account to Manby using much of this iron, is very interesting and gives a clue to some of the trade of the Coalbrookdale Company. The Mr. Manby referred to is Mr. Aaron Manby, the manager of the Horsley Coal and Iron Company, near Horsley Bridge, where Joshua Field had visited only a few days earlier. In his description of Manby's works he says:

The 3 Furnaces tap into a large Foundry where the largest castings can be made. Here were large columns for the London Docks and many castings for the Calcutta Mint Rolling Mill for Rennie, beds, large wheels, shafts . . . these castings are not all made from the blast Furnace but a mixture of ½ Shropshire iron of which they use a great quantity from Lightmoor Furnaces belonging to the Colebrook company.

Judging by this, the larger part of the Lightmoor output must have been sold as smelting pig, to the Horsley Company, the rest, with some from Dawley Castle furnaces going to Coalbrookdale and Horsehay.

The steady growth of the Company through these difficult years can perhaps be shown by the increasing capital, for which for the first time we have some detailed figures available. These figures are for the years 1798 to 1805 derived from the books of the Company, where a payment of interest on a quarter share is entered regularly, with a note of the capital increase and of dividends paid out. For the period 1805 to 1851 there is an annual inventory and profit and loss account, which will be noted later.[1] The earlier years are as follows.

	Total capital value	*Capital increase*	*Capital withdrawn*	*Dividend*
1798	£95,424			
1799	97,414	£1,990		
1800	101,670	4,256		
1801	109,346	7,676		
1802	118,762	9,416		
1803	120,490	1,728		
1804	129,715	9,225	£12,000	
1805	134,665	4,950		£5,950
1806	143,636	8,971	2,000	10,971
1807	154,827	11,191	4,000	15,191
1808	161,397	6,570	3,000	10,343
1809	165,997	4,600	2,000	5,895
1810	164,594			

The total value of the Coalbrookdale works, collieries and pits in 1796, was £90,404, with debts against this of £50,546. In 1805 these valuations were £113,788 with debts of £4,002. In addition, the Horsehay works were now to be added as part of the Coalbrookdale Company and these bring the value up to £144,856 with debts

[1] Summarized in Appendix No. 7.

amounting to £10,191, net value of £134,665. In 1809 the Dawley Castle furnace was added and the itemized inventory becomes as follows:

A Summary of the Value of the Concerns belonging to the Coalbrookdale Co. at 4th. of the 8th Month, 1810

Coalbrookdale Foundry		£27,118. 6. 9
do Pan shop		114.17. 4
do Farm		1,050. 5. 0
New Work Colliery		2,473. 7. 4
		30,756.16. 5
Lawley & Dawley Do		50,999.10.10
Castle Furnace		6,998.16. 7
Debts owing to the Concern		52,256.17. 6
		141,012. 1. 4
Horsehay Furnaces		19,098. 1. 7
do Forges		2,824.17. 1
do Rolling Mill		12,011.14. 2
do General Warehouse		1,000.14. 1
do Dwelling Houses		3,780. 7. 6
Brickwork at Brandlea		213. 8. 2
Forges at C Dale		2,381.12. 5
		182,322.16. 4
Deduct Debts owing by the Concern		
	10,004.11. 4	
Miscellaneous Inventory	6,043. 0.10	
Bad debts written off	1,680.11. 1	17,728. 3. 3
		164,594.13. 1

Profit and Loss Dr.

1810. 8 Mo 4.	To Interest Acct. for Cash paid to the Partners this year	6,639.17. 3
	Do for Balance of Interest & Discount etc.	1,456. 9. 2
	Miscellaneous Inventory	6,043. 0.10
	Bad debts written off	1,680.11. 1
		15,819.18. 4

Profit and Loss Cr.		
By Coalbrookdale Works		9,841. 9. 5
Horsehay do		3,190.12.11
Dawley do		939.15. 8
Castle Furnace		445.14. 8
		14,417.12. 8
By Sarah Darby for her share of the decrease of capital	467. 8. 6	
Rebecca Darby do	132. 8. 8	
Exrs Saml. Darby	175. 5. 8	
Estate of Edd. Darby	292. 2.10	
Francis Darby	83.15. 0	
B & A Dickinson	83.15. 0	
Hannah Darby	83.15. 0	
Richard Darby	83.15. 0	1,402. 5. 8
		15,819.18. 4

When Joshua Field visited Coalbrookdale in 1821, the place appeared much neglected, but its valuation for that year, though reduced, was still £20,210.8.11 for the foundry and £3,366.0.11 for the forges at Coalbrookdale, and for all the concerns £144,737.12.3. This reduction was of course due to the very bad years following the wars, from which the Company was not yet in a position to recover; in fact it was not until 1833 that the concerns really turned the corner and embarked upon their period of maximum prosperity, under the management of the brothers Abraham and Alfred Darby.

Chapter Fourteen

ABRAHAM DARBY IV AND ALFRED DARBY, 1827–1851

JOSHUA FIELD in his description of the Coalbrookdale works, ascribes the neglected appearance partly to the fact that the lease had not long to run. This was not strictly correct, but it is true that some leases and properties had been under review, and that many conditions in the Dale were in a state of flux. The Coalbrookdale works and the Manor of Madeley belonged to Richard Reynolds, and he had leased both to the Company in 1806 for a term of twenty-one years, the leases to terminate on 1 July 1827. On his death in 1816 the property had passed to his son Joseph and to trustees for the children of his other son William. Joseph's action in dismantling Ketley soon after his father's death may have raised queries in the Coalbrookdale Company as to their eventual position. Three years earlier, a new agent acting for Mr. Robert Slaney, who owned much of the land in Dawley, the Horsehay Farm, the land on which the Horsehay works were built and some of the coal mines they were working, wrote to Barnard Dickinson, offering to sell all this estate to them on fair terms.[1] George Bishton, the agent, points out that one lease has forty years to run, and the other one has twenty-six years. 'The object of my interview with you was to make the Coalbrookdale Co. an offer of the Dawley Estate upon fair and reasonable terms, and if they refuse the same to express my readiness to offer them any particular part of it that was an object to them and that would not be detrimental to the interests of Mr. Slaney in disposing of the remainder. . . .' In case of a partial purchase there would be many difficulties in securing acceptable conditions for the making good of damage through mining, and there may have to be many clauses which might prove restrictive to the Company's development at some future date. The request to consider selling a part was favoured at first by Dickinson but Bishton replied on 2 February 1813 that 'I do not see any other Plan to give the Company what they want or in other words to prevent them getting into difficulties than their determining to

[1] The correspondence is in the Shropshire County Records MSS. Nos. 72, 73, 81 of the *Coalbrookdale papers*.

purches the estate. The selling price is £65,000.' The consideration of these matters took a very slow course and it was not until September 1815 that a draft agreement was drawn up for the sale of the property at Dawley to Barnard Dickinson and Miss Darby [Sarah], on behalf of the Coalbrookdale Company. This secured their position at Horsehay and made it possible to plan alterations and rebuilding to suit themselves.

In 1825, with their lease of Coalbrookdale nearing its end, Dickinson suggested that when it was renewed, it should be terminable by seven year periods if need be, but Joseph Reynolds would not accept this suggestion. It is evident from Reynolds's next letter that Dickinson had mooted the possibility of their giving up the Coalbrookdale works and concentrating at Horsehay.[1] The suggestion was taken into account when Reynolds made a valuation of the works for rent, and his estimate of values has many points of interest. In the course of it he says:

> More papers reached me yesterday evening and confirm me in my former opinion that if the foundry business is discontinued, an income equal to that which the Dale Company now pay, would be obtained. I have received from W. Smith an estimated rental of the dwelling houses, Geo. Morgan's Mill[2] and the Malthouse, on the supposition that you do not take a new lease: he reports that they want something done to them to make them in good tenantable repair, and making allowance for repairs and expense of collecting rents, he values them independent of the works at £256.12.0 per annum. He also values the material in the offices and works if pulled down and sold at £2,773.5.0 but as it is obvious that a part would be set for houses and other purposes distinct from the foundry trade, the value may be estimated as under, viz: £2,100. Probable income from the works and houses if the former stood still £450. But it is not likely that so complete a foundry would stand entirely still, it is therefor probable that a better rent than £450 might be obtained for them and that less than £420 could not be anticipated in any event. I therefore consider it as no small proof of my wish to do as I would be done by that I consented at Bristol to renew the lease at the present rent. . . .

This was £400 per annum.

After further discussions the lease was renewed on the suggested terms on 18 August 1827, between Joseph Reynolds on one part, and

[1] Shropshire County Records MSS. *Coalbrookdale papers*, Nos. 114, 115, 116 and 117.

[2] The Corn Mill, Coalbrookdale.

on the other part, for the Coalbrookdale Company, Francis, Richard and Abraham Darby and Barnard Dickinson.

During these ten years 1818 to 1828, Coalbrookdale was at the lowest ebb in its history with most of the Company's activity concentrated at Horsehay and Lightmoor. The plan that was drawn for the purposes of the 1827 lease has some points of great interest and gives a clear picture of Coalbrookdale at that date. The works are best followed if taken in three groupings. The dominant group is the one referred to on the plan as the Upper Furnace. This centres around the Old Blast Furnace, which is the one standing at the present day, just below the bank of the Upper Furnace Pool. Near to it there is a second furnace, described as 'unfinished.' That also still stands and is in its unfinished condition even yet. Some years ago, part of its lining of unused fire bricks was removed and used in a time of shortage, but otherwise, except for the growth of trees around and upon it, it is still just as it stood in 1828. This is perhaps the best testimony we have to the radical change that was made in the first quarter of the nineteenth century, when all the smelting was removed to furnace units placed much nearer to the newer pits on the east portion of the coalfield, and Coalbrookdale was developed primarily as a foundry and engineering shop. The Old Blast Furnace is shown on the plan as part of a large block of moulding rooms with an air furnace, and there are three other moulding rooms, one called Tilley's with an air furnace, which we recognize as occurring by name in the records a hundred years earlier. The other two moulding rooms each had two air furnaces. The remaining buildings include a turning mill, engine shop, shops for smiths, carpenter, wheelwright, sawyer, file cutter and nailers, and a warehouse. This grouping of blast furnace and six air furnaces forms one unit. The Upper Furnace Pool is augmented by a second, New Pool, which was made in 1720 by Richard Ford.

The Lower Furnace is grouped below the Lower Furnace Pool, with the New Blast Furnace (built about 1715) as its central feature. This is a block with four moulding rooms and three air furnaces around it. There are three other moulding rooms and one air furnace, a blowing machine, grinding mill and blacking mill, smiths' and joiners' shops, and a pattern room. Many of the buildings of the Upper Furnace group can be recognized today or traced among their successors, but all the Lower Furnace has disappeared, the pool is filled in and the whole area covered by the present assembling shops.

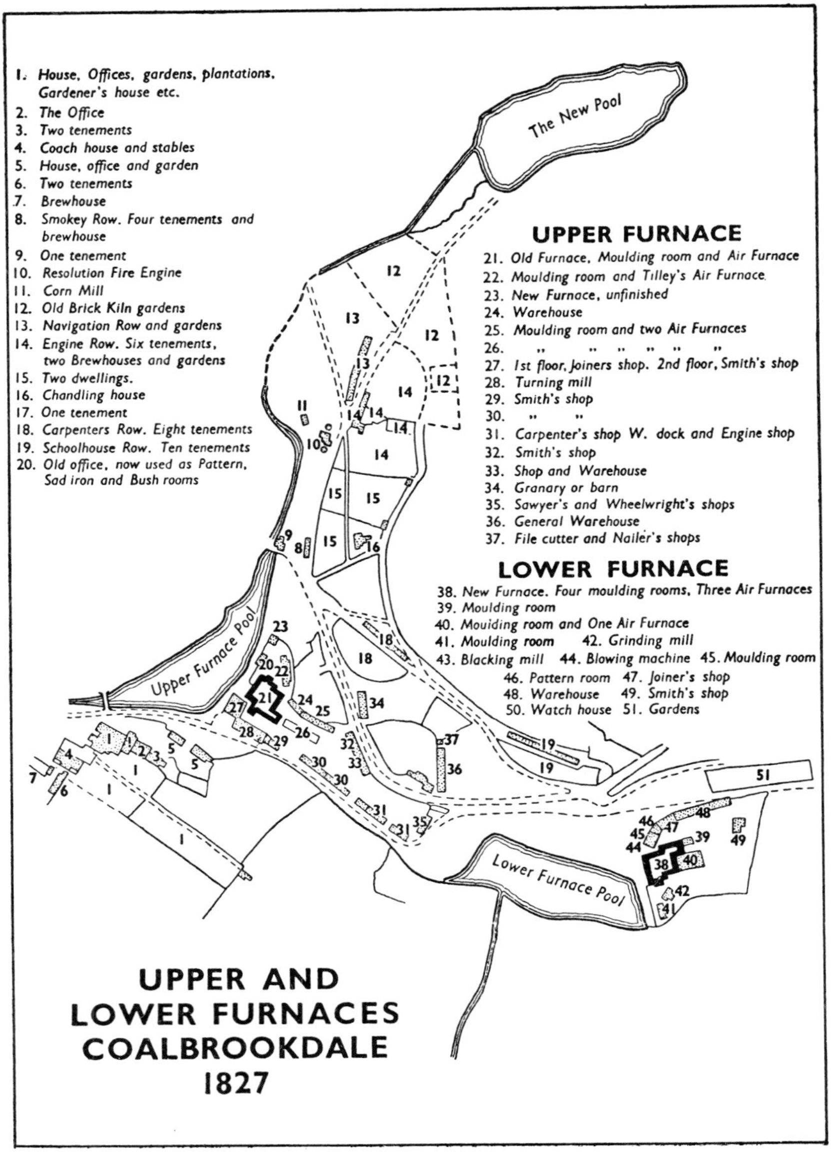

1. House, Offices, gardens, plantations, Gardener's house etc.
2. The Office
3. Two tenements
4. Coach house and stables
5. House, office and garden
6. Two tenements
7. Brewhouse
8. Smokey Row. Four tenements and brewhouse
9. One tenement
10. Resolution Fire Engine
11. Corn Mill
12. Old Brick Kiln gardens
13. Navigation Row and gardens
14. Engine Row. Six tenements, two Brewhouses and gardens
15. Two dwellings.
16. Chandling house
17. One tenement
18. Carpenters Row. Eight tenements
19. Schoolhouse Row. Ten tenements
20. Old office, now used as Pattern, Sad iron and Bush rooms
The New Pool
UPPER FURNACE
21. Old Furnace, Moulding room and Air Furnace
22. Moulding room and Tilley's Air Furnace.
23. New Furnace, unfinished
24. Warehouse
25. Moulding room and two Air Furnaces
26. " " " " " "
27. 1st floor, Joiners shop. 2nd floor, Smith's shop
28. Turning mill
29. Smith's shop
30. " "
31. Carpenter's shop W. dock and Engine shop
32. Smith's shop
33. Shop and Warehouse
34. Granary or barn
35. Sawyer's and Wheelwright's shops
36. General Warehouse
37. File cutter and Nailer's shops
LOWER FURNACE
38. New Furnace. Four moulding rooms, Three Air Furnaces
39. Moulding room
40. Moulding room and One Air Furnace
41. Moulding room 42. Grinding mill
43. Blacking mill 44. Blowing machine 45. Moulding room
46. Pattern room 47. Joiner's shop
48. Warehouse 49. Smith's shop
50. Watch house 51. Gardens
Upper Furnace Pool
Lower Furnace Pool
UPPER AND LOWER FURNACES COALBROOKDALE 1827

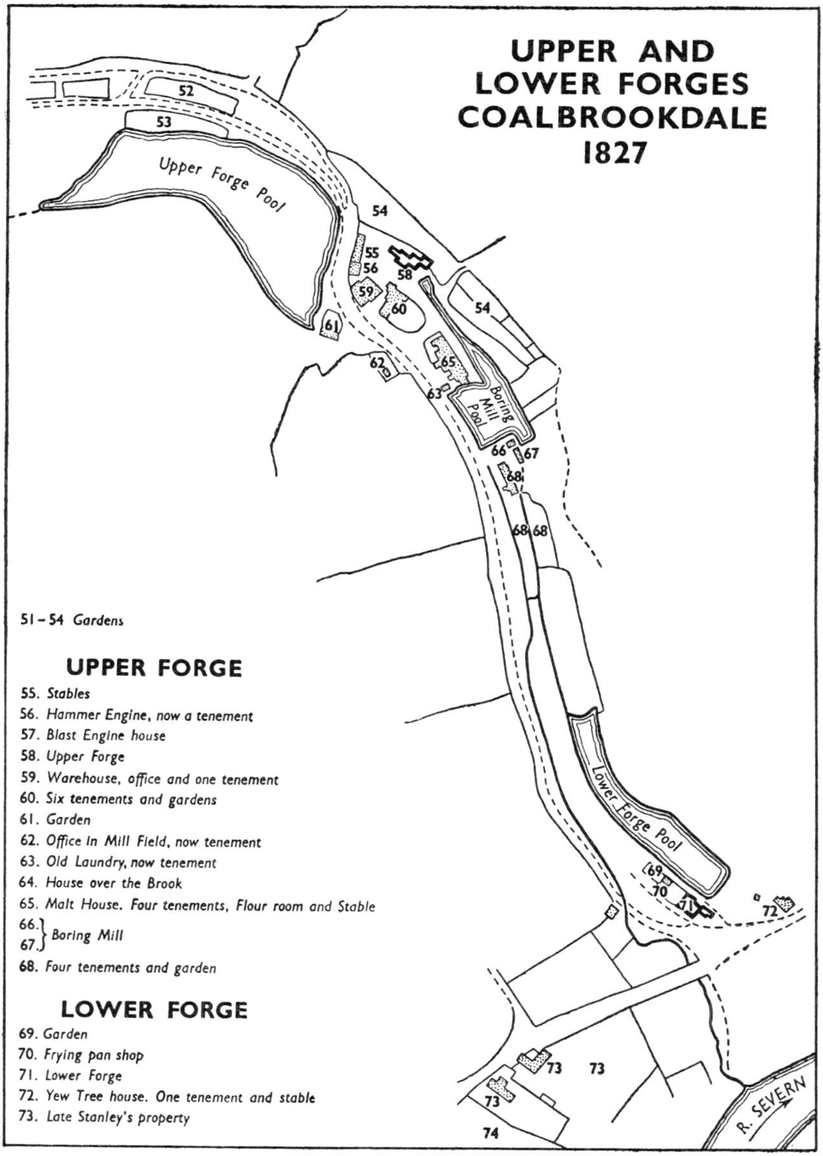
UPPER AND
LOWER FORGES
COALBROOKDALE
1827
52
53
Upper Forge Pool
54
55
56
58
59
60
61
54
62
65
63
Boring Mill Pool
66
67
68
68
68
Lower Forge Pool
69
70
71
72
73
73
73
74
R. SEVERN
51–54 Gardens
UPPER FORGE
55. Stables
56. Hammer Engine, now a tenement
57. Blast Engine house
58. Upper Forge
59. Warehouse, office and one tenement
60. Six tenements and gardens
61. Garden
62. Office in Mill Field, now tenement
63. Old Laundry, now tenement
64. House over the Brook
65. Malt House. Four tenements, Flour room and Stable
66.
67. Boring Mill
68. Four tenements and garden
LOWER FORGE
69. Garden
70. Frying pan shop
71. Lower Forge
72. Yew Tree house. One tenement and stable
73. Late Stanley's property

The remaining group is somewhat scattered along the lower course of the stream. Water from the furnace pools is again collected into the Upper Forge Pool and below that stands the Upper Forge with blast engine and hammer engine, and just below it, with its own pool, the Boring Mill. In this Upper Forge grouping there is the Malthouse and the building called on a plan of 1753, 'Mr. Darby's Old House.' These with many of the forge buildings are occupied as tenements and suggest that the forge work had been greatly contracted here. At the foot of the valley there is the Lower Forge and Frying Pan Shop, a site now covered by the weigh-house and garages.

At the upper end of the valley, the offices, the Darby house and some cottages lie to the west of the Upper Furnace Pool, and at the east end of the pool, at the foot of Jigger Bank, there are the Resolution Fire Engine and the Corn Mill. Apart from the buildings so far mentioned there are several rows of cottages and tenements, and many buildings in the forges group are also tenemented, so that the plan accounts for not less than fifty-two cottage dwellings as well as Navigation Row, which contained ten or a dozen more. All the tenements have gardens and there are areas of garden at several other places near the buildings.

The abandonment of Coalbrookdale as a smelting centre was only part of a general movement that was affecting the whole coalfield. The Coalbrookdale Coalfield has two distinct divisions, the areas of the Middle and Upper Coal Measures. Because of the geological structure and the effects of erosion, the Middle Coal Measures are at the surface and well exposed around Coalbrookdale itself, but to the east the Upper Coal Measures cover them and, as these upper strata are almost barren of coal, the older workings were limited to the exposed field from Coalbrookdale to Ketley and Donnington Wood. By the beginning of the nineteenth century these old collieries were approaching exhaustion and at the same time the improvements in steam engines and pumps made deeper mining possible so that new pits could be sunk to the east to penetrate the cover of Upper Coal Measures. This migration of coal and ironstone working to the east was followed by the migration of the furnaces, new and enlarged ones being built on the new coalfield and the old ones being gradually abandoned. It was considerably cheaper to smelt the ores near the fuel and carry only the pig iron to the foundries, than to carry fuel and ore several miles to the old furnace sites. This migration is seen in the Coalbrookdale Company's transfer of the smelting, successively to Lightmoor and Priorslee.[1]

Barnard Dickinson remained as the general manager of the Company until 1830, with an assistant manager in charge at Horsehay. Until 1827 this had been Daniel Rose, but on his death Joseph Dickinson, the son of Barnard, succeeded him. Joseph, though only a young man of 21, had had like all the Darbys, a good early training in the works and was capable of carrying heavy responsibility. Horsehay forge was well equipped but much of its plant, especially the engines, was old and ready for replacement. The workmen had grown up with the place and their ways were set; in many things the regulation of the works had become slack, so that inefficiency was creeping in. Joseph Dickinson felt that much of the laxity could be removed if the manager were resident on the works, but he never completed the house he planned and began to build at Horsehay.

The Horsehay works at that time had three blast furnaces, two forges and a rolling mill, with a foundry and boiler shop. The weak link in the structure was in the blast engines which were not in a condition to meet the heavy duty demanded of them. In addition to the furnaces, blast was required for the refinery and smiths' shops and for the foundry cupola. Of the two engines in use, one was a Boulton and Watt type, built at Coalbrookdale and in fairly good condition, and the other was a much earlier, improved Newcomen type. The older engine also pumped water back from the forge pool and was seriously overloaded. The arrangement of the blast was somewhat complicated. A cylinder blowing machine was driven by each engine; from this air was delivered to a regulator which had been devised by William Reynolds. The regulator was a cement-lined vaulted brick chamber, 20 yards long, 6 feet high and 3 feet wide, erected in a brick tank of nearly double the width. The inner chamber communicated at the bottom with the outer one, which was open at the top, and both were filled half full of water, when at rest. Air from the blowers was forced into the inner chamber which now had a water seal, and the tuyers drew air from the same chamber. The engine speeds were kept such that the pressure of the water in the inner chamber could maintain a three feet difference in level between the water inside and the water outside, which gave the

[1] This general movement of the centres of the iron industry is more fully discussed in a paper by Birch, T. W., 'Development & Decline of the Coalbrookdale Coalfield.' *Geography*, XIX, 1934, pp. 14–126.

best effective air pressure for the blast. The level of the water outside the regulator was thus a visible measure of the strength of blast. The regulator was very flexible, and it is obvious that if there were an extra demand on the blast, the inner pressures fell and the water head was lowered, or when the blast were shut off too quickly at a casting time, the water seal might blow out unless the engine was checked quickly. Fortunately we possess a drawing of the regulator at Hollins Wood furnace, on this pattern, in 1793, and this is reproduced in the plate facing p. 241. In spite of its trickiness, this regulator made it possible to combine the air from two very different blowing engines, and seemed to work well with careful handling. With this blast arrangement the furnaces had reached an output of 50 to 55 tons a week each, by 1825.

From the furnaces pig iron went to three refineries, which were fired with the best quality coke, where the pig was converted to plate iron, at a rate of about 650 tons a month. This was carried to the forges and broken up for puddling. In the upper forge there were eleven puddling furnaces, and one ball furnace which was used exclusively for making boiler plate slabs from the best quality, only, of the plate iron. The forge had two hammers with metal helves, worked by an old and rather decrepit steam engine. The puddled balls were hammered here into blooms and half blooms for the rolling mills. In the lower forge there were four puddling furnaces and one for heating scraps in special clay pots made at the Company's own brick works. Two of the furnaces were always employed making the very best stamped iron. The helve hammer and a pair of roughing rolls were worked by a large and rather shaky water wheel.

The rolling mill was considered to be one of the best designed in the area, and had four trains of rolls. These were one for boiler plate, one for large Merchant bars, one for small Merchant bars, and one for rod slitting. There was also a large and cumbersome shears. The boiler plate slabs were drawn to gauge under the hammer, before rolling, and the finished plates were usually not more than 4 or 5 cwt. each. The output of the mill was from 520 to 550 tons a month. The old rolling mill, built about 1790, had been taken down when the new one was built in 1806, but its buildings were used as the boiler yard, and part of it as the sugar pan shop. Here and on the works there were a cupola and eleven smiths' hearths.

To complete the survey of the whole concerns at this time, it is necessary to include the Dawley Castle furnaces and the Lawley and

Dawley collieries. Two furnaces at Dawley Castle, a little smaller than the ones at Horsehay, had been brought into blast in 1810. The blast engine which had been built by the Coalbrookdale Company was using about 280 tons of coal a month and was regarded as wasteful. This was caused by the engine being overloaded and so working with a lowered efficiency. However the furnaces were of an improved design and by running with a higher pressure of blast, their output was kept up to 55 to 60 tons a week, each.

Abraham Darby took a keen interest in all the mines but allowed Benjamin Tranter to manage them according to his own discretion so long as he maintained the output demanded of them. Of the pits, twelve were winning coal, and thirty-one were working ironstone beds. The pits among them employed sixteen engines, mostly Sadler's or Heslop's types made at Coalbrookdale. The coals worked were from six seams, Tops, Clods, Randles, Doubles, Big Flints and Sulphur, and the total output was about 9,000 to 9,500 tons a month, and about 4,200 tons a month of ironstone. The ironstone worked was the Topenny, Blue Flat, White Flat, Ball Stone and Spar, little change from the earliest days. The ironstone was calcined at the pit bank in heaps of from 1,000 to 3,000 tons each, with coal and slack got specially for the purpose.

In 1827 some of the wages and costs were as follows. At the furnaces—Keepers 20/-, fillers 15/-, labourers 14/-, cinder fillers 13/6, engine men 14/- a week; cokers and others from 2/- to 2/6 a day. At the pits wages were about 2/- to 2/6 a day, and the cost of coals was 3/9 per ton on the bank, and of ironstone, 6/9 per ton.

The available description of the works in 1827 might easily give a false impression of neglect and decrepitude. The concerns were actually passing through one of the quieter and conservative periods of their existence, but the life of a new and vigorous expansion was already stirring. It is never possible for a business to pursue a steady upward and unbroken line of progress. Political conditions, the state of the markets, the loss of a driving personality can all or any of them carry a business on to a peak of prosperity or sweep it into a trough of depression. On the whole the Coalbrookdale concerns had suffered less violent fluctuations than most, and its peaks had not been so spectacular as say those of the Wilkinsons, nor had its troughs been so deep as many others experienced. The contributory causes were many. The variety of interests and the very early integration of the works from raw material production to finished goods, had tended towards a self-contained stability; its leaders of the Darby and Reynolds families had never sought large fortunes, nor spent the profits which came to them on large establishments and country mansions, but whenever possible had translated leases into ownership both in the works and the collieries. One factor is difficult, if not impossible, to assess but should nonetheless be kept in mind, the fact that during the first four generations, most of the Darby men were short-lived. The successive managers took charge at the following ages—Abraham Darby I, 30; Richard Ford, 28; Abraham II, 21; Richard Reynolds, 27; Abraham III, 18; Edmund Darby, 21; Barnard Dickinson, 29; Abraham IV, 23; Alfred Darby, 23. Thus between 1708 and 1828, there had been nine infusions of young or comparatively young and venturesome blood. It is no wonder that the affairs of the Company give the feeling of virility and flexibility all through its history.

In 1827 the Company was about to receive a double infusion of young blood, the energy of which, along with outside circumstances, was to carry the concern to its greatest level of prosperity. When Edmund Darby died in 1801 his two sons, Abraham and Alfred, were only 6 and 3 years old respectively. In 1826 Abraham went into the Dawley colliery office, under Benjamin Tranter then in charge of all the mines, both coal and iron, which were worked by the Company. His training there was very thorough and he acquired an interest in mining which remained with him all his life. During his four years with Tranter, he familiarized himself also with the blast furnaces. His brother Alfred, in 1828, took a position in the office at Horsehay and there studied the forge and foundry side of the business along with the office methods. In 1830 Abraham and Alfred took over the entire management of all the Company's affairs, Abraham maintained his outside interest in mines and furnaces, and Alfred found his place largely within the forges and offices, so that they formed an ideal complementary couple who worked together in perfect harmony for the next twenty years. Both not only were respected by the men but secured their friendship and trust and never lost it.

The joint management of Abraham and Alfred was initiated by almost revolutionary changes, not only in plant and technical processes, but in the regulation and relationships of labour and in working conditions. When the new management took over in 1830, Francis Darby, son of Abraham III and a man of 47 was still in the works, but his greater interest was in art. He was living at the White House in the Dale, and presumably had the oversight of the Coalbrookdale Foundry. His brother Richard was widely engaged in public work, and spent a great deal of his time and effort in the fight for the emancipation of the slaves.

The depression that was marked in 1816 and the following years by a drastic blowing out of furnaces and the closing down of Ketley and some other works, showed signs of recovery in the 1820's and, by 1824, 41 furnaces were in blast in Shropshire, with a make of 60,000 tons of iron. The Coalbrookdale Company's furnaces were again in full blast at Horsehay and Lightmoor and the demand for coal by the blowing, winding and pumping engines increased in proportion. Abraham Darby discovered that by careful firing, slack coal could be used efficiently on all their boiler fires, and ordered that nothing but slack be used, except for certain emergencies. This at once effected a saving of 600 to 700 tons of good coal a month, and also reduced and prevented two great nuisances. The 'pit slack' in the past had largely been tipped near the pit bank, or in some cases stowed underground in the pit 'gob' behind the workings. In both positions it eventually fired, and polluted the whole district with pit 'stithe' and also made some of the pits unworkable. This great saving in engine coal enabled the collieries to extend the 'Severn Sale,' the shipping of coal to Bristol, which had always been carried on on a small scale.

The first big alterations were made in the furnace management. A good deal of laxity and careless work had crept into the furnace working, largely because the oversight and direction had been somewhat neglected. Abraham and Alfred found lodgings at Horsehay and Abraham cultivated the habit of visiting all departments at all times of day and night, and was regularly seen on the furnaces at least three nights in the week. He altered and improved the furnace filling and left a trustworthy and skilful foreman in charge who made regular reports to the office. A bounty agreement was made, by which the normal make of the furnaces was reckoned 60 tons, and a bonus was paid on all in excess of that amount. For a time this had one unforeseen and awkward result, in that a few furnacemen, to increase the make, were not above collecting any loose iron they could find, spare wheels, rail sleepers, castings, anything that could be thrown into the furnaces to swell the melt; however, a night watchman soon corrected this.

The greatest immediate change in technique was the introduction of raw coal in the furnace charge, which increased the quantity but lowered the quality of the iron made. The old and overworked blast engines were taken down and a new one substituted, which would have been quite adequate for all the furnace blasts, but which was hampered by having a heavy pump attached, to return water to the forge pool. The very heavy load on the pump sometimes made the blast rather irregular, but this was never considered a sufficient disadvantage to call for a separate engine.

The hot blast, invented by Neilson in 1828, was applied at Horsehay and Dawley Castle furnaces in 1838. This again increased the output but was accompanied by a change in the quality of the iron which made it a little less amenable for forge use, but left it quite a good foundry iron. The make of the furnaces was increased from about 60 tons a week to between 80 and 90 tons. One other introduction was the use of refining and mill cinder in the furnace, which was found to be advantageous to the quality of the iron.

With the furnace improvements well in hand, attention was next turned to the forges. At the upper forge a new engine was built with a train of rolls that would roll a billet 5¼ inches wide, and along with this eight new puddling furnaces were made. The puddlers experimented with pig iron and were successful in dealing with raw pig, so that by the end of 1832 the refining of the pig iron before puddling was discontinued except for special purpose iron. The pig 'boiling process,' which had by this time been discovered at Joseph Hall's iron works in Staffordshire, was adopted as the regular process. The forge was rapidly expanding and when the furnaces had increased to twenty-four, and the helve hammer proved incapable of keeping pace with the shingling required, a monster pair of squeezers was introduced to supplement the work of the hammer. This treatment proved very unsatisfactory, so a second hammer was brought in to replace the squeezer. The forge now had 26 puddling and 2 ball furnaces and was considered to be quite up to its work and capable of making 1,200 tons of iron a month. The addition of a new engine and a pair of rolls to take 7¾ inch widths, completed this phase of reconstruction.

In 1837 a new code of rules for the working of the forge was introduced, and unfortunately provoked a good deal of discontent, though only indirectly. The rules regulated the puddling and laid down a minimum yield, with a definite quality requirement; there

PLATE XXIII *The Lower Works Coalbrookdale in about 1860 before the Much Wenlock Railway No. 2 was constructed. The buildings and site had changed little since the eighteenth century, and the works show no outward signs of being the place where the latest decorative metalwork was produced. Abraham Darby IV was responsible for Holy Trinity Church, seen here on the right, which was consecrated in 1854.*

PLATE XXIV *The Upper Furnace pool, Coalbrookdale, about 1860. The main building in the centre background is Dale House, built for Abraham Darby I in 1715 but not completed until after his death. Next to it, immediately above the bridge is Rosehill House occupied in the 1730's by Richard Ford, manager of the works, and behind these buildings is Tea Kettle Row, built by the Coalbrookdale Company between 1735 and 1742.* (See PLATE VI.)

were offtakes for deficiencies in either the yield or the quality of the iron made. The alterations to the blast furnaces have already been noted as increasing the output but at the same time altering the quality of the pig iron, and the puddlers maintained, with much truth and reasonableness, that it was no longer possible to make a better quality iron with the quality of pig sent to them. For some years this contention continued until the increasing complaints from customers compelled the serious attention of the management. The principal alteration made was in the smelting department, more attention being paid to the proportions of the furnace charges and to the regulation of the blast,with a willingness to sacrifice some of the output for the sake of a better quality product. It was possible for this production of poorer quality forge iron to persist so long, only because the Company were rapidly increasing their foundry business, for which the pig iron was quite suited.

These remarks on quality apply only to the bar iron produced. Special care was taken with iron for boiler plate, and for many years Horsehay forge was one of the leading makers of boiler plate. The plate mill in 1838 could produce five feet wide plates and was said to be the only forge in the world at that time capable of rolling such plates. There is an account in the *Mechanic's Magazine* for 1838, which quotes from the *Liverpool Standard*:

> *Enormous Plate of Iron*—we were lately shown in Messrs Fawcett, Preston & Cos. yard two plates of iron which are said to be the *largest ever made*. They measure 10ft. 7ins. long, 5 ft. 1 ins. wide and 7/16 of an inch thick, and weigh between 7 and 8 cwt. They are intended for the bottom plates of two steam generators on Mr. Howard's plan, and were made by the Coalbrookdale Iron Co., Shropshire, who, we were informed, are the only Company in Britain (we may say in the world) that can make plates of this size, or even approach to it.[1]

In the rolling mill, guide rolling was started in 1833 and after some experiments on rolling small sizes and wire, a wire mill was built and put to work in 1834. The principal changes made in the mill were the substitution from time to time of new engines for the old ones. In fact one can say that from 1830 to 1850 Coalbrookdale engine shop and foundry produced a succession of bigger and better engines for all departments of the works, mines, furnaces, forges and mills, each engine being carefully designed for the job it was to do.

[1] Quoted by Jenkins, Rhys, *Boiler Making*, in his Collected Papers, 1936, p. 129.

The technical alterations were largely the work of Abraham Darby but, during the ten years in which these were being carried through, Alfred introduced no less important changes in labour and personnel. He found that many processes in the forge and the furnaces were in the hands of small cliques or family groups of men, who had grown careless, and he also found that the methods of payment and calculation of wages were no longer adequate for a business whose labour roll was approaching two thousand strong. All these things were brought up to date with more consultation with the workmen, and the best men were brought forward as foremen or managers of a process or department with more responsibility than before. The change was from the older family business organization with the manager in and about the works, taking a hand here and there and accepting the responsibility for all decisions, to a business on modern lines with foremen and heads of departments, under-managers and a responsible office staff, with regular reports and consultations. The changes were especially welcome at the pits where they were long overdue.

The works were now rapidly expanding and employed nearly two thousand men, so that it was natural that social problems should become more acute. The most pressing problem was that of housing, and the first step was taken by the building of a row of twelve cottages of a rather better type, suitable for the foremen and more responsible workmen. In the construction of these cottages and in much of the rebuilding in the works, the shale from one of the ironstone waste heaps was used for the brick making and was found to be very good. In 1838 the Company bought the Pool Hill Estate and found on it a good brick clay which was suited for best quality brick production; to utilize this clay a new brickyard was established and quickly brought into production. Sandy Bank Row of eighteen cottages, Pool Hill with six cottages, and Frame Lane Row of eight brought the number of cottages built at this time up to forty-four. This was Alfred's building programme for four years.

The transport department under Alfred saw great changes. Horsehay Farm was purchased and put in charge of a bailiff who was a good horseman, and the Company purchased horses until at one time they had a hundred of their own at work. All the carrying necessary was now done by the Company's own horses and men, and many of the difficulties and abuses that had crept in through the great amount of hired labour and horse teams formerly needed, were corrected. A greatly increased bulk of products was carried direct to the Midland markets, and a system of regular delivery journeys was made to most of the Midland and southern centres two or three times a week. The Company still delivered much of their goods direct to the trader, but was also developing their own agencies and warehouses in many parts. On the canals and the river Severn they had twenty boats in a very well organized shipping department.

Under the vigorous management of Abraham and Alfred, the Coalbrookdale foundries were not neglected. Abraham's first interest was still with the mines and furnaces, but Alfred and his uncle Francis took an equally keen interest in the foundry side of the works. During the reconstruction of Horsehay and Dawley Castle furnaces and forges, all the engines needed were both designed and made at Coalbrookdale foundry, and to accomplish this the engine shop had to be developed with its necessary pattern shops and machine shop departments keeping pace with it. These were now sufficiently equipped to make a number of engines for sale after meeting the demands of the Company, and also to make much of the forge machinery for Horsehay—roll trains, hammers, shears and other requirements. With roll turning and running repairs in addition, it is no wonder that a busy engineer's department was soon in full swing, and the old tradition of engine making was continued with the addition of the production of heavy machinery.

The principal development was however along a new line, that of the art castings department. We have noted that at an early date in the firm's story, railways and balustrades were being cast, and these products were being made in a small way throughout the eighteenth century. At the beginning of the nineteenth century the castings were a little more ambitious and were linked up with the bridges and other structural work. The architect John Nash was obtaining architectural ironwork from them for some of the larger town and country houses on which he was employed.

It is to Francis Darby that one must look for the inspiration of the great expansion which took place and which carried the Coalbrookdale foundry to the leading position in art casting, by the middle of the century. Randall[1] speaking of the Darbys says:

> Of the later members of the Darby family we may speak in part from personal knowledge. Whilst adhering to the grand cardinal doctrine of the Inner Light they indulged their own ideas of the extent to which the

[1] Randall, J., *History of Madeley*, 1880.

strict discipline of the body should control their tastes. They were birth members but lax in their opinions and did not live by their strict Quaker rule. Francis Darby of the White House, had great taste and loved high art. He filled his rooms with costly paintings. Others indulged in a love of music and luxury.

This love of contemporary art and his general artistic sense led Francis to introduce artist designers and among them some from France. These designers had an immediate influence on much of the domestic casting, and found an almost empty field ripe for their exploitation in the application of art motifs in cast iron. The world at large was just realizing the flexibility of cast iron—it was the first real 'plastic' medium which could produce or reproduce carved and sculptured ornament in infinite number. Architects were awaking to the possible beauty of cast iron in rails, balconies, gates, and in finer ornament, and the world was ready to accept and admire the infinite variety possible in the use of this new material. Not only did the new designers at Coalbrookdale apply their art to domestic objects, gates, rails, stoves, and a multitude of things, but they began to produce statuary, and many articles of pure ornament.

Abraham and Alfred Darby like their forbears were interested in liberal education for the children of their workmen and in the general well-being of their employees. Among the workmen at the Horsehay forge there was a voluntary sick fund, for which a few coppers a week were collected by one of the men. From an early date it had been the custom in all parts of the Company's concerns to take a collection for a fellow workman who was prevented by sickness or accident from working, but it was not until 1835 that these *ad hoc* collections were translated into a weekly subscription. About two hundred of the men joined the club which proved of value in the next few years. In 1840 Alfred Darby helped to draft a set of rules for the club and gave to its funds all the fines levied in the works, as well as the half of all deductions made for bad work or under-yield in the forge and rolling mill, in addition to his own subscription on behalf of the Company. The club was extended over the furnacemen at Horsehay and Dawley Castle, and then over all the works, and the collection of weekly subscriptions was undertaken by the office staff, by a deduction from the wages.

The club soon had a substantial fund and, as a surplus over their needs was mounting up, the club agreed to use some of this fund towards the education of more of their children. Richard Reynolds and Abraham Darby III had built small schools for the miners' children in the eighteenth century, but these were quite inadequate to meet the needs of the rapidly increasing population and the much larger number of employees of the Company. Alfred Darby fitted up a temporary school room in the large lofts over the stables at Horsehay Farm which, after a short experimental run, proved so successful that he decided to build more suitable premises. The club funds made a monthly contribution to its running so that the men felt that in a measure it was their own venture. In 1846 Alfred Darby built a large school at Pool Hill to serve seven hundred children, so that boys and girls were now able to go to school from an earlier age. No children were taken into the works after this until they had completed a satisfactory training in the school, which they were not allowed to leave before the age of twelve.

The religious life of the workpeople was not ignored. A Quaker meeting had been held from the very beginning of the works and Abraham Darby II had built a Friends Meeting House in the Dale. A second meeting house was established at Dawley before the end of the eighteenth century. The accounts of the Company include gifts of timber and labour to make seats and a pulpit so that a building could be fitted up as a chapel, and plots of ground were leased or sold at a nominal figure for chapel sites. Abraham IV and Alfred, with their sister Mary, built and gave the present Church of England building in the Dale, in the design and building of which Alfred took a great interest. He gave the fine peal of bells which is a notable feature of the church, and also had much of the Gothic tracery for the windows and many other parts of the church, designed and cast in iron at the works. Shortly after the deaths of Francis and Alfred Darby in 1850 and 1852, the constant efforts and suggestions which they had made to improve the educational facilities in the Dale and to encourage the desire for this improvement to develop naturally among the workpeople, came to fruition in the decision to plan an Institution for the acquirement of Useful Knowledge. A meeting was called in the Infant School, Coalbrookdale, on Friday, 21 January 1853, with the Reverend Charles Marshall in the chair, and ten other men attending. At this meeting after some discussion it was resolved :

> That it is highly desirable to found an Institution in Coalbrookdale for the purposes aforesaid and that the name thereof be 'The Coalbrookdale Literary and Scientific Institution.'

That in order to carry out this object the Gentlemen present Mr. C. Crookes, Mr. H. C. T. Dickenson, W. Sankey, W. Norris, Mr. John Fox and Mr. Cowper do form a Committee (with power to add to their number) to conduct the business of the Institution until the first General Meeting.

That a draft copy of the Rules for the government of the Institution submitted to this Meeting, be brought before the next Committee Meeting for further consideration.

The Institution was at once popular and well supported, and at the Annual Report made in 1857 it was possible to speak of the great encouragement received in the project.

It is also satisfactory to conclude from this circumstance [increased support] that the establishment of the Institution has been productive to the neighbourhood of benefits and advantages which have attracted the sympathy and support of the now large body of Members.

The principal subject for congratulation, however, is the prospect that through the kind patronage of the Coalbrookdale Co., the Institution will be provided with excellent rooms in the new Building now in course of erection in Paradise.

From the improved accommodation, the central situation of the Building and the union under one roof of the Library, Lecture and Reading Rooms, the Committee anticipate many advantages that will increase the efficiency of the Institution and will contribute to the convenience of Members.

The Buildings were of course being erected in only an earthly Paradise, the strip of land and coppice on the hillside, overlooking the Lower Furnace Pool site, and carrying the pleasant field name so suggestive of the after life. The new buildings were completed and opened in 1859 and the Annual Report says:

The year that has passed will be an epoch in the history of the Institution from the occurrence in the course of it, of the opening to the use of the Institution of the handsome and commodious Building which has been erected for its accommodation and from that opening having been attended with circumstances of no ordinary interest.

Whilst recording this event it is due to the Coalbrookdale Co., that the Committee should acknowledge the enduring obligation under which the Members of the Institution at all times are, and will be, placed by the Company's liberality in providing this Building, and it is fitting that the exertions of the Vice-President of the Institution, Mr. Crookes, should be thankfully remembered by the Members. That the Institution may exist as long as the Building and that in its new abode it may exercise a permanent and beneficial influence in the Dale must be the ardent wish of all its Members.

Soon after the formation of the Institution, in 1856, a School of Art was founded with a very representative committee drawn from the surrounding area, Coalbrookdale, Madeley, Ironbridge and Broseley, and with G. W. Norris as the Hon. Secretary. There is no doubt that this school of art and the designing rooms of the Coalbrookdale foundry had a considerable reciprocal effect and that the extraordinary wealth of the Coalbrookdale designs owe something to the vitality of this school. Some of the designers at the foundry, Charles Crookes, John Bell, M. Carrier, B. W. Hawkins, and others, no doubt provided a constant example and encouragement to the students, and the Company was a reliable and attractive prospective employer.

From the years 1805 to 1851 there has survived an annual statement of profits and the valuation of the works, and this reflects many years of difficulty in which the family followed its constant habit of returning capital into the Company.[1] The years 1810 to 1813 were years of loss, though never very great, as also were the years 1816 and 1817, 1820 to 1822, and 1826 to 1831. Over the whole period 1805 to 1851 however, the profits amounted to £400,000 within a few pounds and the losses to £83,500, both of which are modest sums when compared with the wealth taken from the industry by some of the contemporary ironmasters. The valuation of the works and properties rose with set-backs and fluctuations from £134,664 in 1805 to £365,824 in 1851. The ownership remained entirely within the Darby family if the son-in-law Dickinson is included; as the older members died out, it was gradually concentrated in the hands of Alfred and Abraham who thus obtained the major portion of all the shares.

[1] These figures are of sufficient importance to be reproduced in the Appendix, No. 7.

Chapter Fifteen

THE LATER YEARS 1850-1966

A CONVENIENT measure of the progress of the Coalbrookdale foundry during the reconstruction of the works from 1830, and the efficiency it had achieved, is perhaps to be seen in its response to the Great Exhibition of 1851. In the catalogue of the Exhibition the Coalbrookdale Company figures as an exhibitor mainly in the section of General Hardware, with an amazing variety of exhibits. The introductory paragraphs to the description of their exhibit says that 'the total number of men and boys in the employment of the Coalbrookdale Company, at the Foundry and at Horsehay, is between 3,000 and 4,000'. At the beginning of the century the roll of employees was 'over a thousand' but we have no intermediate figures.

The Great Exhibition marked for the Company, in many ways, the end of an epoch. In 1849 and 1851 Abraham and Alfred Darby had virtually retired, and had removed their homes to other parts of the country: Alfred came back to Stanley Hall, Shropshire, but died in 1852. Francis, their father's cousin and joint manager of the works died in 1850, so that the works were left without any Darby in the management. The designer Charles Crookes took on the management for a while but as he had no knowledge of iron making the affairs at Horsehay soon drifted into a very unsatisfactory condition. This persisted until 1866 when William G. Norris took over the management of the whole works and initiated what we may regard as the modern period of its development. Although there were many technical difficulties at the forges, the foundry seemed to carry on under its own momentum, stimulated and fed by an ever increasing demand for its products. At the close of the Great Exhibition the works were turning out 2,000 tons of finished iron per week, and was thus, in actual production, the largest foundry in the world. Among other changes the furnaces at Priorslee and at Dawley Castle had been blown in and supplied all the pig iron required for the forges at Coalbrookdale and at Horsehay, and the furnaces in Coalbrookdale were closed down for good.

The difficulties at the forges which Abraham had dealt with between 1837 and 1842 reasserted themselves. Soon after Darby's retirement, with the advice and energy of William G. Norris a permanent solution was found and the Company were able to compete in all markets with a very high quality product. In this final reformation Abraham took the position of advising expert.

During the management of Norris two major expansions of Coalbrookdale works were made. The first was the development of a great variety of stoves, with associated work on smoke abatement for which the Silver Medal of the Smoke Abatement Exhibition, South Kensington 1882 and several other awards were won, up to 1911. The second great change was in the engineering section. A great number and variety of steam engines were made including the Parker High Speed engine, 500 revolutions per minute, which was supplied to many of the early electric power stations. High pressure and heavy duty pumps were made for mines in many parts of the world and also for docks and harbour work. Their engine shop at the turn of the century had some unique machines—a lathe with a faceplate 20 feet diameter, a planing machine with a bed 20 feet by 8 feet and a full complement of other machinery in proportion. They produced a small contractors' locomotive which was very popular. At Horsehay some very heavy duty rolling mills were developed to make a vast number of beam sections, boiler plates and ships deck plating. A bridge department made large bridges for many parts of the world. The Horsehay works were eventually sold to the Simpson family, whose firm specialised in the gigantic cranes needed for the largest steel plants, lifting up to 420 tons. The Simpsons were Quakers and remained in close friendship with Coalbrookdale.

William G. Norris retired in 1897 and was followed by two men who only served the Company for short periods. Duncan Sinclair 1897 to 1904 and B. S. Brooksbank 1904 to 1906. The next manager of the Company was W. S. Malcolm who served from 1906 to 1929. During his management a major change was effected. In a period of change and depression the idea of an alliance of ironfounders was discussed and in 1922 Light Castings Limited was formed. This was an alliance of the Coalbrookdale Company Limited, Planet Foundry Company Limited of Guide Bridge, Manchester, M. Cockburn and Company Limited of Falkirk and McDowall Steven and Company also of Falkirk. All were old and well respected companies and each kept its own name and specialities but joined in major matters of policy with a clear expression of the old Coalbrookdale expressed ideal of 'Industry coordinated for service'.

In 1929 when world industry was beginning to experience an increasing depression, Light Castings was taken into a larger grouping, Allied Ironfounders Limited. This made possible considerable reconstruction in the various constituent companies of the Alliance with a vastly improved sales organisation of which W. T. Wren was Managing Director. In the Coalbrookdale Company the management pattern was revised but it remained an almost autonomous company. David Sturrock, a Director of Allied Ironfounders and of Sinclair Iron Company Limited, was appointed to supervise the operations of the Coalbrookdale Company from 1929 to 1942, but in 1932 Charles W. Edwards was appointed Managing Director and held that position until 1937 when Thomas Offley Lander became Chairman of the Company. At the same time Charles W. Edwards and John W. Jones were joined with Offler Lander as joint Managing Directors. Edwards served until 1941 and Jones until 1949; Offley Lander served until 1954 when G. Frederick Williams became Managing Director of the Company.

We must now take a short backward look at the works. Although the management of the company by a member of the Darby family came to an end when Abraham IV and Alfred retired in 1849 and 1851, members of the Darby family have continued their interest in the Dale and its workpeople right up to the present. Alfred Edmund William, son of Alfred became the Chairman of the Coalbrookdale Company and kept that position until the formation of Light Castings Limited in 1922. During the time of Charles Crookes as Manager, the Literary and Scientific Institute was formed. That was in 1853 and it was followed in 1856 by the School of Art. The Secretary for both was William G. Norris who in 1866 became Manager of the Company. Though not a Darby he had intimate connections with the family. His mother was Ann Luccock a direct descendant of Thomas Luccock who was apprenticed to the first Abraham Darby. That Thomas' father and grandfather had worked respectively with Abraham's father John Darby and with grandfather John. In 1686 John Darby, Abraham's father had married Joan Luccock, his second wife. Both Alfred and William Darby were keen supporters of the Institute and all its work.

Alfred II had two children, Alfred Alexander Maurice who was killed in the war in 1915, and Frances Muriel who married Mordaunt Leckonby Cope but took the name Cope-Darby. In 1925 she came back to live in Coalbrookdale, inheriting her father's estates of Adcote and Sunniside in 1927. This was not the Sunniside of Abraham II and Abiah but a new house on the other side of the valley and near the Institute. Muriel took a great interest in her family history and continued the collections of Darby records, furniture, dresses and small articles which Alfred and Francis had started. A part of these collections is now in the Museum of Iron and the rest at Rosehill House. She was very active in many ways in the Dale community, starting a choir and many other associations. At her death she left many Darby family possessions to her relation Rachel, Lady Labouchere.

To return now to the main stream of the Company management under Allied Ironfounders, many changes had been made. The engineering shops had been closed down and the main section of the Dale works was the foundries with among other innovations the highly developed stove production lines with the now universally known and used Rayburn stove and some parts of the Aga. There was a mining section providing coal for the furnaces, now used direct without coking. Also fireclay was being mined for an extensive manufacture of fire bricks for every variety of stove and fireplace, both domestic and industrial. By 1947 the Company had perfected and put into operation their invention of the first ever mechanical moulding and sand conditioning plant and were using it in the production of between 300 and 500 Rayburn stoves each week.

In these improving conditions it was possible to give some attention to the history of the Company. In my book *Quakers in Science and Industry*, 1950, I included an account of the Coalbrookdale Company and through a Friend, Harold Simpson of Horsehay, I visited the works in 1946. There I got to know G. F. (Fred) Williams, General Manager of the Northern Group of Allied Ironfounders Limited and Managing Director of the Coalbrookdale works, and already I knew William T. Wren a Director of Allied Ironfounders Limited. While a Fellow at the Quaker College of Woodbrooke, Selly Oak, I got to know Roger and Basil Darby who discussed with me the idea of a history of the Coalbrookdale Company and the Darby family. When the idea had been discussed in more detail and accepted, I asked for some precise detail of the Old Furnace and in 1947 G. F. (Fred) Williams made some excavations about the furnace sufficient to enable him to make the measured drawing used in this book which was first published in 1953. It is here that the story of the excavation and preservation of the furnace has its origin. It was in response to my further request for photographs or drawings that the secretary of Coalbrookdale Company replied on 28th August 1950 that Mr. Williams 'was considering the possibility of photographing and drawing the Old Furnace prior to dismantling it and making full use of the surrounding area'. This followed instructions from Allied Ironfounders for a total clearance of the site. It was suggested that the named beams might be saved and used sometime in a reconstruction somewhere. George Cadbury soon after that came to see the furnace and with Professor Court asked a young Birmingham Friend, David Eversley to make a study of the Company. They approached Allied Ironfounders with a request for the presentation of the whole site to Birmingham University as a study area for their students and for possible full excavation. This was refused as work had already started with Fred (later Dr.) Williams and some of the Coalbrookdale staff. W. P. Wren secured a decision from the Board to save the Furnace and a formal excavation was begun. By late 1951 Dr. Williams had cleared the interior and started on a restoration of the tapping area and the whole front of the furnace. Nothing more was heard from Birmingham University and as excavation proceeded a report of progress was made about every month to a small group of interested persons, one of whom, Michael Rix, from time to time gave reports to the press and to the BBC.

Exploration proceeded quietly and the area around the furnace was extended and the second 'New' furnace which had never been blown in was cleared. In 1957 the Board of Allied Ironfounders decided that the excavations were to be completed and that the restoration of the Old Furnace would be an ideal event with which to commemorate the 250 year existence of the Company and the first smelting of iron with coke. Dr. Williams and I were asked to make a report of the possibility of this and our plans, with the addition of a small museum were accepted. All was completed and officially opened on 15th October 1959.

The furnace we know as the Old Furnace is in fact the one which Abraham III built ready for the casting of the members for the Iron Bridge, on the sand floor between the two furnaces. In excavating along the furnace at the opposite side to the tapping hole, we uncovered, projecting from beneath the Old Furnace foundation, the even earlier foundations of the original furnace of 1638 which was leased by Abraham I and in which all his experimental work was done and which served the works until 1777. This foundation is well displayed exactly as it was found. The Museum was arranged to display some of the products of the Company together with an outline of the Darby Company history. After twenty years of very popular use it was demolished to be absorbed into the Museum of Iron.

In the course of the excavations many problems were encountered and a few surprises like the 1638 foundations gave a welcome degree of encouragement. The bellows wheel pit of the early furnace was a reward for much painful trenching. The wheel pit of the wheel which powered the early bellows was another welcome discovery. The wheel pit of the grinding shop wheel and the elaborate system of tunnels and drains made to keep soil water from the 'New' furnace were cleaned up and made available for visitors to explore in safety. The gates and lamp at the entry to the furnace area were designed and cast in the works. The Boy and Swan Fountain now in the entry to the Museum of Iron has an interesting history. It was designed and cast for a prominent position in the Great Exhibition of 1851 and stood not far from the splendid gates which at the close of the Exhibition were moved to the entry to Hyde Park where they are still to be seen. The Fountain went to a park in Wolverhampton and was after long service dismantled with most of the parts relegated to a council store. It was discovered and recognised there by W. K. V. Gale who secured it for Coalbrookdale. Several smaller parts were damaged or missing but these were replaced in the foundry and the completed fountain was placed at the centre of the space between the Old Furnace and the foundations of the old grinding shops. It remained there until the opening of the Museum of Iron.

Deterioration of iron and brickwork after the exposure of the Old Furnace led to at first a pyramidal top being added in plastic to prevent water penetrating the structure and in recent years a complete building cover has now provided long term preservation.

All this work was planned and carried out under the management of Dr. G. F. Williams who himself took frequent part in the digging and probing among the deeper trenches. Until his retirement he served on the Ironbridge Gorge Museum Trust and with Reginald Morton had a great deal of responsibility and share in the excavation of the Blists Hill furnaces and design of the Museum. With the cooperation of E. Bruce Ball, Manager of the Lilleshall Company, Dr. Williams obtained for Blists Hill Museum two magnificent blowing engines when the Priorslee furnaces were blown out. The twin beam engine David and Sampson made in 1851 and exhibited in the Great Exhibition is to be seen at the first entrance to Blists Hill Museum. A second blowing engine, a vertical engine of very large size, is now installed in the restored blowing house of the furnaces where it is a great attraction to all visitors.

Dr. Williams retired from the management of the Coalbrookdale Company in 1966 but continued his interest in the Ironbridge Gorge Museum Trust until his death in 1987.

PLATE XXV *The Coalbrookdale Company displayed a number of its decorative iron-castings at the 1851 Great Exhibition, including the very ornate gates seen in this view. The gates were later rebuilt in a slightly modified form in Hyde Park, where they can still be seen.*

PLATE XXVI *The Coalbrookdale Company produced its first decorative cast-iron fountain in 1845, and during the next 50 years developed many different designs. One of these is seen here erected in the yard next to the Old Furnace for the official company photograph about 1880.*

Chapter Sixteen

THE NEXT THIRTY YEARS

by Stuart B. Smith, MSc, FMA, FRSA,
Director, Ironbridge Gorge Museum Trust

AT the Annual Conference of the Association for Industrial Archaeology held in Ironbridge in 1979, Arthur Raistrick delivered the Rolt Memorial Lecture on the Old Furnace at Coalbrookdale. In his account, the chronology of development was set out starting in 1950 with Dr. Williams on behalf of Allied Ironfounders Ltd., clearing the area of the buried old furnace in the Upper Works at Coalbrookdale in order to find the extent of the remains.[1] In 1953 *Dynasty of Iron Founders* was published and Arthur Raistrick and G. F. Williams worked unstintingly to open the original Coalbrookdale Museum and Furnace in 1959.

Looking back on these events with hindsight, it is easy to see that the preservation of the Old Furnace was the first step in the establishment of the Ironbridge Gorge Museum. Whilst nowadays it seems unthinkable that such a monument could be destroyed, only forty years ago the future of this site was in considerable danger, the concept of industry preserving history was a novelty and young people learned little of the Industrial Revolution whilst they were at school. The pioneering work of Raistrick and Williams is reflected in the spectacular growth of the Ironbridge Gorge Museum, a flowering of industrial preservation throughout the world and the focusing of educational attention on more recent history.

Preparations for the Ironbridge Gorge Museum 1959–1967

The celebrations surrounding the opening of the Old Furnace and Museum came at a time when the Shropshire Coalfield was going through a period of decline although ideas were being formulated about its future and regeneration. People were leaving the area, firms were closing and there was a general air of despondency in the

[1] Ref: Industrial Archaeology Review IV 2 Spring 1980.

locality. The local authority was deeply involved in slum clearance programmes and many buildings were under threat from either deliberate demolition or natural decay. At this time the only other structure which was preserved was the Iron Bridge which had been closed to vehicular traffic in 1934 and scheduled as an Ancient Monument, the first industrial monument in this country. Even this did not guarantee preservation as the bridge required major structural repairs. During the 1950s a group of local people came together to form the Coalbrookdale Archives Association and were successful in rescuing books, archives and objects which would otherwise have been destroyed.[2]

The Coalbrookdale Company continued to operate on a reduced site but the tile works of Craven Dunnill closed in the 1950s and that of Maw & Co. continued for only a few more years. Over the river at Coalport, the Coalport Company had left the area in 1926 and virtually all mining and brick making had ceased in the Gorge by the 1950s. The only event to have any real significance in the Ironbridge Gorge during the 1960s was the construction of the second Ironbridge Power Station which gave employment for many people and a brief period of prosperity.

However, some farsighted people saw that the derelict area of the Shropshire Coalfield could be revitalised and in the early 1960s a delegation of Birmingham Councillors was invited to come and see the southern half of the Coalfield centred on Dawley. This subsequently led to the establishment of Dawley New Town in 1964. Whilst most new towns resulting from the New Towns Act of 1946 had been built on green field sites, Dawley, subsequently renamed Telford New Town, was one of the first deliberately to choose a derelict industrial area where land reclamation and the creation of new housing, factories and infrastructure would go hand in hand with the enhancement of established urban societies. It was in fact to the New Town of Telford that the Museum owes it birth. On 3rd February, 1967, a meeting was convened by Dawley Development Corporation to consider setting up a Museum Trust. The leading figure in this meeting was Emyr Thomas, later to be Secretary of the Museum Trust and at the time Solicitor to the New Town and subsequently General Manager. Prior to the establishment of the Museum Trust itself, a feasibility study had been

[2] Actually this began in 1948 as the Archives Sub-Committee of the Coalbrookdale W.I.

PLATE XXVII *On the 15th October 1959, Allied Ironfounders opened the area around the Darby Furnace, and in an adjacent building created a small museum of Coalbrookdale Company products. In this photograph taken at the opening, G. F. Williams (on the left) talks to Vicountess Bridgeman. To the right is the Furnace, and in the background the Coalbrookdale Company locomotive no. 5 recently returned from Bardon Hill quarries in Leicestershire.*

PLATE XXVIII *Movement of the river banks had caused early fractures in the Iron Bridge. One of the first efforts of the new Ironbridge Gorge Museum Trust was to raise funds for work on the north abutment, and for the construction of a subaqua reinforced concrete slab between the two abutments to prevent further movement. This was the state of work in September 1973 after flooding a month previously had swamped the site. The slab was completed by Tarmac mid summer 1974.*

PLATE XXIX *Before Ironbridge became part of Dawley New Town in 1963 (later renamed Telford), the area had become very run down with some buildings unsympathetically modified and others simply abandoned. This view shows shops on the Wharfage, Ironbridge before Telford Development Corporation restored them for use as their own and Ironbridge Gorge Museum Trust offices.*

PLATE XXX *Thousands of people now visit Ironbridge every year, and the Wharfage and Ironbridge square have regained their function as the trading centre of the Gorge.*

commissioned from a firm of Birmingham architects which led to the first report of the working party which set out the framework for the projected Museum. This report identified the major sites which the Museum should occupy and restore, including Coalbrookdale, Coalport, Blists Hill, Bedlam Furnaces, the Iron Bridge and several lesser sites. Much of the material in the report was based on visits or correspondence with other open air museums in Europe although it is doubtful if any of the working party realised that their report was in fact fundamentally different from any other open air museum, as it was founded on five principles which at the time were revolutionary but which are now commonplace. They were:

(a) that the Museum would be a charitable trust and not rely on funding from local or central government,

(b) that it would be funded from its visitors as far as the day-to-day operations were concerned,

(c) that a development trust would be established in order to raise capital from industry and elsewhere for the development of the Museum,

(d) that it would be based on the local community and therefore a strong supporters group, later to be called the Friends, would be established, and

(e) that it would be a museum based on a multiplicity of sites which related to the original industries of the Gorge rather than being housed in a museum building in the conventional sense.

This first report of the working party, however, failed to grasp the future size of the Museum operation; its recommendations on future staffing, revenue and capital projections were inadequate and there was no concept of a business plan. However, the framework for a new breed of museum had been established and all it required was the people and money to put the scheme into effect.

Pre-dating these discussions at a local level, the framework for industrial preservation had been established from the late 1940s with the mushrooming of interest in the preservation of railways and canals, largely spearheaded by L. T. C. Rolt. The success in the preservation of transport systems had developed into a general interest in Industrial Archaeology, a term which had been first coined by Michael Rix in 1955 where he referred extensively to the Ironbridge Gorge. Local societies for Industrial Archaeology were sprouting around Britain in the 1960s, and the first national body in

Great Britain was established in 1973: the Association for Industrial Archaeology.

In late 1967 the scene was set: Telford New Town was established, deliberately including the area of the Ironbridge Gorge and Coalbrookdale so that the area could be preserved; interest in Industrial Archaeology was growing rapidly and the Ironbridge Gorge Museum was just about to be formed.

Early Days 1967–1972

On 1st April, 1968, the formal foundation of the Ironbridge Gorge Museum Trust took place under the Chairmanship of E. Bruce Ball, who literally took on a second career in developing the Museum. The Trust was set up as a company limited by guarantee, registered as a charity, and governed by an Executive Board of 15 of whom the County and District Councils and the Development Corporation nominated two members each. The objectives of the educational charity were the preservation, restoration and interpretation of historic sites and properties within the Shropshire Coalfield. It was now essential to rally support from all areas and to establish the various sites of the Museum. Some of the sites which the Museum would occupy were already in the ownership of Telford Development Corporation, such as Blists Hill, Bedlam Furnaces and eventually Coalport, whereas the other sites were in public or private ownership. One of the earliest acquisitions was the Quaker Burial Ground in Coalbrookdale which was leased to the Museum in order that it should be maintained. The Museum Trust quickly acquired Rose Cottages in Coalbrookdale, the derelict Severn Warehouse building from Dawley Urban District Council and Carpenters Row from private owners.

An exhibition at Priorslee Hall in 1967 had generated considerable interest in the Museum project and collections started to be accumulated. Initially storage was in the basement of Priorslee Hall and then with the occupation of Blists Hill by the Museum Trust, objects were transferred to the warehouses which were on site. The Development Corporation had been using the Blists Hill site as a tip in order to fill in the excavation which had been carried out in the 1940s to reclaim slag from the site. Even at this late stage some of the industrial buildings on the site were threatened, particularly the remains of the brickworks and some of the blast furnace complex.

An early appointment therefore was a residential caretaker who lived on this exposed site which was criss-crossed with a public road and with public footpaths. On the 1st November, 1969, the first part-time employee was taken onto the Museum payroll, initially to save items at Blists Hill as well as organising volunteer working parties to rescue equipment from other sites, notably Milburg Tileries. Shortly after that date the Museum acquired its own offices at Southside, Church Hill, which had been recently vacated by Dawley Urban District Council. These offices not only provided a headquarters but also better storage facilities for the growing collection of tiles, which were being rescued by volunteers from the old works of Maws and Craven Dunnills.

By a judicious deal the Museum Trust acquired from Shropshire County Council the tollhouses on Coalport Bridge and the Iron Bridge, and the Ironbridge Tollhouse was quickly opened as an information point. Work started on the restoration of Rose Cottages in Coalbrookdale to provide accommodation for a blacksmith and for a house. Bedlam Furnaces which were in the ownership of Telford Development Corporation were investigated by a working party who cleared away much of the undergrowth and did some remedial work on the furnace lining. Another excavation took place at the site of the Lloyds Engine House and Shaft and a report was compiled, this being the first archaeological work undertaken on behalf of the Museum which began a long tradition of the publication of such work. The Shropshire Mining and Caving Club were busy looking for the Tar Tunnel which everyone knew was somewhere at Coalport but the location had been lost. When it was discovered that the tunnel had originally been adjacent to the Inclined Plane, however, the mystery was solved when a brick wall in a cellar was broken down and the Tar Tunnel was exposed. Working parties consisting of the Shropshire Mining and Caving Club and Borstal boys then carried out a massive clearance operation in order to get people into the Tunnel. Public interest in the Museum had been stimulated by holding Open Days the first of which was held on the 28th September, 1960. These featured the sites already in the Museum's care, such as Blists Hill and Bedlam, and also sites which it was hoped would pass to the Museum in the future such as the Coalport China Works, where the Coalport Company helped by providing demonstrators in order to generate interest in this possible project. The Coalbrookdale Museum continued to be run by the Coalbrookdale Company, cared for by two retired employees. In the summer of 1970, however, Her Royal Highness Princess Margaret handed over the lease of the Coalbrookdale Works Museum and Furnace from the Glynwed Group to the Museum Trust, thus ensuring that all the major sites in the Gorge were now under the Museum's care.

Whilst Blists Hill was the largest of the Museum sites and a master plan had been drawn up, little had been placed on the site apart from the construction of the Miners Walk and some mining exhibits. At the top of Blists Hill, a potter took up residence, providing much needed life and activity on an otherwise open site. Volunteers did some excavation and consolidation in the Brick Works and the line of the Railway Siding was also excavated and consolidated. The first major exhibit to be brought to the site was the Beam Blowing Engines, David & Sampson which had previously been located at the Priorslee Works of the Lilleshall Company. The Chairman of the Museum Trust, E. Bruce Ball was, as ex-Chairman of the Lilleshall Company, very concerned about their preservation and was responsible for raising the funds for this major exercise.

The Honorary Curator of Blists Hill, Reg Morton, did much to mastermind the development of the site, formulating some of the earliest plans for the future Ironworks. At this time, however, Blists Hill was envisaged very much as an open air park containing industrial remains with areas set aside for mining, iron-making, coke production, etc. and there were grandiose schemes for moving Longdon on Tern Aqueduct to the site and the development of a very elaborate canal system. Although a scheme did exist for moving domestic property to the site, in particular the re-erection of numbers 61/65 High Street, Madeley, as the entrance to the complex, no thought had been given to the large scale introduction of domestic or commercial property or in fact the demonstration of any of these exhibits. Whilst the initial report of the working party had been far sighted in envisaging the scale of the Museum operation in terms of buildings, collections and sites, it had not really come to terms with the capital requirements of the Museum, its revenue operation nor in fact the staffing of such a mammoth operation. A curator manager had been appointed in 1970 but this had not been a success.

Plate XXXI *An aerial view of Coalbrookdale in 1984 showing in the centre the Long Warehouse, opened by Sir Keith Joseph (then Education Secretary) on 11th February 1983 as the Ironbridge Gorge Museum's Library and Elton Gallery, and later providing accommodation for the Ironbridge Institute. On the right of this building is the Great Warehouse opened as the Museum of Iron by HRH The Prince of Wales on 5th July, 1979, and behind this the Glynwed foundry occupying the site of the original Coalbrookdale Company lower works.*

Plate XXXII *The Coalbrookdale Company built this transhipment warehouse with gothic details at the end of its plateway network beside the River Severn in the 1840's. It had a very short life as a warehouse, but survived until 1976 when it was restored as a visitor centre by the Ironbridge Gorge Museum Trust. In 1989 it was refurbished again and was opened on 8th May by HRH The Prince of Wales as the Museum of the River.*

PLATE XXXIII *At the opening of the Ironbridge Institute's accommodation in the Long Warehouse, Coalbrookdale, 30th May 1984. From left to right: Stuart Smith, Director of the Ironbridge Gorge Museum Trust; Dr. G. F. Williams; Sir Alex Jarratt, then Chancellor of the University of Birmingham; Dr. Arthur Raistrick; Lady Labouchere, then President of the Museum Trust; Dr. J. R. Harris, Head of the Department of Economic & Social History in the University of Birmingham.*

PLATE XXXIV *The study at Rosehill House displays the partner's desk (believed once to have belonged to Abraham Darby III) and Francis Darby's portrait on the wall. The house was extensively restored by the Ironbridge Gorge Museum after a period as a hotel, and opened to the public in mid-nineteenth century form on the 29th June 1985, by Sir Adrian Cadbury.*

PLATE XXXV *The Blists Hill foundry was opened by Gareth Davis, Chief Executive of Glynwed, on 21st June 1985. It allowed the Ironbridge Gorge Museum Trust to show visitors the basic techniques of iron-casting, and it took the Museum on from the traditional display of objects to the innovating demonstration of industrial processes.*

PLATE XXXVI *Suggestions for an operational wrought-iron works at the Ironbridge Gorge Museum's Blists Hill site were first made in the 1970's, but it was not until 1982 that work began in earnest with considerable help from Shell, Tarmac and English Heritage. The 1860's equipment was retrieved from Thomas Walmsley's Atlas Works in Bolton after it closed in 1976, and the building, designed by John Rennie and erected in 1815, came from Woolwich Dockyard. The ironworks was opened by HRH The Prince of Wales on 6th March 1987.*

PLATE XXXVII *Coalport China Works was established in 1795 and continued to grow, producing varied high quality ceramics until 1926 when the company moved to the Potteries. Fifty years later the surviving buildings on the banks of the River Severn, restored to display some of their best products, opened as part of the Ironbridge Gorge Museum Trust.*

PLATE XXXVIII *The restoration of the former tile works of Craven Dunnill at Jackfield is one of the Museum's most ambitious projects. The model factory was completed in 1874, but after tile production ceased in 1952 it became a foundry and was modified accordingly. The Ironbridge Gorge Museum Trust bought the property in 1983, and since then has been gradually refurbishing it to display an impressive collection of tiles.*

The fledgling Museum now had many of the raw materials required for the development of a truly fine Museum but it seemed possible at this time that the whole concept might fail through lack of staff and money. The Executive Board at this time wisely realised these problems existed and called in the Museums Assocation. Their advice was that the Museum Trust should set up a separate Development Trust in order to raise capital for development and this took place in August 1971. They similarly advised that the Museum required to be run by a museum professional and accordingly Neil Cossons was appointed as Director in October 1971. The following Spring the present author was appointed Curator of Technology, charged with the responsibility of converting, restoring and building the Ironbridge Gorge Museum. At the same time technical staff were appointed and the stage was set for the next period of intense development.

The First Rush 1972–1979

With the appointment of professional staff and the heartening success of a fund-raising programme the first priority was to prove to the public that there was a viable Museum which was worthy of support and which would eventually generate revenue income. In 1972 there was not a great deal to be seen. In Coalbrookdale there was the Quaker Burial Ground, the Old and New Furnace and Furnace Site which had been laid out in 1959. On this site was the Boy and Swan Fountain, two steam locomotives and some columns. The pioneering Coalbrookdale Museum was unchanged but unsuited to the number of visitors it was likely to receive. The Coalbrookdale Company catalogues and records were left lying on the entrance table which was acceptable when each visitor could be supervised by the custodial staff but not suited to an increasingly popular museum. Work had started on Rose Cottages, and preliminary work had been carried out at Bedlam Furnaces. The Ironbridge Tollhouse continued to function as a small shop and information centre selling the early publications which had been generated by the Friends of the Museum. However, the restoration of the Tollhouse left much to be desired with an unsuitable shop front having been inserted. The largest of the Museum sites, Blists Hill had by now received David & Sampson, although the removal work to the site had precluded its future operation under steam.

Another steam blowing engine, also from the Lilleshall Company, had been installed in the North Engine House of the Blists Hill Blast Furnaces and volunteers had been working hard clearing the Inclined Plane, in particular the transfer basin, and the railway siding, warehouses and Brickworks. A machine shop had been laid out and with the acquisition of a matbro digger, heavy pieces of equipment could be moved. Southside was the Museum office at which was based a small team consisting of the Director, Curator of Technology, Development Trust Fund-Raiser and secretarial staff. The first appointments to be made after this were the Head of Interpretation and the Retail Manager, indicating the priorities which the first Director felt were required at Ironbridge.

One of the very first objectives of this new team was to develop the Blists Hill site. Miles of fencing were begged, transported and re-erected, largely by teams of Borstal boys coming from Stoke Heath, public footpaths had to be diverted outside the site, the canal was excavated by Telford Development Corporation and the fill used to flatten the area now occupied by the Ironworks. Public toilets were acquired, an entrance building lent by Tarmac and the Steam Winding Engine from Milburg Tileries was re-erected on the site of the old Blists Hill mine by the Museum technical staff. His Royal Highness The Duke of Edinburgh came to see work in progress on this project in July 1972 and by March 1973 the Museum felt confident enough to invite the Earl of Plymouth to open Blists Hill officially to the public. A minimal charge was made and visitors were happy to explore this largely vacant site, although they could witness the re-erection of Shelton Tollhouse, the first building to be moved to the site.

One of the greatest achievements of the Chairman of the Museum, E. Bruce Ball was to persuade Shropshire County Council and the Department of the Environment to join with the Museum in the restoration of the Iron Bridge. The Museum covered its share of the restoration cost via a donation from John Smith (founder of the charitable Landmark Trust) and from the summer of 1972 through to October 1974 the mammoth task of forming coffer dams in the bed of the river, excavating the bed rock and then casting in situ a large concrete beam were undertaken. The task was not without its problems but it is fortunate that this was one of the first tasks undertaken in Ironbridge, as to have delayed longer could have prejudiced the future of the Bridge and would have made the subject exorbitantly expensive. During this time the Department of the Environment also took the brave step of listing almost every building in the Gorge that survived unaltered, thus ensuring that the slum clearance programme which had been previously put in hand came to an end and that many dozens of empty and derelict buildings would be preserved. It is not easy to imagine now that in the early 70s only a few shops were occupied and only a handful of public houses were still in business.

Work on Blists Hill and the restoration of the Iron Bridge was only the first phase of a planned development of the Museum which would culminate in 1979 with the bicentenary of the Iron Bridge. The plan was to increase the retailing ability of the Museum, to open Museums at Coalport, the Severn Warehouse and the Museum of Iron, to make the various ancient monuments in the Museum more accessible to the public and to develop a Youth Hostel. During the seven years between 1972 and 1979 all these objectives were achieved in a frenetic burst of activity. The Shop In The Square was opened in 1973 allowing the Museum to sell a good range of Coalport China and its award winning publications. Similarly, the Ironbridge Tollhouse was restored, with the upper floor giving a history of the Bridge and the lower floor used as a Tourist Information Centre and retailing point. On Blists Hill the Shelton Tollhouse was opened to the public in 1973 and a debate took place as to the date to which the interior should be furnished. It was eventually agreed to seek a late 19th-century date, although at this time there was no overall concept that Blists Hill itself should be of any fixed and particular period. The second building on Blists Hill, the Printing Shop, was also opened during 1973, the contents having been bought by the *Sunday Times* and donated to the Museum. The shop front came from St. Georges and it was during the construction of this exhibit that the idea of a terminal date for Blists Hill first came about. With the opening of these exhibits the first demonstrators were appointed, and when later put into costume, live interpretation became a reality at the Museum.

A building which was not envisaged in the original programme was Rosehill House, one of the homes of the Darby family. Lady Labouchere had become President of the Museum in 1973 and it was at her instigation that Rosehill House was purchased from private owners in 1975. This has now been completely restored and houses much of the Darby furniture and other material. The other Darby home, Dale House is in the process of restoration. In the same year work on Rose Cottages was completed and the residential section was let to one of the Trust's employees following a tradition established at Carpenters Row, where the end cottage had been converted to residential use. The other half of Rose Cottages was restored as a Blacksmith's Shop and the first blacksmith started work shortly afterwards. Promotion of the Museum also continued with extensive editorial coverage for the Museum's activities and increased awareness from television companies. A bicentenary exhibition was held in the House of Commons in 1976 and interpretation of the Museum and its sites was enhanced by the listening post scheme which was inaugurated by His Royal Highness The Duke of Gloucester in 1976.

The programme for Museum development relied on the conversion of the Coalport China Works into a Museum. This became possible when the previous owners who were making exhaust pipes agreed to move out during 1976. Permission to carry out the scheme was given on 1st January 1976, on condition that the Museum was completed and open in the following July. This enormous task was undertaken with heroic efforts by the Museum's technical staff and there began a long association with Robin Wade & Pat Reade Design Associates which continues to this day. The task was made doubly difficult by the fact that the industrial occupants of the factory, although co-operating with the Museum, did not finally vacate the premises until one month before the official opening. The display of Coalport China inside the kiln was instrumental in winning first of all the Museum of the Year Award and then the European Museum of the Year Award in 1978. Several archaeological excavations took place around Coalport at the time of the restoration and the results of these were displayed in the Archaeology Room adjacent to the River.

As soon as the opening of the Coalport China Museum had taken place the Museum seized the opportunity of selling to Telford Development Corporation the freehold of the offices at Southside and then moving into offices provided by the Corporation on the Wharfage. This move was of fundamental importance: not only did it give the Museum capital to restore the Severn Warehouse, but it also placed the Museum offices firmly in the centre of Ironbridge. The Wharfage Offices were not entirely occupied by Museum staff, who were still small in number, but most of the premises were given over to providing accommodation for the Severn Gorge Project Group. This group consisted of architects, planners, surveyors, secretarial staff, all being charged with the responsibility of restoring Corporation properties in the Gorge and co-ordinating the work of all other bodies in the restoration of the infrastructure of the valley. Officers met regularly to discuss planning issues, the undergrounding of services, the restoration of property, a town scheme of grants and many other issues. This happy combination of Museum and Corporation staff continued for over four years and was vitally important in the regeneration of the area.

The Museum has been involved since the very beginning with Government schemes to assist unemployment, including the Short Term Employment Programme, Youth Training Scheme, Youth Opportunities Programme, Community Programme and many other programmes now consigned to history. Many hundreds of unemployed people, both young and old, have worked for the Museum on these schemes. None have been more successful than the various programmes which have helped the tile collections, both at Maws and subsequently Craven Dunnill and at Blists Hill where Community Programme has constructed the entire Wrought Ironworks. At the height of unemployment in Telford the Museum had over 380 employees on the Community Programme and 60 young people on the Youth Training Scheme.

Whilst the refurbishment of the Coalport China Museum had been funded largely by Telford Development Corporation, the Museum itself undertook the restoration and conversion of the Severn Warehouse into a Visitor Centre. This was achieved by May 1977 and the audio visual programme proved vital in selling combined tickets to the various Museum sites. When the Heritage Education Group visited the Museum in the same year, they were entertained to a banquet in the Tar Tunnel at which Lord Asa Briggs delivered a momentous subterranean speech. Such Ironbridge spectaculars have become commonplace and reflect the determination of both staff and Board Members to make sure that Ironbridge is always seen as something different.

In 1977 the Museum won the Museum of the Year Award with all its attendant publicity. Also in that year E. Bruce Ball retired as Chairman and was replaced by Tom Honess from Guest Keen Nettlefold plc. The following year the Museum established its own

Trading Company as a non-charitable subsidiary, which became heavily involved in promoting the Museum outside Ironbridge via mail order and many other activities. The year also saw a bitter controversy as to the allocation of the Elton Collection, a large collection of prints, drawings, engravings, books and memorabilia concerned with industrialisation which had been left to the nation by Sir Arthur Elton. The contestants for the Collection included Bristol Museum, Manchester Museum, The Science Museum and Ironbridge and it was largely due to the efforts of Lord Northfield, Chairman of Telford Development Corporation that Ironbridge was the successful applicant. Lord Northfield promised that the Collection would be available to the public within six months and that the Collection would be properly curated. The Development Corporation eventually became the owners of the Collection and appointed immediately a Curator of Art, a Librarian and a Documentation Assistant who were responsible for cataloguing the Collection and preparing it for display.[3]

The Ironbridge Bicentenary in 1979 was a momentous series of events inaugurated by floodlighting the cooling towers at the Ironbridge Power Station. During the year the Coach House Gallery was opened for the Elton Collection, also the Walker Study Centre and at Blists Hill the Squatter Cottage was completed. In June of that year Granville Colliery closed—the last deep mine in Shropshire—and the miners marched to Blists Hill to lay up their lodge banner in the Miners Mission Church which had been opened the previous year. A Bicentenary parade took place in July of that year and a few days later His Royal Highness The Prince of Wales came to open the new Museum of Iron which later won the Come to Britain Trophy. This Museum had been made possible by the sale of the Great Warehouse and the Long Warehouse by Messrs Glynwed to the Ironbridge Gorge Museum. Enormous help was received from Telford Development Corporation in landscaping the site and the original Coalbrookdale Museum opened in 1959 and housed in unsatisfactory premises was demolished, in order to create the car park. The entire contents of the original Museum were transferred into the new Museum of Iron and laid out to tell the story of the history of iron in general but also in particular of the Coalbrookdale Company and the Quaker connection. For the first

[3] Telford Development Corporation had already brought together a collection of material pertaining to Thomas Telford which was looked after by the Museum.

time a Museum was not purely devoted to the technology of iron making but also the influence of the Quaker families and the social history of this unique valley. An exhibition was held at the Royal Academy entitled 'A View from the Iron Bridge' where every known illustration of the Iron Bridge was placed on display. Altogether the Bicentenary focused a great deal of attention on Ironbridge but it also placed great strains on the financial resources of the Museum, for the Trading Company had been too ambitious in their plans to generate income. 1979 therefore provided a watershed: the major Museum sites were now developed, Rosehill House was under restoration, as was the Youth Hostel, and conservation work on Bedlam Furnaces had taken place. The Museum had successfully demonstrated the large scale use of MSC teams and Maws Tile Works was being busily restored and put to work as a Tile Museum and manufactory. The Museum, however, was not in a very healthy financial position. The next ten years were destined to be ones of spectacular growth and consolidation.

The Last Ten Years 1979–1989

As the euphoria of the Ironbridge Bicentenary came to an end it was a time to take stock and to consider the ways and means of stabilising the Museum. Visitor numbers were the prime area of concern and it was therefore decided to concentrate on building Blists Hill into a major visitor attraction. The second objective was to strengthen the academic part of the Museum and the Institute of Industrial Archaeology came into being in 1980, set up jointly by the Museum and the University of Birmingham. Initially their courses were run from the Museum offices which also contained the Museum Library and store for the Elton Collection but it was not long before all these functions could be transferred to the Long Warehouse in Coalbrookdale, a building converted largely by Telford Development Corporation.

The Trust as an educational charity had always been keen to maximise the number of school visits and this concept was extended and improved to include all educational parties by means of a generous grant from the Carnegie Foundation. Subsequently the Museum was fortunate to have seconded to it a senior Education Officer from Shropshire County Council who is now backed by his own educational staff.

The third aspect of the plan, to improve the financial stability of the Museum involved the application of a stringent financial control system, coupled with reporting systems and accountability to the Finance Committee which are a model for any other museum. Similarly, the Trading Company which had over stretched itself was brought back to operate at a more modest level.

Philip Trevor-Jones, the new Chairman in 1981 saw as his task the completion of this three point plan assisted by the Museum's Treasurer, Mike Lowe, and Secretary, Emyr Thomas. Exhibits at Blists Hill were the main priority and these were completed at the rate of almost two per year. The Candle Factory opened in 1981, Sweetshop 1982, New Inn 1983, Foundry 1984, Chemist Shop 1984, Slaughterhouse 1984, Blacksmiths 1984, Ironworks offices 1985, Locksmiths 1985, Doctor's Surgery 1986, Ironworks 1987, Foundry Machine Shop 1987, Bakery 1988, Plumbers & Tinsmiths 1989, motorisation of David & Sampson 1989. The spectacular growth of Blists Hill in the last ten years has been largely instrumental in boosting visitor figures from 151,127 in 1981 to 404,000 in 1988. *The Spry* was rescued from Diglis Basin in Worcester and transported to Ironbridge in 1983 and work on the boat since then has proved an immense visitor attraction.

The Museum has always been helped by the existence of voluntary advisory groups who have come together on a regular basis to discuss particular projects. The general advisory group took under its wing the planning of the Blists Hill Ironworks. Equipment was brought to the Museum from Bolton in the early 1970s and a memorial fund to Reg Morton, the Honorary Curator of Blists Hill raised sufficient funding to allow the piling for the Ironworks to go ahead. There was then a long gap until a Community Programme team came together in 1982 when over seventy men at any one time were busily engaged in constructing the Ironworks. The first spectacular event took place in January 1983 when the huge anvil of the steam hammer was lowered into place. Unfortunately unemployment in Telford in the early 1980s was extremely high and this allowed the Museum to recruit extremely skilled people under Community Programme with a wide variety of craft and trade skills. Ted Sutton, the Ironworks Manager brought to the project a lifetime of experience in the heavy engineering industry and Brian Howl started to help the project as a volunteer, eventually becoming a member of the Finance

Committee and then the Board. This form of long apprenticeship by which Board Members are selected is one of the great strengths of the organisation.

With the re-erection of the New Inn at Blists Hill, for the first time the Museum could start to cater for the public in a reasonable fashion. After a considerable debate it was eventually agreed that the public house should be run by the Museum directly, a precedent which has been followed on all subsequent occasions. This means that everyone working on the Museum site is either a member of staff, or a volunteer. As visitor numbers increased then much greater attention had to be paid to visitor facilities and in the late 1980s there was considerable attention paid to toilets and catering in particular. At the same time, due to a cautious approach to retailing, the Trading Company was beginning to return a healthy profit to the Museum Trust.

As the emphasis for development moved towards Blists Hill, not a great deal of work was carried out on the Museum's ancient monuments, although a cover building was erected over the Coalbrookdale Furnace to protect it from the elements. This was opened in July 1982 by His Royal Highness The Duke of Gloucester. A year after that the Museum's first Director, Dr. Neil Cossons, who now saw that the Museum was firmly on the road to international stardom, left the Museum to become Director first of the National Maritime Museum, then of the Science Museum. The author was appointed Director in July 1983 and by now the emphasis in the Museum changed subtly from intensive capital development to making sure that the Museum functioned on a day to day basis and that visitors had an enjoyable experience. Over the last five years there has been an incessant procession of VIPs, government ministers, television programmes and events too numerous to mention which have all helped to lift the profile of the Museum and ensure that it receives good publicity, both locally, nationally, and internationally. On the development side a further new Museum opened at Rosehill House in 1988 after a long period of conversion. Work started on the difficult and expensive conservation of the adjacent Darby home, Dale House, with the long-term intention that this will eventually be a centre for Quaker meetings and study.[4]

[4] At present local Quakers meet on the last Sunday in every month in the Long Warehouse.

The other major development has been the acquisition of the tile works of Craven Dunnill and the removal there of all our collections and operations from Maws Tile Works. The Craven Dunnill property is being rapidly restored and is already one of the Museum's most exciting sites. The largest single acquisition of property which the Museum has seen was the purchase from the Glynwed Company in 1987 of the redundant buildings to the north of their works including the old offices, the engineering building and the Northern Lights Building. This acquisition was assisted by the National Heritage Memorial Fund who have been consistently helpful to the Museum.

The transfer of ownership of these buildings marked the last major phase of the gradual transfer of Glynwed properties into Museum ownership which was started in 1970. Throughout this time Dr. G. F. Williams had maintained his association with the Museum and was now a Vice-President. It was therefore particularly gratifying that G. F. Williams knew of the acquisition prior to his death in August 1987 and he also knew of the return to Shropshire of the Lightmoor Beam Engine which he had been involved in dismantling and transporting to the Henry Ford Museum at Dearborn, Michigan some 60 years previously. This engine when re-erected will form a memorial to the late G. F. Williams.

The funding for all these major capital projects has been greatly helped by the continuing good work of the Ironbridge Gorge Museum Development Trust. The Development Trust Director works energetically to motivate his fund-raising committees in London, Birmingham and locally and the various Development Trustees and helpers have heroically struggled to ensure that the Museum has sufficient money to continue to develop. This has been of immense benefit to the Museum as at any one time well over a dozen projects are in hand and the public return time and again to see what has happened since their last visit.

The Institute for Industrial Archaeology has continued to grow and sensing the change in society a second course, Heritage Management was established in 1987 and led to a necessary change in the Institute's title to the Ironbridge Institute. Research programmes have been funded by Leverhulme, Nuffield, Carnegie and the Institute has successfully run under MSC a very large archaeology programme working both in Ironbridge and elsewhere. Similarly, the Institute has taken on consultancy work at a wide range of sites, both in this country and abroad and its continuing series of short courses have been immensely successful.

In 1987 William Waldegrave, the Minister for the Environment came to Ironbridge to unveil the World Heritage plaque making Ironbridge the first site in Britain to be placed on the UNESCO register of sites of such unique cultural importance that they are worthy of preservation by all mankind. At the same time as he visited the Museum he also announced that the Museum would be receiving an endowment from the Government as part of the transfer of assets from Telford Development Corporation to the Museum. This announcement in fact brings the Museum to possibly the most important time of decision making since its inception. From the very beginning Telford Development Corporation have been in the background to help the Museum, both publicly and also privately in the carrying out of its objectives. From 1991 the Corporation will cease to exist and therefore all sites and land currently owned by the Corporation must pass to some new body. Currently the Museum is being restructured in order to accept the Government Endowment and details are being drawn up of the various sites which the Museum will take over from the New Town. There are, however, other sites in the Museum's ownership which still await restoration: Carpenters Row, the John Rose Building, Coalport and Coalport Tollhouse, together with the recently acquired Glynwed properties. As visitor numbers continue to grow it is not envisaged that these sites will become Museums but will be used to provide accommodation and visitor services. Diversification of income is vitally important as the Museum receives no income from outside of any consequence and has to survive by its visitors.

Increased visitors also place pressure on the road network in the area and during 1988 a firm of consultants carried out a major study on the future of transportation within the Gorge. The recommendations from this study will take time to assimilate but it is likely that the Museum will play a major role in the future operation of transport systems. Several cut backs in MSC schemes eventually left the Museum in 1988 with virtually no MSC employees apart from a very successful Youth Training Scheme. Towards the end of 1988 those previous MSC employees who were vital to the Museum's operation were taken onto the Museum staff and a

Monuments Manager and Archaeologist was appointed in order to care for the Museum's archaeological sites and monuments, a task which it has not fulfilled adequately in the last ten years. Management of this large and dynamic organisation has led to the development of a complex staff structure.

The Executive Board of the Museum meet every six weeks and has sub committees concerned with Finance and General Purposes, Academic and Curatorial matters and Development. There is also the Ironbridge Trading Company and the Jackfield Tile Company which are non-charitable subsidiaries. The Friends of the Museum are, of course, an autonomous body but their Chairman is invited to attend Museum Board Meetings. Similarly, the Development Trust has its own Trust structure but has representatives at Museum Board Meetings. Many members of the Board, their spouses, Development Trustees and members of the Friends are active volunteers within the Museum and give many hours of their spare time to the furtherance of its objectives. The Director of the Museum reports directly to the Executive Board and internally operates the Museum via a weekly Management Group. The Senior Staff consist of Administrator and Head of Visitor Services, Head of Finance, Head of Education, Curator of Art, Curator of Technology and Public Relations Advisor. Until the appointment of a General Manager of the Trading Company the Department Heads responsible for catering and retailing are also responsible directly to the Director. Professor John Harris of Birmingham University shares with the Director the distinction of heading the Ironbridge Institute which is once again poised for a period of expansion and the possibility of acquiring new subject areas.

During 1988 the Museum celebrated on several occasions its 21st Anniversary and this was an opportunity not only of looking back but also of considering the future. Emyr Thomas retired as Secretary, to be followed by Michael Osborn. Lady Labouchere retired as President and was replaced by Philip Trevor-Jones and Mike Lowe became Chairman in his stead. Considerable emphasis has been placed recently on customer services and in particular catering and retailing, with a Commercial Manager now appointed. His task will not only be to increase the profitability of our existing retailing and catering operation but also to expand manufacturing, accommodation and other income-generating areas. During 1989 the Museum published its development plan for the next 21 years which not only outlines possible capital developments but also looks again at its philosophy and objectives.

In the 1950s the urgent necessity was to rescue the Old Furnace and such records of the Coalbrookdale Company as could be preserved. This need to rescue continued throughout the 1970s but in the 1980s the emphasis had to shift to the management and care of nearly half a million visitors per annum. Great challenges face the Museum as it takes on wider responsibilities in a period of increasing competition from other leisure attractions. Considerable thought is now being given to the educational role of the Museum, not only for the conventional educational parties but also for the average visitor. Ironbridge and Coalbrookdale have a unique place in world history and the entrepreneurial zeal which spurred the early Darby's is still present in this unique valley. Lord Hugh Thomas described this as the 'Ironbridge Spirit' and it is this same spirit which has inspired and continues to inspire the Ironbridge Gorge Museum. As we move into the future, it is with the fervent hope that the Museum will be able to go on forging the vital link between the heroic past and the changing present, that we will stimulate and challenge all those who come to Ironbridge with the relevance to their own lives of the great events which took place here, and that, in so doing, we shall have deepened their appreciation of the past and enriched their aspirations for the future.

FRIENDS IN SCORN CALLED QUAKERS

A new 1989 Postscript by Arthur Raistrick

WHAT does it mean that the Coalbrookdale Company was a predominantly Quaker Company?

The seventeenth century saw the advent of George Fox with his new religious message and his 'convinced' followers in the latter half of that century. A first generation of Friends was rapidly collecting and among these early Friends was one John Darby (1618-1700) of Wrens Nest near Dudley, a small farmer and iron worker who was a lockmaker. His son John also became a Friend and his grandson was Abraham Darby I. As the son of a Friend family, Abraham was reared in strong conformity with all the tenets and ways of life of the Quakers. He was apprenticed with Jonathan Freeth of Birmingham, a very strict Friend, and with him Abraham not only learned his craft but attended the Meetings for Worship in mid-week and on First Day (Sunday). The organisation of the Society of Friends included the Monthly Meeting in which the smaller local Meetings in an area met to worship and then to carry out their business of the Society. Monthly Meetings were grouped in Quarterly Meetings, often for a whole county, and over all was the Yearly Meeting. Abraham attended these functions throughout his life and was soon noticed as a 'public Friend', zealous in attending Meetings and active in the business of the Society.

At some of these Meetings he would meet several Friends from the Midlands and the Welsh Borders of whom some were ironmasters, such as Crowley, Lloyd, Milner, Darby of Sedgley, Osborne of Wolverhampton. After Abraham had completed his apprenticeship and moved to Bristol he would meet another small group of Friends in the iron trade, Reynolds, Champion, Harford, Goldney and Prankard, with some others at Quarterly Meetings which covered a wide area. When he moved to Coalbrookdale in 1708 he became Clerk of the Friends Meeting in Broseley and before long Clerk of the Monthly Meeting. Although all this was in the stress of establishing his new work, he still attended to all the business of the membership and visited widely among the Meetings in Wales. Abiah, his daughter-in-law says of him 'he was a religious good man, and an eminent minister among the people called Quakers'.

His son Abraham II continued the clerkship of Monthly Meetings and for a time travelled among and drew together Friends in Wales to form a General Meeting of Wales. A Half Yearly meeting was formed which Abraham always attended even though it met at Swansea, Cardiff or other towns remote from Coalbrookdale. His daughter Hannah usually accompanied him and on some occasions with a few others she went to visit Friends in Quaker families while in Wales.

Abraham built the Meeting House in the Dale in 1745 and another one at New Dale in 1759. William Norris, a manager in the Coalbrookdale Company, a sincere and active Friend, gave Abraham his valued support. Besides care for the business of the Society of Friends and the careful practice of its principles the Darbys also cared for the housing and education of their workpeople, as has been recorded in earlier chapters. A basic Quaker belief and practice is the complete equality of the sexes, 'that of God in all humanity' so that women equally with men took part in the Ministry—not ordained but moved to speak by the leading of the spirit, the Inward Light. Some of the Darby women were famous, and early Quakers called them 'weighty Friends'. They visited meetings and Friends' families in all parts of Britain and in many parts of the world. Abiah, wife of Abraham II, preached in most parts of Britain and in some parts on the continent of Europe; Deborah, wife of his son Samuel, spent two years visiting Friends' groups in America. Both women travelled widely as companions when visiting Friends in this country. Abiah's daughter, Sarah, was strong in the ministry and also spent much time in prison visiting: she was very concerned for the condition of the prisoners and did a great deal to help them. Elizabeth Gurney spent some time at Coalbrookdale where the work of Abiah and Sarah helped her, after she married Joseph Fry, to devote herself to work in the prisons.

Coalbrookdale as well as being the location of the famous ironworks was at the same time, through the activities, care and hospitality of several generations of Darby men and women, an active centre, to and from which Quaker visitors and others came in large numbers. It was a centre for rest, inspiration and renewal of spiritual strength. The magnitude of this contribution to the spread of Quakerism can be realised in the life of Abiah, only one of a long stream of Quaker men and women who served the young Society of Friends here and abroad. As one stands in the quiet burial ground near the site of Abraham II's Meeting House (no longer there) with the simple stones not only of Darby's but of Luccocks, Dickinsons, Rose, Reynolds and many of the families who figure through the long record of the Company, looking over the works where they laboured, it is easy to sense the persistent love they had for the Dale, and to appreciate the strength of the friendship and fellowship which the Darbys shared and enjoyed with their workpeople. Their true memorial is in the works they left behind them and the respect which their names still command here and in the world at large.

One of Abraham III's sons, Richard, was of a political turn of mind and an enthusiastic worker in the movement for the abolition of slavery, on behalf of which Richard spent much time travelling widely. He was what was called a 'plain Friend', very strict and simple in his living and habits. One of his nieces records in her diary 'that parties arranged by him at Rosehill were not very exciting and rather dull'. His cousin Edmund, who for a short time was Manager of the Works, shared in Richard's work against slavery but did not travel so far. This same concern against slavery had been held by Richard's Aunt Sarah and Uncle Samuel Darby.

The beliefs of Friends did not separate the affairs of their religion from those of their secular life. The lifelong habit of gathering together to wait silently for the leading of the spirit, and their implicit belief that in all and every event, serious or trivial, the Inward Light would direct them, gave them a stability that was proof against all the shocks and trials of either failure or success. With such an integrated world where no divisions were erected between the affairs of the spirit and the ordinary avocations of daily work, there was little danger of decisions being made on a basis of short term expediency or solely on the ground of personal gain.

Although Abraham Darby IV left the Society of Friends for the Anglican church, he retained his interests in the Dale and built a fine church near the Works and his brother, Alfred Darby I, gave the peal of bells. The son of Alfred I, Alfred Edmund William, became Chairman of the Coalbrookdale Company and served it in this capacity until 1922. Alfred II's daughter, Frances Muriel married Mordaunt Leckonby Cope, but she retained the name of Muriel

Cope Darby and lived in Coalbrookdale after inheriting the estate from her father. She was deeply concerned for the welfare of the community and kept alive all the traditions of the Darby family character. She took an interest in the Institute and provided classes as well as training the Church Choir. She encouraged research into the history of the Dale, had an Archive Society and collected much Darby material.

Of the later generations two members have been very active in the affairs of Coalbrookdale, Rachel Labouchere, wife of Sir George, and Michael Darby descended respectively from Samuel and Abraham sons of Abraham II and Abiah.

Lady Labouchere, seventh generation from Abraham I, was for many years President of the Ironbridge Gorge Museum Trust and during the last few years has spent much time on research into the lives of Abiah and Deborah Darby. As part of that concern she has worked at the restoration of the two houses Rosehill and Dale House both of which were built as Darby family homes. The restoration of Rosehill was completed in 1988 and Dale House is to be ready in 1990. The simple life of the Quaker families can nowhere be better appreciated than when viewing furnishings, clothing and everyday articles which past generations (Alfred Darby II and Muriel Cope Darby) have been so careful to save and which, inherited by Rachel, have now been so lovingly displayed in the homes where they were used. The heart and spirit of the Darbys is enshrined in these splendid restorations and in the research done on Abiah and Deborah. The key to the Quaker and spiritual life of Coalbrookdale is now made clear to us in Rachel's two books *Abiah Darby* (1988 Sessions of York) and *Deborah Darby* (Sessions of York, forthcoming), and are a valid part of these restorations.

Michael Darby, son of Roger Sorton Darby, has done much to preserve the Coalbrookdale story. He shared his father's interest in the excavation of the Old Furnace and from its formation has been a member of the Ironbridge Gorge Museum Trust and active in all it has done. He was very responsible in securing the conversion of the old Institute to a high quality Youth Hostel, where young students can spend a few days if they wish to study Coalbrookdale and its Museums. Michael has followed the example of Abraham I and many of the succeeding Darbys by serving for some years as Clerk of the Monthly meeting of Friends to which he belonged.

Coalbrookdale is not only the scene of a world famous iron making and engineering firm which contributed heavily to the Industrial Revolution; it has contributed equally to the growth of the Society of Friends and to its nurture and development here and in many parts of the world.

The Industrial and the Quaker history are inextricably combined in this Darby story.

APPENDICES

1. Profit and Loss Accounts.
2. The valuation of the works, 1718.
3. Some Darby and Ford agreements, 1734–1738.
4. Some steam engine accounts.
5. Account for Trevithick's experiments.
6. List of steam engines made by the Company.
7. Profit and Loss Account 1805–1852.
8. Rules for the preservation of good order at Ketley works.

Appendix 1

PROFIT AND LOSS ACCOUNTS

There are no regular returns of profits and losses, but between 1732 and 1745 there are two fragmentary sources. In the Richard Ford letters there are occasional notes which show something of how dividends were determined and distributed. Writing to Thomas Goldney 15 November 1733, Ford includes the following summary for Goldney's approval.

Dr. Thom^s Goldney To Dale Comp^y		Cr.	
To a Ball. Settled in Dale Ledger	2385. 9. 6		
By Sundry Piggs not yet recd for	162.12. 1½		
Aug 25 By R F to Tho. Lea	10. 0. 0		
By Sundry Drafts for Trustees	763.14. 0		
Balance in his Hands	1449. 3. 4½		
	2385. 9. 6		
To Ball: as pr Contra & to be divided as under	1449. 3. 4½		
In Tho: Goldneys Hands as above	1449. 3. 4½		
a Dividend on 4 shares at £177.15.1½ each	711. 0. 6	remains in his hands	738. 2.10½
Hannah Goldney hath drawn on 1 Share	157.17. 1		
Her dividend on Do.	177.15. 1½	due to her	19.18. 0½
Eliz. Goldney hath drawn on 1 do	157.17. 1		
her dividend on Do	177.15. 1½	due to her	19.18. 0½
Mehet. Goldney hath drawn on 1 Do	157.17. 1		
her dividend on Do.	177.15. 1½	due to her	19.18. 0½
Añn Goldney hath drawn on 1 Do	157.17. 1		
her dividend on Do	177.15. 1½	due to her	19.18. 0½
Martha Vanderwall hath drawn on 1 Do	82. 9. 0		
her dividend on Do.	177.15. 1½	due to her	95. 6. 1½
Jos. Sergt. hath Drawn on 1 Do	175. 8. 7		
his dividend on Do	177.15. 1½	due to him	2. 6. 6½
Gabl. Goldney hath drawn on 2 Do	283. 6. 2		
his dividend on Do.	355.10. 3	due to him	72. 4. 1
Rich. Ford hath drawn on 2 Do	186. 2. 5½		
his dividend on Do.	355.10. 3	due to him	169. 7. 9½
The Trustees have drawn on 2 Do	36. 4. 1		
their dividend on Do.	355.10. 3	due to them	319. 6. 2
			£738. 2.10½

On 12 September 1735 there is a long letter concerned with the financial affairs and as it gives some light on Ford's management, it can be quoted in part.

Esteemed Friend, Thomas Goldney,

I have Recd thyne of ye 2d. Inst. wth ye Bristoll Accots to Aug. wch find to be right & have Settled ye Ball: in thy hands at £2589.13.7 on Accot. of Dale Compy. . . . A Dividend Accot. now I think might be made, but what money will be wantg. from yee before next Fair I cannot yet Calculate, I must first try ye Success of two or 3 Journeys one wch I Purpose going next Week & ye Week after to Chester wch if they turn out Well I shall want none from yee this Michaelmas quarter otherwise I shall, & then against Xmas there is always large calls by Carryers & Ironstone Royalty of Do Colliers Workmen &c that will take a Large Sum & tho there is Debts owing sufficient to discharge 'em, Yet tis so hard to get 'em in, that I dont think it prudent to leave ourselves without a Bank of 4 or £500 whether twill be wanting or not, I will use my best endeavours to prevent its being Calld for. I have as under sent yee Every Partners accot. Dr. as it stands, & wn yee have made up a Dividend Accot. please to let me know it. . . .

Thomas Goldney on	4	Shares	£2589.13. 7
Gabl. Goldney on	2	do	357. 7.11½
Martha Vanderwall on	1	do	82. 9. 0
Hannah Goldney on	1	do	157.17. 1
Mehetable Goldney on	1	do	157.17. 1
Ann Goldney on	1	do	157.17. 1
Joshua Sergeant on	1	do	320.17. 8½
Richd. Ford on	2	do	557.19. 0½
Trustees on	2	do	156.14.11½

For the years 1739 to 1745 there is a summary 'Accot. of ye Profits of Dale Works' in the handwriting of Abraham Darby, and a detailed sheet for the year to 28 September 1740. This is endorsed 'This sheet is Ruled like That on Which ye Profit of Dale Works was Wrote (being the same size) to 28th 7mo. 1740 and sent to Thos. Goldney.

Memo. AD had not Finished it till 24th 11mo. 1740 & RF Designes sending it & Bristoll Fair Accots together. AD Wrote Thos. Goldney Word he hoped he should never be so Long againd Doing it Whilst he had anything to do with the Books.

Tis Profit of Dale Works made up to 28th. 7mo. 1740.'

The form of this account is very simple—first an Inventory of Coalbrookdale, then the debts due to the Company and those owing by the Company. These are brought into a summation as follows

Dr. To ye Quick Stock in ye Works at ye Commencing of ye Accot. as pr ye Credit side of last Years Accot. Amounting to	17762. 6. 6¼
To Debts due from ye Co. at ye Closing this Accot.	795.12.11
Ball: is which is the Profit	2765. 9. 3
	£21323. 8. 8¼

Cr. By Debts due from ye Compa. at ye Commencing of this Accot. and Discharg'd this year	546. 0. 7
By ye Amount of ye Inventory this year	7553.11. 5½
By Debts Due to ye Compa. at ye Closing of this Accot	9223.16. 7¾
By Amount of Cash Dividend as pr Dividend Acct.	4000. 0. 0
	£21323. 8. 8¼

The next document gives the summary in this form for each year, and from it we can take the following figures—

Year	*Dividend*	*Profit*	*Total*	*Profit/share*
1739	£1600	£2293.14. 4¾	£3893.14. 4¾	£143. 6. 7¾
1740	4000	2765. 9. 3	6765. 9. 3	172.16.10
1741	2400	3157. 4. 10	5557. 4.10	197. 6. 6½
1742	3200	2704. 8. 6½	5904. 8. 6½	169. 5. 6½
1743	4000	2659. 2. 7¼	6659. 2. 7¾	166. 3. 1¾
1744	2400	4627.18. 0	7027.18. 0	289. 4.10½
1745	4800	6084.15. 9¼	10884.15. 9¾	380. 6. 0

On this sheet a note is made each year of what is due to Abraham Darby, excluding dividends, and taking the two together we can get an idea of his personal income.

Each year the sum is written as profits on two and a half shares, plus salary, plus profit of the Malthouse.

Year	*Profits plus salary plus Malthouse*	*Dividend*	*Total*
1739	£713. 6.11¾	£250	£963. 6. 11¾
1740	1215.10. 2	625	1840.10. 2
1741	1033.11. 1¼	375	1408.11. 1¼
1742	1098.11.10	500	1598.11.10
1743	1179.18.10	625	1804.18.10
1744	1310. 3.11	375	1685. 3.11
1745	1899. 7. 2¼	750	2649. 7. 2¼

Appendix 2

AN INVENTORY OF QUICK AND DEAD STOCK IN THE IRON WORK ATT COALBROOKDALE TAKEN IN YE BEGINNING OF JULY 1718 viszt—

[*Folio* 1] *In Ware-house*

	£. s. d.
431 Potts & Kettles & 304 Furnacs &c q.101.19 @ 14/–p	70.16. 4½
10 Halfe Ware 1.2.26 att 8/ p.c.	13.10
38 Skillets 1.2.5 att 16d a ps	2. 10.8
7 Mortars 1.1.4 att 2¼d p lb.	1. 8.10½
5 Skillets 0.1.20 att 1/4	6. 8
148 Smooth Irons 6.0.21 att 12d a ps	7. 8. 0
Heaters 0.3.16 att 2d	16. 8
1 Grid iron 0.0.10 att	2. 6
Cart Boxes 8.0.26 att 11/ p c.	4.10. 7
40 Fire backs 13.3.6 att 10/6 p c.	7. 6. 4
10 Bake Stones 2.3.25 att 10/6	1.11. 2
1 Anvill & Tue Iron 1.0.5. att 12/ p c.	12. 6
2 Brass Potts 0.1.3. att 7d p lb	18. 1
1 Brand Iron 0.1.14 att 12/ p c	4. 6
2 Plates 2.0.18 att 14/ p c	1.10. 3
6 Iron Screws and Boxes att £7 a pr	21. 0. 0
1 pair of Scales & Ropes 2 Iron Beams	2.17. 0
Iron Weights with Rings 11.3.14 att 12/ p c	7. 2. 6
A pcell of Wood Bush Moulds	16. 0
2 Dale Boards	5. 0
1 Rowle Mould att	2. 0. 0
	134.17. 6

In the Dark Store Room

66 Potts, Furnaces & Kettles 32.3.0 att 14/ p c	22.18. 6
124 Potts & Kettles from Stowerbridge 25.1.9 att 10/	12.13. 0
101 Cart Boxes 4.1.4. att 11/ p c	2. 7. 1
A pcell of Wooden Moulds	13.13. 0
A Stove with a Pipe	3.17. 0
	55. 8. 7

In the Dressg Room in UpprForge

51 Coal Basketts att 8/ p Dozn.	1.13. 4
11 Doz & 5 of Mine Do. att 4/	2. 5. 8
Horses, Tables and Planks	7. 0
1 Furnace Pattern of 42 gallns att 2/	4. 4. 0
4 Hhds of Stowerb. Clay	1. 0. 0
A pr of Scales and Roaps	8. 0
Old Iron 4c att 6/	1. 4. 0
I Ingot Mould 1.1.0 att 11/	13. 9
	11.15. 9

Between Uppr Air Furnace & Forge	*£ s. d.*
1 Loom Furnace for a Bosh	6. 0. 0
1 Do sound 5.2.20 83 gallns att 19/ p c	5. 7.10
22 Furnaces 32.1.5 att 14/	22.12. 1
4 Tarpulins att £6.5. a ps	25. 0. 0
2 Old Screws 3c att 6/	18. 0
2 Ingott Moulds 3 c att 11/	1.13. 0
1 Old Cart Wheel	5. 0
	61.15.11

In the Coal-Yarde	
Brayes computed 35 doz. att 30/6	52.10. 0
Wood 9 Cord att 14/	6. 6. 0
Turfe valu'd att	30. 0. 0
	88.16. 0

[*Folio* 2] *In the Smith's Shop*	
4 New Kettle Boxes 2.2. att 10/ a ps	2. 0. 0
3 Old Pott do 2.1 att 40/ a ps	6. 0. 0
2 Iron Pott Patterns 3.2 att 2/ p gall.	14. 0
½c of Old Iron	5. 0
1c. of Old Brass	3. 0. 0
2c of New Iron	2. 2. 0
2 Vices	1. 0. 0
3 Dozn of Files att 12d a ps	1.16. 0
5 Pott Dozn Ware Boxes unfinished att 10/ a ps	2.10. 0
8 Pott Boxes 3.3 att 10/	4. 0. 0
2 Old do of 6.3	6. 0. 0
1 Do of 11 gallns	5. 0. 0
1 Pr of Bellows Anvill and Tools	7.14. 0
1 New Mine Strike	12. 0
1 New Kettle Box of 42 gallns	8. 0. 0
1 Brass Fire Engine	6. 0. 0
Check Patterns	1. 0. 0
Odd Leggs & Ears	4.10. 0
Sundry odd things	10. 0
4 small Flasks	4. 0
	62.17. 0

In the Old Blast Furnace	
1 large Bosh for holdg Water	4.10. 0
A Pump	3. 0. 0
A Bell	10. 0
Sundry Plates	15. 0
1 Kettle Pattern 42 gallns att 2/	4. 4. 0
Moulds	10. 0
Odd things	1. 0. 0
Furnace Utensills	4. 0. 0
3 Great Ladles 10/ sundry small do 32/	2. 2. 0
	20.11. 0

In the Bellows Room

	£ s. d.
A Pair of Bellows &c	80. 0. 0
4c & ½ of old Iron us'd p Jno Dawe att 5/ p c	1. 2. 6
4 Kettle Boxes of 5 gallons att 10/	2. 0. 0
4c of Piggs to weight Boxes	1. 4. 0
1 Large Dutch Back Pattern	1. 0. 0
Odd things	3. 0. 0
	88. 6. 6

In the Room over the Bellows

4 Dutch Back Patterns	4. 0. 0
3 Engines and odd things	10. 0. 0
	14. 0. 0

Att ye Tunnell Head

9 Doz and 7 Coal Basketts att 8/ 18d Mine do att 4/	7. 8. 8
Coaks & Stack att 6/9 is 40/6 Mine 6 Doz att 13/ £3.18.0	5.18. 6
12 Chargs in ye Furnace viz 17 Boxes of Mine, 3 of Brays 6 of Coal	10. 2. 6
Limestone 11 Ton att 4/–	2. 4. 0
Hammers, shovells &c	5. 0
Old Iron 24.1.10 att 5/	6. 2. 1
1 Mine Barrow 2 Cart do	15. 0
Wash Mine 10 Dozn att 13/ p dozn	6.10. 0
	39. 5. 9

[*Folio* 3] *In the Mine Yard*

396 dozn & 5 Strike of Iron Stone att 13/ p Dozn	257.14. 0
Coaks att ye Coal hearths 15 Stack att 6/	4.10. 0
	262. 4. 0

In Dannll Richardson's Mould Room

6 Kettle Boxes of 3.2. 3 do of 3. 7 do of 5 gallns att 8/ a ps	6. 8. 0
2 more do of 5 gallns att 8/, 2 do of 6 & 2 do of 7 gallns att 10/ each	2.16. 0
1 Pott Box of 5 gallns att	7. 0. 0
1 Iron Kettle Pattern 5 gallns 1 do 8.2. 1 do 7 att 2/ a galln	2.13. 0
1 Iron Pott Pattern 5 gallns att 2/ p galln	10. 0
2 Risers 5/ Odd things Utensills &c 20/ Sand 20/	2. 5. 0
5 Mortar Patterns att 5/, 1 Pan 3 gallns, 1 do 3.2 att 12d	1.11. 6
4 Setts of Leggs & Ears att 20/ 34 Bottome Boards att 18d	6.11. 0
	29.14. 6

In John Thomas's Mould Room

	£ s. d.
1 Furnace Box 42 gallns £8. 1 do 32 £4. 1 do 24. £3 1 do 18. £3	18. 0. 0
1 Do 16 Gallns 50/, 1 do 12.2.50/ 2 do 10 gallns att 50/ each	10. 0. 0
1 Iron Pattern 28 gallns 1 do 24 g 1 do 21, 1 do 18, 1 do 16, 2 do of 12.2 & 10	12.19. 0
1 Old Iron Pattern 34 gallns £3.8, 1 do of 19 38/ 1 Kettle do 4/ Ladle do 1/	5.11. 0
8c of Piggs to weight Boxes att. 6/. 2 setts of Leggs & Ears att 20/	4. 8. 0
Bottome Boards 20/ Sand 20/ Odd things & Utensils 30/	3.10. 0
	54. 8. 0

Att the Furnace Door

1 Furnace Box 50 gallns att £3.10. 1 do 24 att £3	6.10. 0
1 Furnace Pattern 24 gallns 1 do 34. 2 do 32. 1 do 50. 2 do 19 att 2/	17.16. 0
1 do 16 gallns. 1 do 15. 1 do 27. 1 do 12. 1 do 36 att 2/ 1 brim pan do 36/	11. 8. 0
1 Kettle Pattern 5 gallns 1 do 4 1 do 6 att 2/ p gall	1.10. 0
2 Press Plates 8c att 10/ sundry odd boxes in ptts 10/ Tongs &c 18/	5. 8. 0
	42.12. 0

In the Pigg Yard

3 Garden Rowles 12.1.25 att 20/c. £12.10. 1 Furn 28 gallns 56/	15. 6. 0
1 Furnace Pattern 62 gallns 1 do 14 gallns att 2/	7.12. 0
Piggs 8 Ton att £8.10. p Ton £68. 1 Furnace 56 gall	72. 0. 0
1 Pair of Pigg Scales &c £5. 1 Beam, Scales & Triangle 15/	5.15. 0
Iron Weights Ringed 4c 1 53/. 2 Old Screws 20/ Weights unring'd 15/	4. 8. 0
1 Large Old Box 20/ 3 Furnaces ½ Ware 3c 1 39/6	2.19. 6
Sculls 70 Tons att 40/ p Ton £140. Iron 0.3.6 6/3	140. 6. 3
4 Cast Furnace Rings 5c att 10/. 2 Copper Ingott Moulds 3c att 10/6	4. 1. 6
	252. 8. 3

In Samll Roden's Shop and before ye Door

Wood cut for 8 Boxes 7, 4 & 3 gallns att 7/6p box and for 18 gallns	3. 7. 6
2 Grind Stones hangd 5/ odd Boards & Utensills 28/	1.13. 0
500 Stowerb. Brick att 4/ 2 Dale Boards att 2/6 odd ps of Wood 20/	2. 5. 0
	7. 5. 6

In the Bellows House att New Furnace &c

1 Pair of Large Bellows with Gearing valu'd att	80. 0. 0
2 Pair of Finery Bellows Boards	2. 0. 0
Sundry Plates	1. 0. 0
Furnace Tools	4. 0. 0
8 Ladles	1.10. 0
1 Large Bosh to hold Water	5. 0. 0
A Lead Pipe and Cock	10. 0
A Hearth to be Laid	9.15. 0
	103.15. 0

[*Folio* 4] *In the Mould Room att ye New Furnace*

	£ s. d.
1 Pott Box 15 gallns 1 do 11, 2 do 9.3. 3 do 7.2 6 do 6.3. 9 do 5.1 att £7 a ps	154. 0. 0
5 Do of 4.1 att £7.6 do 3.1., 10 do 3 att £3 6 Dozn Ware att 50/	98. 0. 0
1 Kettle Box 7 gallns 10/. 2 small do att 5/ each 1 Grid Iron box 8/	1.14. 0
1 Brass Pott Pattern 15 galls £10. 1 do 11. £8. 1 do 7.2 £7. 20 do 6.3 £14	39. 0. 0
2 do 5.1 £12. 1 do 4.1 £6. 1 do Dozn Ware 40/ 1 do Iron 3.1 12/, 1 do 3 galln 12/	21. 4. 0
1 Brass Kettle Pattern 2 gallns 40/, 1 do Dozn Ware 40/ 1 do Iron 5/	4. 5. 0
1 Lead Mortar Pattern & Box 7/6 54 Bottome Boards att 2/ each	5.15. 6
9 setts of Leggs & Ears £9 Sundry Tools 20/ Sand 40/	12. 0. 0
A new Air Furnace with Utensills	40. 0. 0
1 Iron Pott Pattern 9 gallns ¾s att	2.10. 0
	378. 8. 6

In the Pigg Yard

Pigg Iron 16 Ton 10c att £8.10 p Ton	140. 0. 0
1 pr of Pigg Scales £5 1 pr of Scales, Beam & Triangle 50/	7.10. 0
Iron Weights ringed 8.3.14 att 12/	5. 5. 6
1 Furnace 66 gallns att 16d £4.8 14 cast Rings 10c £5. 5 wrote do 1c.3. 35/	11. 3. 0
1100 Stowerb Bricks att 4/ p hundrd 200 Foot of Boards att 26/	3.16. 0
	167.14. 6

In the Old Forge

A Beam and Scales	10. 0
1 Old Wrought Iron Cannon	1.10. 0
1 Forge Hammer & odd things	10. 0. 0
Centers	2.10. 0
	14.10. 0

Att the Tunnell Head

Coal Baskets 6 Doz 9 att 8/54/ Mine do 4 dozn att 4/	3.10. 0
18 Stack of Coaks att 6/9 £6.1.6 1 doz of Mine 13/	6.14. 6
Wheel Barrows Rakes, Shovells, &c 30/ Old Iron 4c att 5/ is 20/	2.10. 0
Lime Stone 5 Ton att 4/ Cinders 3 Ton att 15/ Wash Mine—8 dozn att 13/	8. 9. 0
	21. 3. 6

In the New Warehouse att New Blast Furnace

1 pr of Large Bellows pipes 10/ 2 Small Cramps for Air. Furn. 5/	15. 0
400 Potts & Kettles 100.2.14 att 14/ p c .	70. 8. 9
6½ Ware do 1.2.8. att 8/ p c	12. 0
1 Grate 93 Bushes 5c att 10/6	2.12. 6
	74. 8. 3

In the Mine Yard	£ s. d.
Iron Stone 250 Dozn 4 Strike att 13/ p dozn	162.14. 8

In the Old Store Room

315 ½ Ware Potts & Kettles 70.0.21 at 8/ p c.	28. 1. 6
13 Bake Stones 2.1.11 att 14/, 2 Mortars 28lb att 2/6 Bushes 36lb 1/8	18. 2
7 Brasses 36lb, 1 Anvill 8 lb. 5 Bullets 31lb all att 6/ p c.	10. 4
Old wrought Iron 1.3.7 att 10/. 6 ends of Iron 0.3.4. att 10/	1.13. 8
3 Malt Mills & 1 Wheel £4.3. Ladles 9/. 1 Rod of Iron 84lbs att 20/	5. 4. 0
17 Patterns 2.0.24 att 14/ is 31/. 1 Gudgeon Mould 1/. 1 Back & 1 Grate do 6/	1.18 0
White metal 4c att 4d lb £7.6.8, 1 Barrell of Black Lead 2/6	7. 9. 2
Tallow 0.2.18 att 4d p lb 25/ Old Leather 1.3.14 att 4d p lb. £3.7.8	4.12. 8
5 Pieces of New Cloth att 15/ £3.15 4 Charcoal Baggs 20/	4.15. 0
6 Dozn & ½ of Roaps for tying Potts att 3/, 19/6 2 Large Roaps 15/	1.14. 6
An Iron Chain 6/8 11 Box att 10/ £5.10 A Clock £3	8.16. 8
29 Bottome Boards att 18d 43/6 Nails 46lbs att 3½ Odd things 40/	4.16. 6
	70.10. 2

[*Folio* 5] *In the Coppr Ware House*

151 Potts & Kettles 31.2.8 att 14/ p c	21. 8. 0
46 ½ Ware do 8.3.21 att 8/ £3.11. 124 Grates 36.0.15 £18.19.4	22.10. 4
39 Bake Stones 10.0.20 att 10/6. 43 Fire Backs 17.2.21 att 10/6	14.11. 0
2010 Cart Boxes 102.0.23 att 11/ p c	56. 4. 0
A Beam & scale 15/ a Large pr of Bellows £20	20.15. 0
Iron Weights 2.2.21 32/ Lead do 0.2.20 8/. 3 Hams. 1c.0.1¼ 10/6	2.10. 6
An Old Malt Mill 10/ Sculls 26 Tons att 40/ £52.	52.10. 0
	190. 8.10

In the Coppr House

800 Stowerb Bricks 32/ Cinders 9c att 7/ Coal 12c att 6/6	2. 5. 0
2 Air Furnaces with ye Utensills £80. 1 Old do £30	110. 0. 0
1 Iron Kettle Pattern 5 gallns 10/ 1 do 3 gallns 6/ 1 Riser 1/	17. 0
2 Wooden Grate Patterns 2/ a Cieve 2/6 a Sledge 2/.	6. 6
1 Wooden Ingot Mould Pattern 1/ 2 Hams. 7/6	8. 6
A pcell of Old Furnace Iron Braces &c 4c att 29/ p c	4. 0. 0
2 Wooden Fire Back Patterns 42/ 1 Bakestone do 6d.	2. 2. 6
2 Wooden Fire Back Patterns 42/ 1 Iron Barrow 2/ a Ladle furn 40/	4. 4. 0
In ye Stamping Mill Stowerb Clay 3 Ton att 30/	4.10. 0
	128.13. 6

In Upper Air Furnace	£ s. d.
An Air Furnace with its Utensills	50. 0. 0
11 Pott Boxes 4.1 £77.8. do 3.1 £24 9 do 2.3. £27 21 do 2.1 £52.10	180.10. 0
1 do 7.2. £7.2 do 4.1 £8. 2 do 3 £6. 16 dozn Ware do £40	61. 0. 0
11 Kettle Boxes 2 gallns £4.8. 4 smaller do 32/	6. 0. 0
12 Dozn Ware do att 8/ £4.16. 3 Skillet Boxes att 8/ 24/	6. 0. 0
1 Brass Pott Pattern 7.2. £6. 1 do 4.1 £4.10. 1 do 3.1 £4	14.10. 0
2 Doz 2.3. £7. 2 do 2.1 £5. 3 dozn Ware do £6. 1 Izop do 20/	19. 0. 0
1 Brass Kettle Pattern 2 gallns £2. 2 Pitch Pan do £2	4. 0. 0
1 Small Brass Kettle 10/ 1 Kettle Pattern 3 gall 6/	16. 0
A hand Fire Engine Brass 20/ 10 Setts & 2 odd Leggs 10 pr Ears £11	12. 0. 0
1 Iron Pott Pattern 4.1. 9/ 1 do 3.6/ 1 Kettle 2.2.5/	1. 0. 0
2 Dozn Ware Kettle Patterns 10/ 4 Lesser do 10/	1. 0. 0
1 Pitch Pan do 2/6, 2 Skillet do 5/ 2c of old Iron Kettles 10/	17. 6
1 Large Furnace £6. 1 Ingot Mould 12/ a Bell 1/	6.13. 0
1 Ladle Furnace 50/ Odd things 20/ Sand 20/ Bottm Boards £4	8.10. 0
	371.16. 6

In the Office	
New Cppr 12lbs 12/ and Iron Paddle 2/ 3lb of Sawder3/	17. 0
White Mettle ½ a c. 42/ a Pewter galln 10/ Chairs	3.13. 0
A Writing Desk 2 Tables & Shelves 30/ 2 pr of hooks & Hinges 2/	1.12. 0
A Sett of Weights for Standards 1c 12/ a Sett of Leggs 1 pt wantg 10/	1. 2. 0
Paper 3 Reams & ½ att 6/ is 21/ 1 Ream att 12/4 pr of Brass Leggs 24/	2.17. 0
Brass Pott Pattern 10 gallns £8. 1 do 8 £6	14. 0. 0
1 do 9 gallns 1 do 5. 1 do 3. 1 do 6. 1 do 4 1 do 2 1 do dozn ware	12. 0. 0
1 Large Brass Mortar Pattern 40/1 do smaller 15/ a pr Pistolls 20/	3.15. 0
2 Brass Dozn Ware Kettle Patterns 20/ 30lbs of Brass at 7d. 17/6	1.17. 6
1 Iron Pott Pattern 5 gallns 10/ 1 do 3 6/ a new Riddle 4/	1. 0. 0
25 Sheets of Tin 6/4 a Spring Lock 3/, 5 Cieve Bottomes 2/6	11.10
A Spring Lock from ye Office Door 10/ A Brass Pott Pattern 3.1. £3.10.0	4. 0. 0
	47. 5. 4

Brot from Folio 1	352.13. 9
Brot from Folio 2	225. 0. 3
from Folio 3	752. 7. 3
from Folio 4	889. 9. 7
	2957.15. 0

The Total Amount of ye Inventory
The Buildings £1242.5.0 not charged here.

Appendix 3

Leases to Darby & Ford, 1734–1738

Indenture 7 June 1734 between John Unett Smitheman of Much Wenlock and Catherine his wife and John Giffard of the city of London and Rose his wife on the one part and
Richard Ford of Coalbrookdale and Abraham Darby of do. on other.
ALL THOSE Iron Furnaces commonly known by the name of the Old Furnace and the New Furnace with the appurts. situate in Coalbrookdale and all that parcel of land on part whereof the Furnaces or one of them stands by estimation ½ acre and all those three iron forges or iron smithies commonly called the Great Forge, the Upper Forge and the Plate Forge with a house or building commonly called the Steel House but lately converted into a Malthouse
and also that part of the waste ground and bushes and underwood growing there, adjoining the sd Forges intended by the sd lessees to be enclosed by setting up a gate on a road there which waste is bounded on the north by Old Furnace Pool, on the East by Duddell's Coppice, and the lands of Thomas Stanley on the south and Geo Dukesills lands on the west also all and singular the dwelling houses . . . pools . . . dams . . . except the wood timber etc. the lessees having power to enter to cut down any and make saw pitts and to dig and set cole fires in and upon the land, and also liberty for employees etc. etc. and horses and carriages to pass Paying £102.10.0 per ann and maintaining buildings etc. and also all such cynders as they shall at any time find within the waste of the said Manor [of Madeley] making and paying reasonable satisfaction for the damage done by carrying and taking the cynders etc.
Lessees to buy all such coales and Ironstone as they shall spend in and about the sd ironworks from and out of the coleworks and ironstone pitts of the sd lessors and not elsewhere provided such coals and ironstone be fitt to their use and there be sufficient to be had at and from the sd coalworks and that the same be sold at a marketable and reasonable price.
Lessees not to sublet any wharfeage at Ladcroft to any person.

1735 Mar 26 Agmt between Richard Ford and Abm Darby Whereas in Jan 1734 John Unett Smitheman . . . etc. did let to A. D. and R. F. the two furnaces known as the Old and New furnaces and Great, Upper and Plate Forges, and the Steelhouse, Now R. F. and A. D. agree that R. F. shall receive ¾ and A. D. ¼ of all rights and privileges and advantages under the same.

1738 Oct 30 Agmt between Richard Ford and Abraham Darby, and Thomas Goldney, Gabriel Goldney merchants, and Martha Vanderwall

Hannah Goldney, Mehetable Goldney, Elizabeth Goldney, and Anne Goldney
recites the lease of 1734 for 21 years and now transfers and assigns to Thos Goldney and his relatives, 9/16ths of the rights etc. the sd Thos Goldney shall have 3/16ths and his relations 1/16th each and to divide all profits of the concern in which Thomas Goldney lately deceased the Father of sd Thos G. and the other parties, was a partner with R. F. and A. D. in these proportions, and 4/16ths to R. F. and 3/16ths to A. D.

Appendix 4

Shrewsbury Mss. 332

Engine for Coalbrookdale Works, 1754–55

Cash Book

Anno 1754

	Fire Engine Dr. to Sundry Accots.		£. s. d.
11.11thmo.	To William Hallen for 3 Bundles of Rod Iron 1c.2.0. @ 22/–, 1 spade 3/–. 16 Round Plates, wt. 1.0.23 @ 28/–, 3 Mothooks 0.0.16 @ 4d. & 117 Engine Plates wt. 33.2.21 @ 28/–	£. s. d.	50.18. 4
18.6mo	To Dale Company for 1 Plate 1.0.4 @ 10/–	10. 4¼	
	To Do for Wrot Iron Blocks & 6 Shivers 1.0.8. @ 1/– pr.	6. 0. 0	
	To Do 9 Cast Iron Barrs 0.1.8 @ 10/–	0. 3. 2½	
	To Do 2 Plain Pipes 8ft Lo 25In. Diam.2 Blast holes 7Ft2Inch 2 Clackseats Do wt 132.3.1 @ 15/–	99.11. 4½	
	To Do 2 Working Barrels 10ft lo.24 Inch 52.2.6 @ 26/–	68. 6. 4½	
	To Do 1 Cylinder 10ft lo.47¾In Diam. 72.0.0 @ 26/–	93.12. 0	
	To Do 2 Engine Pans 125.3.17 @ 15/–	94. 8. 6¼	
	To Do 1 Ring for Engine Pan drill'd 28.2.10 @ 15/–	21. 8.10	
29.10.	To Do 1 Old Furnace Pattern 1 Plate for Engine Pit, 1 Old Forge Hammer, Old Barrs 1 Old Furnace & I Old Loam Pan faulty 54.3.24 @ 7/6	20.12. 2¾	
	To Do 1 Air Vessel & 1 Engine Pan Ring 50.0.0 @ 15/–	37.10. 0	
	1 Gudgeon 2 Brasses & 2 Plates 15.0.12 @ 7/6	5.13. 3½	
27.12.	To Do 1 Cylinder Bottom 14.2.7 @ 16/–	11.13 0	
	1 Air Vessel Top 10.0.14 @ 10/–	5. 1. 3	464.10. 5¼
			515. 8. 9¼

		£ s. d.	£ s. d.
1755			
10.2mo	To William Hallen for 11 Engine Plates 31. 3.12 at 28/– & 18 Round Plates 1.0.4 at 28/–	46. 1. 0	
	To Dale Company for 6 Sleepers & 70 Barrs 29.3.6 @ 7/6, 3 Gudgeons & 2 Brasses 5.2.21 2 Barrs 1.3.7. 2 Bucket Door	13. 6. 2	
	Plates 9.2.6, 2 Door Frames & 1Y Block Plate 10.2.6 in all 22.0.11 @ 7/6	8. 5. 9¼	
	5 Plates & 7 Shivers 13.0.9 @ 7/6	4.18. 1¼	
	1 Working Barrel 6½ftlo 9 in Dia 7.0.19, 1 Sinking Pipe in 2 parts 7.2.18, 3 Injection Caps 1.0.22 & 1 Bucket & Clack 2.1.0, in all 18.1.3 @ 26/–	23.15. 2¼	
	1 Blast Hole Pipe 5.2.0. & 6 Plain Pipes 28.0.5 in all 33.2.5 at 15/–	25. 3. 2	
	1 Timp & 1 Bucket Door Plate 3.3.18 @ 7/6	1. 9. 3¾	
10.4mo	1 Piston Ring in 4 parts 8 Weights 2 Clack weights & 2 Plates, 12.1.3. @ 7/6	4.12. 1¼	
	4 Plain Pipes 9ftlo 10in Dia 24.2.8 @ 15/–	18. 8. 6¾	
	8 Buckets & Clacks 9.3.0. @ 26/–	12.13. 6	
	1 Brass Clack, 1 Regulator & 1 Sinkg Clack 1.2.12½ @ 1/4, 1 Maundrel in Sand 0.3.27 @ 10/–, & 1 Do in Loam 4.1.14 @ 15/–	15.16. 2¼	
	1 Timp 2.0.0 @ 7/6	15. 0	
	2 Pipes 17.1.26 @ 15/–	13. 2. 2¾	
	1 Gudgeon 3.2.14 @ 7/6	1. 7. 2¼	
	To Richard Ford for Bar Iron 13.3.20 @ 20/–	13.18. 0	
	14 Valve Plates 2.2.18 @ 20/–	2.13. 0	
	Bar Iron 25.3.7 @ 20/–	25.13. 6	
	Do 4.0.1. @ 20/–	3.19. 8	235.17. 7¾
	Total		£751. 6. 5

Cost of the New Fire Engine 1758

7.5mo to Dale Co.				
	1 Cylinder Bottom	28.2. 0	16/–	22.16. 0
	2 Pipes 2 Blasthole pipes & 2 Clack Seats	226.0.13	15/–	135.13. 8¾
	1 Piston turn'd	17.0.26	12/–	10. 6. 9¼
	2 Workg Barrels 8 Bucket & Clacks	96.2.14	26/–	125.12. 3
	5 Pipes 1 Blasthole 2 Clack Seats pipes	70.2. 5	15/–	52.18. 2
	1 Gudgeon 1 Brace 2 Bucket door plates	28.1.22	10/–	14. 4. 5½
	2 Clacks	2.0.15	26/–	2.15. 5¾
	1 Clack Weight	1.0. 8	10/–	10. 8½
	1 pipe 1 Elbow Pipe 1 Clack seat & 1 Blast hole	30.0. 6	15/–	22.10. 9½
	2 Buckets & 2 Clacks	0.1.16	26/–	10. 2½

			£ s. d.
1 Clack	1.0.10	26/–	1. 8. 3¾
5 Buckets & 2 Clacks	6.0.21	26/–	8. 0.10½
1 Steam Vessel	21.0. 0	15/–	15.15. 0
1 Cylinder Bottom	31.2. 5	16/–	25. 4. 8½
1 Steam Vessel top in sand	10.2. 5		5. 5. 5¼
5 Pipes & 2 Clack Seats	126.1. 8	15/–	94.14. 9¾
2 Pipes & 3 Elbow Pipes	17.1.21	15/–	13. 1. 6¾
2 Bucket door plates	19.2.25	10/–	9.17. 3
4 Buckets & Clacks	12.1.15	26/–	16. 2. 0
3 Injection Pipes	1.0. 5.	@ 16/–	0.16. 8½
1 Regulator & 2 Clacks Brass	2.2.22	1/4	20. 2. 8
2 Buckets & 4 Clacks	9.3. 3	26/–	12.14. 2¼
1 Pipe & 1 Elbow Pipe	19.2.14	15/–	14.14. 4½
1 Sinking Pipe for hot well	2.3. 7	26/–	3.13. 1½
1 Brass Cock 28lb @ 14/			
4 Brass Braces 10½ @ 1/–			2. 7.10
3 Clacks 26/– 12.3.4 & 1 Brass Clack	0.1.19	@ 1/4	19.15. 1
1 Bucket	0.0.27	26/–	6. 3
77 Sundry Valve Plates etc.	15.1. 6	@ 40/–	30.12. 0
446 Bars Iron	139.0.15	@ 18/6	128.13. 9¾
12 Brasses	23	@ 1/–	1. 3. 0
Cash Paid sundries			30. 1. 7
carr. of 35.2.20 of lead fr London			3.17. 3
			846. 6. 4¾

Cost of Dawley Colliery Engine, 1761

9.2mo. 1761				
	2 Working Barrels unbored.			
	2 Clack Seats	465.1.24	@ 14/–	325.16. 6
	2 Blast hole pieces & 21 pipes			
	1 Gudgeon, 5 Brasses, 3 Plates & 1 Pig	20.3.12	@ 8/6	8.17. 3¼
	140 Barrs	47.0. 8	@ 8/6	20. 0. 1¼
17.4mo	2 Sleepers 6.0.4. @ 8/6			2.11. 5½
	2 Injection Pipes, 2 Steam pipes,			
	1 Cylinder Bottom, 1 Receiver & top 69.3.20 14/–			48.19. 0
10.5mo.	1 Cylinder 10 ft × 60 ins.	72.1. 7	@ 26/–	94. 0. 1½
	1 Cylinder Bottom	17.0.14	@ 16/–	13.14. 0
	1 Pipe Bored 10ft 27½ins.	32.0. 0	@ 26/–	41.12. 0
	1 Do unbored 8 28¼			
	1 Blasthole pipe 7ft 27ins	79.1.14	@ 15/–	59.10 7½
	1 Clack Seat 7ft 27 ins.			
To New Fire Engine				
	12 Clack seats 6ft 30ins	80.2.3	@ 15/–	64.17.10¾
	1 Piston turnd 9.1.18 @ 12/–			5.12.11
	1 Pipe, 4 Barrs, 4 Injection caps			
	1 Cylinder Bottom, 4 Pistn wts 35.2.22 @ 14/–			24.19. 9
				£710. 11.7¾

Horsehay Steam Engines, 1769–1770

fo. 214
Bought of Dale Company.
1769.

				£ s. d.
13.3mo.	7 Flew Brick @ 6d.			3. 6
22 –	4½ days work p John Parker			6. 0
9.5mo	10 Boyler Plates 2.2.1 @ 28/–			3.10. 3
	2 Gudgeons & 2 Brasses 5.0.18 @ 10/–			2.11. 7
3. 6	7 Tewirons 0.1.26 @ 12/–			5. 9
22. 8	5 Dales @ 4/8 & 4 do @ 4/–			2. 3. 4
	1 Tongs Ladle	0.1.15 @ 12/–		4. 7
	1 Axletree pattern & Box			10. 0
28. 9	4 Gudgeons & 4 Brasses 9.0.0 @ 10/–			4.10. 0
10.10	6 Tewirons 0.2.0 @ 12/–			6. 0
1770				
16.1mo	Steel	0.2.3 @ 36/–		19 0
	1 Cylinder 4½–84	49.2.24		
	1 Do	43.1.16	158.2.12	
	1 Cylinder Bottom	34.1. 0	@ 30/–	237.18. 2
	1 Do	31.1 0		
	1 Piston	28.2.14	54.2.25	
	1 Do	26.0.11	@ 12/–	32.16. 8
	1 Pipe 6–6	3.2.10		
	1 Do 7–6	3.1.21		
	2 Small Pipes	1.3. 2	15.1.6	
	1 Receiver	3.1.15	@ 18/–	13.15. 5
	1 Taper Pipes	3.0.14		
	1 Plug	0.1. 3 @ 12/–		3. 4
	1 Collar	9.1. 4		
	1 Do	9.1. 4	18.2.8 @ 14/–	13. 0. 0
	Pins Screwed		4.3.11 @ 2d	4.10. 6
	42 Screws & Burrs		2.0.23 @ 6d	6. 3. 6
	Wrot iron work		2.3.25 @ 4½d	6. 4.11
	131 Boyler Plates		50.1.22 @ 27/–	68. 2. 0
	Rivets iron		6.1.26 @ 18/–	5.16. 8
	Barr Iron		0.0.13 @ 20/–	2. 2
				404. 3. 4

Fo 355
Bought of Coalbrookdale Company
1771. 29.1mo.

48 Links	7.3.13 @ 14/–	5.10. 1
2 Clacks	0.2. 1 @ 30/–	15. 3
6 Tewirons	0.1.21 @ 12/–	5. 3
1 Snifting Pipe	1.2. 6 @ 18/–	1. 8. 0
374 Links	32.1.17 @ 14/–	22.13. 8

			£ s. d.
	1 Pipe 10 in long 12 ins Diam.	1.3.24 @ 18/–	1.15. 4
	2 Do 12 × 25	5.1.17 @ 18/–	4.17. 3
	2 Do 12 × 9	4.0. 2 } @ 18/–	5. 0. 5
	1 Snifting pipe	1.2. 7 }	
14.10mo	12 Tewirons	0.3.16 @ 12/–	10. 8
	2 Buckets	0.1.6 @ 30/–	9. 1
	1 Sinking Clack 1 Regulat. Hand & Cock 1 Injection Cock 1 Hand Hinge & Pin	2.1.10¼	16.17. 1
1772. 19.1mo.			
	20 Files cutt @ 3d		5. 0
	Barr Iron	2.2.22 @ 19/–	2.11. 0
	1 Pump pipe	0.0.14 @ 4d.	4. 8
			63. 2. 9

SHREWSBURY MSS. 333

fo 283
Bought of Dale Company
For the Fire Engines.
1771. 12.3mo.

	1 Communication pipe 8–17 15.3.0 @ 18/–	14. 3. 6
	Paid Smith's wages	7.10½
11.5	6 Buckets & Clacks 18.3.12 @ 30/–	28. 5. 8½
25.	1 Brass Regulator 1.2.19 @ 1/4 & 4 Brasses 14lb @ 1/-	13. 3.10
26.11	1 Piston Plate 14.1.24 @ 12/–	8.13. 7
29.	1 Sinking Clack 0.2.16 @ 1/4	4.16. 2
19.12	1 Gudgeon & Brass 13.1.4 @ 10/–	6.12.10
	Barr Iron 0.2.20 @ 20/–	0.13. 4
		£76.16.10

1770				
11.5mo	For Blast Furnace &c.			
	1 Load Fine Sand			0. 8. 0
	1 Furnace 50 Gallons		2.1.9 @ 11/–	1. 5. 7
	1 Cylinder	40.0.7		
	1 Do	39.3.5	133.1.7 @ 30/–	199.19. 4
	1 Cylinder Bottom	26.3.3		
	1 Do	26.2.20		
	1 Piston	26.3.26	53.2.26 @ 12/–	32. 4. 9
	1 Do	26.3.0		
	1 Air Box & 4 Bellows pipes 26.0.9			
	1 Injection pipes 4.0.10		@ 18/–	27. 3. 0
	1 Collar		9.1. 6 @ 14/-	6.11. 0
	12 Pott Cords			6. 0

		£ s. d.
3 Quarts Sallad Oyl 2/11. 1 gall do. 3/8 Sand 8/–		14. 7
2 Gudgeons & 2 Brasses	5. 1.0 @ 10/–	2.12. 6
6 Tewirons	0. 1.19 @ 12/–	5. 0
20 Strikes Lime @ 4d.		6. 8
24 Dozen Screw Pins	10.0.17 @ 6d	28. 8. 6
		£300. 4.11

fo. 416
Bought of Coalbrookdale Co.
1772

16.3mo.	1 Pipe		1.1. 4 @ 18/–	1. 3. 1
	1 Half Ware Furnace 90 Gallons @ 6d. and making 4/6			2. 9. 6
	1 Large Receiver		38.3.15 @ 18/–	34.19.11
	Screws & Burrs in Do		1.0.12 @ 6d.	3. 2. 0
	1 Brass Stop Clack	1.2. 2		
	1 Do	1.2.18		
	1 Steam Clack & 1 Cock	0.2.2½	4.3. 3½ @ 1/4	35.14. 0
	1 Injection Cock	0.3.10		
	1 Regulator Cock pin	0.0.27		
	1 Pipe 8 ft 15 in diam	10.1.17	18.1.13 @ 18/–	16.10. 7
	1 Do 6 15	7.3.24		
	1 Hot Well Pan in Loam		13.2.8 @ 14/–	9.10. 0
	Boyler Plates	55.1.22		
	16 Do	4.3.7.	60.1.1 @ 27/–	81. 7. 0
	Rivett Iron		10.0.0 19/6	9.15. 0
	40 Strikes of Lime @ 4d			13. 4
	21 Files cutt @ 3d			5. 3
	Barr iron 26 lbs @ 19/– Plate 0.1.2. @ 27/–			11. 8
	22 Boyler Plates		9.0.5 @ 27/–	12. 4. 2
				£208. 5. 6

Appendix 5

Richd Trevithick & Co D^r^ to Warehouse

			£ s. d.
To Castings for trying Experiments now at the Dale.			
1 Boiler	30.2.11	@ 18/-	
1 Case for Do	22.3.21		48. 3. 7½
Sorted Screwpins	4.2.17	@ 8d	17. 7. 4
2 Cast Iron Grates	1.1.27	13/-	19. 4½
1 wrot iron Jaw	24	8d	16. 0
1 Cylinder top & pipe	11.1.13		
1 Stuffing Box	14	32/-	18. 7. 8½
2 Brass Brasses	10	2/-	1. 0. 0
3 Slides	1.3.20	16/-	
2 pillars	1.1.16		2.13. 1½
1 Curve Pipe	2.2.25	20/-	2.10.10½
1 Strait do 4½ft.10 in dia.	4.2.17	18/-	4. 3. 8½
3 Curve pipes	10.1.9	20/-	10. 6. 7
2 Strait do	13.2.23	18/-	12. 6. 8
2 Slides	1.1.4	16/-	1. 0. 6½
1 Working Barrel	8.0.10	32/-	17. 2. 6½
1 Top for Do	1.1.16		
1 Plunger	1.0.25		
1 Strait pipe	7.3.0	18/-	6.19. 6
3 Elbow pipes	19.0.27	20/-	19. 4. 9
1 Clackseat pipe	2.2.15		2.12 8
2 Pillars	1.1.17	16/-	1. 2. 5
5 Clacks	1.3.10	20/-	1.16. 9
2 Chucks & 1 Plate	3.0.23	16/-	2.11. 3
1 wrt pump rod	1.18	1/-	2. 6. 0
Caps, Stuffing, Box & cross Bars	2.2.3	16/-	2. 0. 5
Wrot iron joints & Pins	3.0	8d	2.16. 0
1 Brass Cock, Shell etc fitted	1.2	2/6	3.15. 0
4 Cast iron Brasses	1.2	16/-	4. 3½
1 Brass ring in Boiler Joint	20	2/-	2. 0. 0
1 Piece Cast iron to repair the Boiler	1.0.0		16. 0
1 Cylinder 5in with Skews cut at ends for the floating engine	10.3.20	40/-	21.17. 1½
Expence in Pumping the Engine 18.10mo.1802			
Fitting & Attg Engine Boiler etc making joints & putting up pipes etc 4 Men in all 74¼ days @ 3/6			12.19.10½
2 Men do in all 47¼		2/-	4.14. 6
Work at the Turning Mill & Mens Time in fitting 24½ D @ 7/-			8. 9. 9
John Bratford fitting & helping up with engine 52 at 3/-			7.16. 0
Expence in making a Crank used in working the Barge afterwards broken up			5. 0. 0
Sundry postages unpaid by R.T. when at the Dale			5. 6
			246. 5.11

Appendix 6

Steam Engine cylinders etc. made and supplied by the Coalbrookdale Company between 1722 and 1748, according to three lists.

A. the Coalbrookdale Sales Books. B. the Coalbrookdale Cash Books. C. Stanley Davies list in *Trans. Newcomen Soc.*

	A	B		C
1722		1	Cylinder	
1723				
1724	Rich[d]. Beech Winster mines.	3	,,	Rich[d]. Beech.
1725		3	,,	Stannier Parrot. Aug. Griff Colliery. Nov.
1726		1	,,	Rich[d]. Beech. May J. Beckett. (2). July
1727				Rich[d]. Beech July. Sr. Geo. Beaumont.
1728	Lord Middleton	2	,,	Lord Middleton G. Sparrow.
1729	G. Sparrow Aug.			
1730	Stannier Parrot Mch. S. Lloyd. Aug. G. Beaumont. Dec.			S. Lloyd.
1731	Ald. Ridley. May. Thos. Allan. Aug. J. Hornblower. Sep. J. Griffith. Dec. Rich[d]. Hartshorn. Dec.	7	,,	Jos. Hornblower. Ald. Ridley.
1732	S. Hamer. May T. Pilkington. July W. Green. Aug. Ald. Ridley. Oct.	10	,,	
1733	R. Beech. Feb. Earl Scarborough. Apl. Ld. Middleton. Aug.	5	,,	Earl of Scarborough
1734	G. Beaumont. Sep. J. Hornblower. Dec.	2	,,	Sr. Geo. Beaumont. J. Hornblower.
1735	J. Crow. May R. Beech. May. H. Lambton. Oct. Wo. Richardson Nov.. J. Hornblower. Nov.	6	,,	H. Lambton. W. Richardson.
1736	J. Fletcher. May. Ld. Middleton Aug. Ld. Dudley. Oct. B. Sparrow. Nov. J. Hornblower. Dec.	8	,,	Ld. Middleton. Ld. Dudley B. Sparrow.

	A	B	C
1737	Ld. Dudley. Mar.	3 Cylinder	
1738	B. Sparrow. Jan.		
	Hewish & Co. Mch.		
	R. Ridley. May.		
	J. Lawton. July		
1739		2 ,,	
1740		2 ,,	W. Ferriday
1741		1 ,,	
1742		1 ,,	Coalbrookdale works.
			J. Smitheman.
1743	Coalbrookdale Wks.	4 ,,	Anth. Barker.
1744	Coalbrookdale Wks.	4 ,,	
1745		6 ,,	
1746		4 ,,	
1747		4 ,,	
1748		13 ,,	
		92	

Engines built at the Coalbrookdale works after 1748. The records are very incomplete for this period, and few are mentioned except those built for the works.

1751	Lord Ward.					
1752	William Brown. Throckley Colliery, Northumberland.					
1754	Engine for works.	10ft	stroke	$47\frac{3}{4}$	inches	cylinder.
1755	Horsehay Co.	10ft	,,	$60\frac{1}{2}$	,,	,,
1756	Horsehay Co.	10ft	,,	60	,,	,,
1756	Mr. Broade, Fenton.					
1757	Horsehay Co.	10ft	,,	$60\frac{1}{2}$	,,	,,
1758	Ketley Co.					
1759	Henry Wood's engine.					
1761	Dawley engine	10ft	,,	60	,,	,,
1763	Walker Colliery	$10\frac{1}{2}$ft	,,	74	,,	,,
1766	Madeley Wood					
1767	Killingworth Colliery.					
1770	Horsehay Co.	7ft	,,	56	,,	,,
	Horsehay Co.	7ft	,,	56	,,	,,
1771	Horsehay Co.					
1771	Horsehay Co.					
1776	Handley Wood engine	$5\frac{1}{2}$ft	,,	48	,,	,,
1771	Horsehay Co.					
1771	Horsehay Co.					
1776	Handley Wood engine	$5\frac{1}{2}$ft	,,	48	,,	,,
1778	Boulton & Watt engine, built at Coalbrookdale.					
1780	,, ,, ,, ,, ,,					
1781	,, ,, ,, ,, ,,					
1783	,, ,, ,, for forge hammer.					

1784	Boulton & Watt engine, 6ft stroke 26 inches cylinder.
1785	" " " Coalbrookdale forge.
	" " " Horsehay forge.
	" " " " "
1787	" " " 6ft stroke 20 inches cylinder for shears.
1790	Heslop's engine
1791	" " for Lord Lonsdale.
1792	Sadler's engine at Coalbrookdale.
1793	" " " Bank.
1795	Boulton & Watt engine for North Downs mine, Cornwall.
1798	" " " " " " "
1802	Trevithick's experimental engine.
1803	6 Trevithick engines.
1804	2 10 inch Trevithick engines.
1805	Trevithick engine with barge
	John Burlingham, Trevithick engine complete. 18inch cylinder.
	Rowlands & Co. ordinary engine complete. 27 inch cylinder.
	New Work Colliery winding engine. 20 inch cylinder.
	New Work Colliery winding engine No. 7. 20 inch cylinder.
1807	12 winding engines made for New Work and Lawley collieries.

Appendix 7

Coalbrookdale Company
Profit and Loss Account 1805 to 1852

Cash paid to the Partners	*Valuation*				*Year*
	Coalbrookdale Foundry	*Coalbrookdale Forge*	*Horsehay Works*	*Total*	
£12,588	£81,308	£4,275	£31,068	£134,664	1805
25,178	90,342	3,722	30,749	143,635	1806
30,252	94,178	4,405	33,365	154,827	1807
26,631	96,887	2,471	33,461	161,396	1808
23,397	85,848	2,508	35,491	165,996	1809
8,095	27,118	2,391	38,930	164,954	1810
4,937	31,088	3,402	43,568	162,739	1811
4,882	30,544	3,383	40,811	158,717	1812
3,571	28,642	2,906	38,071	157,373	1813
7,869	29,899	3,897	40,602	165,214	1814
8,261	31,843	5,767	35,061	165,214	1815
6,610	27,264	4,008	32,593	151,802	1816
7,000	24,916	4,663	32,157	145,713	1817
7,202	23,609	5,869	30,012	149,822	1818
12,491	22,733	4,392	30,096	151,112	1819
7,556	23,505	5,072	33,176	146,360	1820
4,396	20,210	5,025	33,531	144,737	1821
5,518	20,903	3,265	31,972	137,367	1822
6,616	17,956	4,066	27,382	137,367	1823
6,602	18,756	3,930	31,603	138,114	1824
14,753	19,891	3,920	30,632	149,434	1825
7,200	19,544	4,670	29,166	140,899	1826
6,903	19,770	3,058	31,947	134,682	1827
4,040	18,649	4,437	33,158	134,221	1828
3,355	18,386	4,671	30,245	132,482	1829
5,013	17,820	2,483	33,262	125,508	1830
3,138	17,078	3,199	36,822	120,052	1831
3,001	16,071	1,774	39,419	120,052	1832
3,001	17,507	948	42,667	120,052	1833
6,002	18,154	3,616	44,612	130,885	1834
6,544	17,242	5,100	53,707	137,853	1835
13,785	16,484	2,296	46,528	162,261	1836
8,319	22,774	4,919	66,545	183,505	1837
18,718	25,257	4,797	67,310	200,170	1838
50,042	23,273	2,448	65,283	212,518	1839
21,252	28,135	6,767	81,512	235,405	1840
11,770	36,263	5,462	91,287	262,628	1841
13,131	35,523	3,031	88,910	262,628	1842
13,131	28,122		89,428	246,347	1843
12,317	27,628		74,098	269,467	1844
13,473	42,491		80,741	301,814	1845
75,454	41,193		73,705	311,327	1846
77,832	42,514		73,683	319,755	1847
31,975	44,065		73,118	351,548	1848
35,155	45,283		75,033	359,280	1849
17,964	44,764		85,328	365,824	1850
18,291	47,422		74,795	365,824	1851
16,919	44,734		82,324	313,461	1852

Appendix 8

RULES

For the Preservation of good

ORDER

in the

Works of William Reynolds and Co.

1. Each Person employed in the Works shall come to, and be engaged in the Employment appointed for them, and at their proper Places from the hours of Six in the Morning to Six in the Evening, Breakfast and Dinner excepted, or forfeit the Sum of One Shilling in Addition to the Time lost by Absence or Indolence, which will be deducted from his Weekly Wages.

2. If the Person has undertaken any Place, and is known by the appellation of a Place or Plackman, or gets Twelve Shillings per Week or more, he shall forfeit in Addition to the above, One Shilling and Six-pence.

3. Those who stay longer at their Meals than the Time allowed, viz: half an Hour at Breakfast and an Hour at Dinner, shall forfeit a quarter of a Day's Wages.

4. The Clock kept at the Work is to be considered as the true Time of Day, and is to be observed accordingly.

5. If any Person is found at Work in a State of Intoxication, he shall be deemed liable to the Fine of absence, and not suffered to work during that Day, nor be paid for what work he may have done in that State.

6. If any Person shall send for Ale or bring Strong Liquors into the Works without leave first had from the Masters or their Agents, he shall be fined the Sum of Two Shillings and Six-pence; and every Person joining in the said Ale or Liquors, shall forfeit One Shilling, besides the fine for Intoxication if that should have taken place, One Shilling.

7. Any One who is prevented from coming to his work by Illness, or some unavoidable Accident, and does not send information of the same to the Clerk or Agent at the Time he ought to be at Work, or if the Party is a Place Man and does not give notice time enough for the Agent to provide a Substitute before the Works sustain any Damage, he shall be liable to the Fine of Absence, unless it shall appear to the Agent that he has exerted himself to give Notice and could not.

8. If any One Strikes another in the Work, or in working Hours, he shall forfeit Two Shillings and Six-pence; and if the other returns the blow he shall pay One Shilling; but if they fight in or near the Work, so as to draw away those who ought to have been at work, they shall pay double the above Sum.

9. If any One suffers a Stranger to be in that part of the Work in which he is employed, he shall forfeit Two Shillings and Six-pence.

10. If any One is found in that part of the Work where his business does not call him, he shall forfeit One Shilling.

11. If any One is detected in receiving Money or other Value, under false pretences, by charging more Time than they have worked, or altering Notes, etc. he shall forfeit Five Shillings besides reimbursing the Value so obtained.

12. If any One leaves his Employment without giving a Month's Notice at the Reckoning to the Clerk or Agent who looks over his work, he shall forfeit whatever Wages are due to him, provided such Stoppage shall not exceed Ten Shillings and Six-pence.

13. If any One after having given Notice as above, and paid his Debts, if any are owing to the Company, asks for his discharge in writing, he shall have the same and his full Money to the Day of the Monthly Reckoning next following such Notice, provided he is not bound by any agreement for a Term of Years then unexpired.

14. If any Clerk or Agent shall refuse to enter such Notice when it is given, or at the end of the next Month to give a discharge in Writing when claimed, after due Notice as aforesaid, he shall forfeit the Sum of One Guinea.

15. The different Agents shall have the power of reducing any of the above Fines to a Sum not less than One Shilling, if they see sufficient Reason for so doing, and nothing herein contained shall be understood to prevent application to the Magistrates for their Assistance of the Law to obtain Satisfaction for the Damages which may be sustained by the Infraction of any of the above Rules.

Index

January 172[illegible]

Date	Fo.	No.		£ . s . d	C . q . lb		£	s	d
			Sundry Acco^ts are D^rs to Warehouse			264			
Aprill 21	216		**Edward Parry** Welchpool			10			
		36	Pots & Kettles q^t 164 Gallons ¼ at 10	6 . 16 . 10½					
		1	Mortar 9 lb at 1¾	0 . 1 . 3¾	8 . 2 . 8				
			4 Backstones q^rs 2 . 11 at 12/ 82 Bushes 3 . 2 . – at 14/ 1 Purgatory at 6/ 1 D^o Least at 5/. 2 Gridirons ground at 2/6. 1 D^o Unground at 2/	3 . 14 . 2¼	4 . 3 . 3		10	12	4½
ye 21	216		**John Willson** Newtown			92			
		15	Pots & Kettles q^t 3 . 3 . 9 at 15 p^r C	2 . 17 . 5¼					
		7	Small ware q^t 1 . 16 . at 18/8	0 . 7 . 4	4 . – . 25		3	4	9¼
ye 21	216		**Randle Bingley** Mould			275			
		19	Pots & Kettles q^t 99 Gall^s at 10	4 . 2 . 6	4 . 3 . 3				
			13 Backstones C 2 . – . 1 at 12/	1 . 4 . 1¼	2 . 0 . 1		5	6	7¼
ye 21	216		**Samuell Mason** Knighton			11			
		4	Small w^e viz 1 at 1/11 . 2 at 1/9 . 1 at 1/7	– . 6 . –	0 . 1 . 26				
			4 Backstones q^t 2 . 23 at 12/	0 . 8 . 5½	0 . 2 . 23			15	5½
ye 21	217		**Andrew Clark** Knighton			68			
		2	Pots q^t 25 Gallons at 10	1 . – . 10	1 . – . 19				
			12 Sadirons at 16 . 50 Bushes C 2 . – . 9 at 14/	2 . 5 . 1½	2 . 2 . 19		3	5	11½
ye 21	217		**Thom^s Bright** Bishopscastle			215			
		35	Pots Kettles & Furnaces q^t 285 Gall^s ½ at 10	11 . 17 . 11					
		18	Small ware viz 3 at 1/11 . 7 at 1/9 . 4 at 1/7 . 4 at 1/5	1 . 10 . –	15 . – . 7		15	1	6½
			54 Bushes C 2 . 1 . 17 at 14/	1 . 13 . 7½	2 . 1 . 17				
May 7th	218		**Godfrey Stubbings** Newcastle			176			
		17	Pots & Furnaces q^t 164 Gall^s at 10	6 . 16 . 8					
		14	Small ware viz 2 at 1/9 . 6 at 1/7 . 6 at 1/5	1 . 1 . 6	8 . 3 . 13		7	18	2
ye 7th	218		**James Eaton** Drayton			205			
		5	Pots q^t 49 gall^s ¼ at 10	2 . 1 . – ½					
		9	Small w^e viz 3 at 1/9 . 3 at 1/7 . 3 at 1/5	– . 14 . 3	2 . 3 . 21		3	10	0½
			24 Bushes C 1 . – . 6 at 14/	0 . 14 . 9	1 . – . 6				
ye 7th	218		**William Stanley** Newport			52			
		12	Pots & Furnaces q^t 141 gall^s ½ at 10	5 . 17 . 11	6 . 2 . 10				
			3 grates q^rs 3 . 22 at 12/ 114 Bushes C 4 . 3 . 9 at 14/	3 . 18 . 11¾	5 . 3 . 3		9	16	10¾
ye 7th	218		**Willm Stoakes** Newport			198			
		12	Pots & Furnaces q^t 110 Gall^s ¾ at 10	4 . 12 . 3½					
		13	Small w^e viz 3 a 1/9 . 3 a 1/7 . 4 a 1/5 . 3 mortars q^rs 2 . 9 at 16/4	1 . 5 . 1¾	6 . 1 . 3		7	18	9
			3 grates q^rs 3 . 4 at 12/ 50 Bushes C 2 . 1 . 3 at 14/	2 . 1 . 3¾	3 . – . 7				
ye 5	219		**Willm Bright** Ludlow			70			
			47 Bushes C 2 at 14/ 3 Pipes C 2 . – . 15 at 22/6	3 . 16 . –	4 . 0 . 15		3	16	–
Aprill 21	217		**George Battersbea** 90 Bushes C 3 . 1 . 12 at 14/	2 . 7 . –	3 . 1 . 12	150	2	7	0
ye 21	217		**Richd Bromley** 80 Bushes C 3 . 1 . 14 at 14/	2 . 7 . 3	3 . 1 . 14	231	2	7	3
ye 21	217		**Sam^ll Bradburn** 100 D^o 4 . – . 7 at 14/	2 . 16 . 10½	4 . 0 . 7	124	2	16	10½
	218		**James Beddard** 4 Backstones q^rs 3 . 2 a 12/	0 . 9 . 2½	0 . 3 . 2	83	0	9	2½
May 5th	219		**Samu^ll Whitten** 15 Dutch Backs C 3 . 3 . 5 a 13/6	2 . 11 . 2¾	3 . 3 . 5	203	2	11	2¾
	219		Pots Kettles & Furn^s q^t	58 . 3 . 23					
			Castware	41 . 3 . 22	100 . 3 . 17		81	18	1½